Introduction to PROBABILITY and STATISTICS

Third Edition

Introduction to PROBABILITY and STATISTICS

B. W. LINDGREN, *Department of Statistics, University of Minnesota*

G. W. McELRATH, *Bayer and McElrath, Inc., Management Consultants, and Department of Mechanical Engineering, University of Minnesota*

The Macmillan Company
Collier-Macmillan Limited, London

THE MACMILLAN COMPANY
COLLIER-MACMILLAN CANADA, LTD., TORONTO, ONTARIO

Printed in the United States of America

Preface

This book is intended as a text for a course of 30 to 50 hours that introduces basic concepts of probability and statistics, mainly to students who subsequently will have no other formal coursework in the area. Various statistical methods are introduced, but this is not a "methods" book; the student who has completed the course will not be expected immediately to be able to handle all statistical problems, nor will he find this book particularly useful as a reference—for finding methods to handle a particular statistical problem he may encounter. However, he should gain some appreciation of the nature, scope, and theoretical basis of methods of statistical inference. Our purpose will have been accomplished in some measure if with this course in his background, a student will know when he may need to consult a statistician, or he is able to read more detailed discussions of methodology with sufficient understanding to make a reasonable attack on his own problem, or he understands better the statistical claims made in literature from his field, or he is motivated to include in his college program still more coursework in statistical theory and methods.

The minimum mathematical prerequisite is college algebra, although students who have had mathematics beyond this will be more comfortable in their study. Certain material requiring calculus is identified as such; this includes a treatment of continuous distributions in terms of calculus, some work on moment generating functions, and a differential derivation of the Poisson probability distribution.

Continuous distributions are first introduced without the tools of formal calculus, in terms of area under a curve—a geometrical concept that can be comprehended without knowing "how to integrate." The analogy with continuous mass distributions exploits the reader's intuition as an aid to understanding the ideas of distributions and moments. In such an approach it is necessary to avoid the mathematical difficulties that are involved in the derivation of distributions of statistics used in inference about continuous populations. However, with an understanding of the theory that can be and is here developed for the discrete case, the student will perhaps appreciate what is needed in the continuous case and be willing to accept the assertion that an appropriate mathematical background would provide the necessary justification.

Fundamental concepts of statistical inference are introduced early, based on discrete populations and involving only the binomial and hypergeometric distributions. The application of these concepts to the problem of acceptance sampling provides an early illustration of the use and power of statistical methods in an important, "real" situation.

A brief course in just the elements of probability theory is available in Chapters 1, 2, 4, and the first part of Chapter 6 (through Section 6.3).

Changes from the second to the third edition include the following: Probability is now defined for general discrete spaces first, rather than for the case of "equally likely" elementary outcomes. The old Chapter 4, with its plethora of new concepts, has been trimmed to a more digestible—and somewhat more classical—introduction to inference for the new Chapter 3. (Much of the deleted material now appears in Chapter 8.) The discussion of sampling and of the presentation and description of data has been restored, in the new Chapter 5, to something like what appeared in the first edition.

We are indebted to the editors of *Biometrika*, *The Annals of Mathematical Statistics*, and the *Journal of the American Statistical Association* for permission to adapt material taken from these journals for use in our tables, and to the American Society for Testing Materials for permission to adopt material from the *ASTM Manual on Quality Control Materials*. We are indebted also to Professor Sir Ronald A. Fisher, Cambridge, to Dr. Frank Yates, Rothamsted, and to Messrs. Oliver and Boyd, Ltd., Edinburgh, for permission to reprint a portion of Table II from their book *Statistical Tables for Biological, Agricultural, and Medical Research*.

B. W. L.

G. W. McE.

Contents

Introduction to PROBABILITY and STATISTICS

1

DISCRETE

PROBABILITY MODELS

It is common experience in making physical, chemical, and economic measurements, and in drawing samples from a population or a manufactured lot of articles, to find that the characteristics of the observations vary from measurement to measurement, or from sample to sample. They cannot be predicted infallibly and are commonly thought of as being "random" or subject to "chance." The phrase *experiment of chance* will be used to describe such processes.

Although one cannot predict accurately the outcome of a single performance of an experiment of chance, experience with sequences of trials of such experiments reveals a kind of regularity that is useful. A "model" or mathematical structure that describes this regularity is of value, and probability theory has evolved to provide models for experiments of chance. A *probability model* is a mathematical structure intended to characterize the laws governing an experiment of chance.

The subject of *statistics* deals with the making of inferences about the "correct" probability model governing a given experiment of chance using the results of experimentation—carrying out the experiment of interest and so obtaining "data." The correct or true probability model usually is not known in every detail, and this is the motivation for obtaining data and drawing conclusions from the data about the true model. Thus, our study

1

begins with probability models and subsequently proceeds to statistical inferences concerning these models.

1.1 Mathematical models

An essential part of applying mathematics to a so-called real situation is the construction of a "mathematical model" for the situation. Consider a familiar example. Newton's second law of motion states that an object subject to a force moves with an acceleration proportional to the force: $F = ma$. The *model* consists of the numbers representing the magnitudes of force, mass, and acceleration, together with the equation relating them. The *law* says that this mathematical model can be used for describing and predicting physical phenomena. Proof of the law in a mathematical sense is impossible; it can only be tested by experiment.

For example, working mathematically with the equation $F = ma$, one can derive a formula giving the distance a dropped object will fall in a given time. Agreement between the motion predicted by this formula and the actual motion of a dropped object is then taken as evidence of the usefulness or "correctness" of the model.

Similarly, in geometry one sets up mathematical points, lines, circles, and so on. These, together with certain axioms, constitute a model. Theorems of geometry are really theorems about this model, *not* theorems about *physical* points, lines, or circles. Of course, the model is found to be useful, and so people study geometry. Indeed, even apparently useless models are studied, with the hope that someone will later find applications for them—as often happens.

There are many phenomena in which the cause mechanisms are so complex that it is futile to attempt to set up a deterministic model based on something like Newton's laws. Yet some kind of model is desirable.

Consider, for example, what happens when a thumbtack is tossed into the air and allowed to fall on a horizontal, hard, smooth surface. Ordinarily, the tack will come to rest either with its point straight up in the air, or with its point touching the surface (see Figure 1-1). These positions will be referred to as "point up" or U, and "point down" or D, and it is assumed that one is interested only in whether the tack lands point up or point down. Conceptually, it is possible to compute (from Newton's laws, from a knowledge of the initial position and velocity, and from a knowledge of the forces acting during its flight) whether the result of tossing the tack will be U or D, but this is surely most impractical. A deterministic model for the toss of a thumbtack—although one may exist—ordinarily is just not feasible to use.

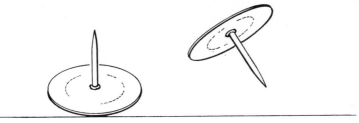

Figure 1-1   Outcomes of the toss of a thumbtack.

Experience with tossing things—and mankind has amassed a great deal of this over the years—has uncovered a phenomenon that has significance and value: When a tack is tossed repeatedly, the *proportion* of tosses in which the outcome is *U* approaches a *limiting value*, and this limiting value is a property of the tack and the tossing mechanism—it is the same in one sequence of tosses as in another. Moreover, although it is a quantity associated with long sequences of tosses, this proportion appears to have relevance to rational people's behavior when they encounter only a few tosses, or even a single toss.

The probability model or *stochastic* model for the toss of a tack consists of a specification of the possible outcomes (*U* and *D*) together with a specification of a number *p* assigned to *U* and intended to represent the long-run proportion of tosses in which *U* would occur. (Clearly, the proportion of tosses in which *D* would occur is automatically $1 - p$.) The number *p* is said to be the *probability* of the outcome *U*, and $1 - p$ the probability of the outcome *D*. These outcomes and corresponding probabilities constitute the model.

A stochastic model such as the one just described for the toss of a thumb tack, like a deterministic model, is a mathematical structure; it may or may not have significance for the phenomenon it is intended to represent. Whether or not it does is a matter for experience to determine.

EXAMPLE 1-a.   In actual tosses of a precision die (a cube whose six faces are marked with 1, 2, ..., and 6 dots, respectively), the following results have been reported:

It is assumed, in this experimentation, that one only keeps track of whether an odd or an even number of points turns up. The model consists of the two outcomes "odd" and "even," together with a number *p* representing the long-run proportion of tosses in which "even" turns up. On the basis of the evidence contained in the above table, the number *p* appears to be somewhere in the immediate vicinity of 1/2.

Number of tosses	Proportion of even numbers
10,000	.5030
20,000	.50075
40,000	.4991
80,000	.5007
160,000	.50055

Although the introduction of stochastic models has been given for situations in which an experiment is or can be repeated indefinitely, there are situations in which the experiment will not or cannot be repeated but for which a stochastic model would be useful. The weatherman may say that there is one chance in four that it will rain next Saturday, and the question is, should a picnic be planned? The weatherman's guess is educated by his knowledge of pressure maps and what usually happens in certain patterns, but next Saturday will not be repeated indefinitely. The question, "what is the probability of war in ten years?" is another illustration of this kind of problem. There are also situations in which chances *are* computed by repeated experimentation, but in which one would like to be able to apply them to a particular case in which "chance" really may not be appropriate. For instance, one is told that a certain medical treatment has a 60 percent record of success; can he then apply this to himself, or is the chance aspect of the treatment overshadowed by particular circumstances in his own case which are more pertinent? (Indeed, one might wonder whether life is really a gamble.) Some people advocate a *subjective* or personal concept of probability, as opposed to the more common view that probability is objective, something attributable to the phenomenon itself without reference to the person computing it. Both views have their uses.

The use of a stochastic model to represent some physical phenomenon should not be taken as an implication that Nature is haphazard, governed by "laws of chance," either in part or in whole. It is just that, in some instances, the stochastic type of model is the only kind of model that has any practical value. Indeed, stochastic models, and stochastic structures superimposed on deterministic models, are coming more and more to be needed and used.

1.2 Discrete probability spaces

In this and the next few chapters, the concern will be with the simpler situations in which the number of outcomes of an experiment—the number of distinct ways in which (according to one's interest) an experiment can terminate—is either finite or, at most, countably infinite.† The set of possible outcomes is called the *sample space* of the experiment. Because this is a finite or, at most, countably infinite set, its elements (the individual outcomes) can be listed, and if not more specifically described, referred to as (say) $\omega_1, \omega_2, \ldots$. The sample space is the set of these:

$$\Omega = \{\omega_1, \omega_2, \ldots\}$$

The possible outcomes, or the ways in which a given experiment can turn out, are usually not uniquely specified by the nature of the problem, but only by decree—by the person setting up the model. For instance, if *two* coins are tossed, one could say there are *two* ways: either they match or they do not match. But one can also say there are *three* ways: the number of Heads is 0, 1, or 2. Or, since the coins can be distinguished from one another—perhaps one is a nickel and one a penny—one could count *four* ways: both Heads, both Tails, Heads on the penny and Tails on the nickel, or Heads on the nickel and Tails on the penny. Of these three formulations, the last is the most generally useful, being the most detailed. That is, if it is known which of those four outcomes listed is the result, it can be determined from this which of the three numbers of Heads is the result, and whether or not the coins match.

EXAMPLE 1-b.   A missile is fired with the intention of destroying a target. This mission may fail or succeed, depending on a multitude of factors. A stochastic model for the firing would involve a sample space with two elements: $\Omega = \{success, failure\}$. (But this model would not take into account a degree of partial success of the mission, such as damaging the target.)

EXAMPLE 1-c.   The number of flaws in a manufactured article usually cannot be predicted from a knowledge of the condition of the machine which produces it; this is best considered an experiment of chance. If one is concerned with just the number of flaws (and if he has a workable definition of what constitutes a flaw), a probability model for what happens in the production of a single article involves a sample space consisting of the various possible numbers of flaws:

$$\Omega = \{0, 1, 2, 3, \ldots\}.$$

Although, in practice, it would be difficult to imagine an article with a million flaws, and even more difficult to count them, there is no particular reason to limit the sample space to a finite set of numbers. One may as well take it to be the set of all nonnegative integers, which is a countably infinite set.

---

† A set is countably infinite if it is possible to "count" its elements—that is, place them into one-to-one correspondence with the "counting numbers" 1, 2, 3, …. This means, in effect, that one can list them in a single but possibly infinite sequence—in a row.

EXAMPLE 1-d.   The names of all of the people in a certain community are typed on individual slips of paper and these slips placed in a hat. After the slips are mixed, one slip is drawn from the hat. The outcome of this experiment is the name on the slip drawn, or the person named. If the names are coded $N_1, \ldots, N_k$, the sample space consists of just these names: $\Omega = \{N_1, N_2, \ldots, N_k\}$.

To complete the construction of the basic model for an experiment of chance, one assigns probabilities to each possible outcome, say p_1 to outcome ω_1, p_2 to outcome ω_2, and so forth. These p's are intended to be the ideal or limiting proportion of times the corresponding outcome shows up in a long sequence of trials of the experiment. As proportions they would have certain properties, and it will be assumed that the probabilities $p_1, p_2, \ldots$ in a probability model have the following properties:

(1) $0 \leq p_i \leq 1,$ for $i = 1, 2, \ldots$

(2) $p_1 + p_2 + \cdots = 1.$

The first simply says that a proportion is not negative and cannot exceed the whole, and the second says that taking into account all possible outcomes, the sums of the proportions for the various outcomes would be the proportion which is the whole.

It is natural to wonder how, in the construction of such a probability model, one determines the probabilities p_i. Although any set of nonnegative numbers adding up to 1 would serve to define a model, the "true" values of the p's (that is, the p's in the model that faithfully describes the experiment being studied) are almost never exactly known. This does not preclude assuming that "true" p's exist.

EXAMPLE 1-e.   A coin is tossed so as to fall on a flat, horizontal surface. The sample space adequate for most purposes is $\Omega = \{H, T\}$, where H denotes the outcome that "Heads" is showing, and T that "Tails" is showing. Denote the probabilities of these outcomes by p and $q = 1 - p$, respectively. Most people behave as though $p = q = \frac{1}{2}$, but this is an ideal model that may or may not represent the actual experiment. (Surely it is possible to construct a coin or to toss one in such a way as to make this choice of probabilities unreasonable.)

EXAMPLE 1-f.   Consider (as in Example 1-d) the sample space $\Omega = \{N_1, \ldots, N_k\}$, where $N_1, \ldots, N_k$ are the names of the k people in a given community. One name is chosen by a blindfolded boy reaching into a container in which all of the names have been placed, and the person whose name is drawn is awarded a prize. This drawing would be considered fair by the people if everyone's name "has the same chance of being drawn," by which they would likely mean that if the drawing were repeated a great many times, the proportion of times each name occurred should be close to $1/k$. Thus, the probability model for an ideal, or fair, drawing is that in which the probability assigned to each outcome is $1/k$. When the drawing is conducted in such a way that this is the true model, the selection is said to be made *at random*.

EXAMPLE 1-g. The sample space used to represent the number of flaws in a manufactured article was taken in Example 1-c to be the set of nonnegative integers: $\Omega = \{0, 1, 2, \ldots\}$. One possible probability model is that shown in the following table:

ω_i	0	1	2
p_i	.4	.4	.2

Since the probabilities p_0, p_1, and p_2 add up to 1, the probability assigned to any number of flaws greater than 2 must be 0. This model might be appropriate for articles that have undergone a screening process to remove articles with more than two flaws. Any model that assigned positive probability to each possible outcome would have to be based on a convergent infinite series. For instance, since the base e (approx. 2.71828) of the natural logarithm system can be calculated as follows,

$$e = 1 + 1 + 1/2! + 1/3! + \cdots,$$

the numbers

$$1/e, 1/e, 1/(2e), 1/(6e), \ldots$$

add up to 1, and being positive they can be used as probabilities for $0, 1, \ldots$, respectively. (This is a commonly used model.)

Problems

1-1. Two persons each toss a coin to decide who is to pay for coffee that day. What would be an appropriate sample space?

1-2. A student is picked from a group of students and asked how many brothers and/or sisters he has. What is the sample space?

1-3. The number of telephone calls coming into an exchange in a given one-minute period is to be treated as a random phenomenon. What would be the appropriate sample space?

1-4. Toss a thumbtack fifty times. After each toss, plot the proportion of U's (point up) among the tosses as a function of the number of tosses carried out up to that point. Observe whether there is any tendency towards a stabilizing of the proportion of U's, and make a guess as to the probability that should be assigned to U. (This will depend on your particular tack, so no "answer" can be given.) Do you think you could guess this probability very accurately after three tosses?

1-5. When two coins are tossed, the result can be recorded in terms of the number of Heads that show. What is the sample space? If there is an argument as to whether the true probability model assigns equal probabilities (1/3, 1/3, 1/3) to the outcomes in the sample space, or the probabilities 1/4 for 0 Heads, 1/2 for 1 Head, and 1/4 for 2 Heads, which side of the argument would you be on? (You may toss a couple of coins several times to help you decide.)

1-6. The release time of a certain relay is designed to be 1/2 second, but is actually somewhat variable around this nominal time. If the release time is measured to the nearest hundredth of a second, this measured time can be thought of as the outcome of an experiment of chance. What is the appropriate sample space?

1.3 Events

The points of a sample space represent the individual, distinct ways in which an experiment can terminate—that is, the possible "outcomes" of the experiment, enumerated according to a scheme that is sufficiently detailed for the purposes at hand. Thus, for example, although one might describe the result of the toss of a coin in terms of the orientation of the coin on the table, this orientation is usually not of interest; the elementary outcomes are taken to be *H* and *T*.

On the other hand, having specified a sample space in terms of certain elementary outcomes, one might be interested in a less detailed classification—in an outcome or result that is not so well defined.

EXAMPLE 1-h.   In the toss of two ordinary dice, of the type used in many games of chance, the sample space that will serve most purposes can be taken to be the different possible total numbers of points:

$$\Omega = \{2, 3, 4, \ldots, 12\}.$$

But in some situations one might care only whether the total number of points were odd or even. The result is odd if any one of the outcomes 3, 5, 7, 9, 11 occurs, and otherwise even. That is, the condition of oddness is satisfied by any of the five outcomes listed; indeed, the description "the result is an odd number" defines this set of five outcomes and is called an *event* in the original sample space.

Definition   An *event* is any set of outcomes in a sample space.

An event can be specified by giving a list of the outcomes that make it up, or by giving a descriptive phrase that serves to characterize them; that is, a condition that is satisfied by each outcome in the event and not satisfied by outcomes not in the event. The event is said to have happened or occurred if some one of the outcomes in it has resulted from a performance of the experiment.

In a *finite* sample space, the number of distinct events that can be defined is finite. In particular, if there are k points in the sample space, there are 2^k events, if one includes as an event the empty set, the set with no points in it (as would be "defined" by any condition that is satisfied by no outcome in the given sample space). This number 2^k is just the number of subsets of a set with k elements, as will be shown in a subsequent section.

EXAMPLE 1-i. The sample space for the toss of a penny and a nickel together can be taken to be $\{Hh, Ht, Th, Tt\}$, where (for instance) *Th* means that the penny has fallen Tails and the nickel Heads. There are then 16 (or 2^4) distinct events, as the following list shows:

$\{Hh\}$	$\{Hh, Ht\}$	$\{Ht, Tt\}$	$\{Hh, Th, Tt\}$
$\{Ht\}$	$\{Hh, Th\}$	$\{Th, Tt\}$	$\{Ht, Th, Tt\}$
$\{Th\}$	$\{Hh, Tt\}$	$\{Hh, Ht, Th\}$	$\{Hh, Ht, Th, Tt\}$
$\{Tt\}$	$\{Ht, Th\}$	$\{Hh, Ht, Tt\}$	Empty set

Examples of events that are defined by a description or condition include these:

The penny falls Heads, which defines $\{Hh, Ht\}$.
The coins match, which defines $\{Hh, Tt\}$.
Neither coin falls Heads, which defines $\{Tt\}$.
At least one coin falls Heads, which defines $\{Hh, Ht, Th\}$.

It is desired to assign probability to an arbitrary event, and this should be both computable from an initial assignment of probabilities to elementary outcomes, and representative of the long-run proportion of trials in which the event occurs. The following definition achieves these ends.

Definition The *probability* of an event E is the sum of the probabilities assigned to the outcomes that make up E. The probability of E is denoted by $P(E)$.

Certainly, the proportion of trials (in any sequence of trials) in which outcome ω_1 occurs plus the proportion of trials in which ω_2 occurs is precisely the proportion of trials in which the event $\{\omega_1, \omega_2\}$ occurs. The extension of this idea is what leads to the above definition for a discrete probability model.

It should be noted that, because the probability of any event E is a sum of nonnegative numbers, it is nonnegative; and because it cannot exceed the total of the probabilities assigned to the outcomes in the sample space, it does not exceed 1:

$$0 \le P(E) \le 1.$$

It also should be observed that, because the probabilities assigned to outcomes must add to 1, $P(\Omega) = 1$.

EXAMPLE 1-j. A student is selected from a class of 30 students of which 3 are freshman boys, 6 are freshman girls, 12 are sophomore boys, and 9 are sophomore girls. One model that might be appropriate consists of the following sample space and probabilities:

ω_i	FB	FG	SB	SG
p_i	.1	.2	.4	.2

The event defined by the condition that the student drawn is a sophomore is $\{SB, SG\}$, with probability $.4 + .2 = .6$. The event defined by the condition that the student drawn is a girl is $\{FG, SG\}$, with probability $.2 + .2 = .4$. One writes

$$P(\text{Sophomore}) = .6, \qquad P(\text{Girl}) = .4.$$

1.4 Combining events

Certain operations and combinations of events will now be introduced, arising from the specification of events in terms of conditions involving other events. First, two conditions define the same event if they specify precisely the same list of outcomes in each case; thus, one writes $E = F$ if the outcomes in (or defined by) E comprise exactly the same outcomes as are in (or defined by) F.

The condition that a certain event E has *not* occurred defines the set of outcomes of the sample space that are not in E.

Definition The *complement* of a set E (relative to a given sample space Ω) is the set consisting of those elements of Ω that are not in E. It is denoted by E^c.

It is almost obvious that

$$P(E^c) = 1 - P(E),$$

because the probabilities assigned to outcomes in the sample space, which add up to 1, would be included either in the sum defining $P(E^c)$ or in the sum defining $P(E)$, but not in both. Notice that since the complement of Ω is the empty set, one has

$$P(\text{empty set}) = 1 - P(\Omega) = 1 - 1 = 0.$$

EXAMPLE 1-k. Consider the model in which the outcomes are the integers $1, 2, 3, \ldots$ and the corresponding probabilities are $1/2, 1/4, 1/8, \ldots$. Let E denote the event that the outcome is a number greater than 2:

$$E = \{3, 4, 5, \ldots\}.$$

The complement is clearly $E^c = \{1, 2\}$, and

$$P(E) = 1 - P(E^c) = 1 - P(\{1, 2\}) = 1 - [1/2 + 1/4] = 1/4.$$

Examples have been encountered in which events sometimes have outcomes in common; those common outcomes satisfy the conditions defining each of the events considered. This leads to the following.

Definition The *intersection* of events E and F, written either EF or $E \cap F$, is the event whose outcomes are all those contained both in E and in F. The intersection of any collection of events, $\{E_\alpha\}$, is the set of all outcomes each of which lies in every member E_α of the collection.

About all that can be said about the probability of an intersection of two sets (in terms of the probabilities of these sets) is that it does not exceed the probability of either one of them. Sometimes there are no outcomes that satisfy each of two conditions; their intersection is then empty. The conditions are said to be "mutually exclusive," and there is no overlapping of the corresponding sets.

Definition Two events whose intersection is the empty set are said to be *disjoint*.

Another combination of events is defined by the condition that an outcome must be included in any one or more of those events:

Definition The *union* of events E and F, written either $E + F$ or $E \cup F$, is the event whose outcomes are each contained either in E or in F (or in both). The union of any collection of events, $\{E_\alpha\}$, is the set of all outcomes each of which lies in at least one member of the collection.

EXAMPLE 1-l. The sample space for the toss of an ordinary die can be taken to be $\Omega = \{1, 2, 3, 4, 5, 6\}$. Let E denote the event that the outcome is a number divisible by 3, and F the event that it is a number divisible by 2:

$$E = \{3, 6\}, \qquad F = \{2, 4, 6\}.$$

Then

$$E \cap F = \{6\} \qquad \text{and} \qquad E \cup F = \{2, 3, 4, 6\},$$

the intersection consisting of that outcome divisible both by 3 *and* by 2, and the union consisting of all outcomes each divisible either by 3 *or* by 2.

Because the condition defining an intersection is usually encountered as "condition *E and* condition *F*," and the condition defining a union as "condition *E or* condition *F*," it is just as easy, for many purposes, to write the intersection as "*E* and *F*" and the union as "*E* or *F*," and this will sometimes be done in what follows.

The probability of a union can be expressed in terms of the probabilities of the sets making it up when those sets are *disjoint*. For, if *E* and *F* have no outcomes in common, the outcomes in $E \cup F$ consist precisely of all those in *E* together with all those in *F*, and so

$$P(E \cup F) = \text{sum of probabilities of all outcomes in } E \cup F$$
$$= \text{sum of probabilities of outcomes in } E$$
$$+ \text{sum of probabilities of outcomes in } F$$
$$= P(E) + P(F).$$

As a particular case, and because *E* and E^c are disjoint, observe that

$$P(E) + P(E^c) = P(E \cup E^c) = P(\Omega) = 1,$$

which verifies again the relation given earlier for $P(E^c)$.

EXAMPLE 1-m.   Suppose that the probability that a manufactured part (according to set standards) will be too long is .05 and that it will be too short is .02. The events "too long" and "too short" are disjoint, so the probability that the part will not be too long or too short is

$$P(\text{not too long or too short}) = 1 - P(\text{too long or too short})$$
$$= 1 - [P(\text{too long}) + P(\text{too short})]$$
$$= 1 - [.05 + .02]$$
$$= .93.$$

Problems

1-7.   Given the sample space {1, 2, 3, 4, 5, 6} for the toss of an ordinary die, how many distinct events could be defined? How many events including the outcomes 1, 2, and 3 could be defined? List the latter.

1-8.   Suppose that the model for a rather unusual die and tossing mechanism is as follows:

Outcome	1	2	3	4	5	6
Probability	1/4	1/4	1/4	1/12	1/12	1/12

Determine the probabilities of each of the following events:

> E: the outcome exceeds 3
> F: the outcome is even
> G: the outcome is not divisible by 3
> H: the outcome is not 3 or 4.

1-9. List the outcomes in the complement of each of the events E, F, G, H in the preceding problem, and give the probabilities of each.

1-10. Referring to the events in Problem 1-8, determine the following intersections (answer by listing the outcomes):

(a) $E \cap H$,   (b) $F \cap G$,
(c) $E \cap F \cap G \cap H$,   (d) $F^c \cap G$.

1-11. Referring to Problem 1-8, determine the following unions (answer by listing the outcomes):

(a) $E \cup H$,   (b) $F \cup G$,
(c) $E \cup F \cup G \cup H$,   (d) $F^c \cup G$.

1-12. Referring to Problem 1-8, determine x such that

$$P(E \cup F) = P(E) + P(F) - x.$$

Can you identify x as the probability of a certain relevant intersection and deduce a *general* formula?

1-13. Referring to Problem 1-8, show that $P(E \cap H) = P(E)P(H)$. Is this a general relation—is the probability of an intersection of sets the product of their probabilities in every case?

1-14. Show that if every outcome in E is included in F (written: $E \subset F$), then $P(E)$ does not exceed $P(F)$. [*Hint:* Express F as the union of E and another set disjoint from E.]

1.5 Equally likely outcomes

There are a number of simple experiments for which the ideal model assigns equal probabilities to all of the outcomes. Because the sum of the probabilities of the outcomes in a sample space is finite (that is, 1), the number of outcomes in the sample space must be finite if they are to be equally probable or, as is often said, *equally likely*. Indeed, if there are N outcomes in a sample space and if they are to be equally likely, the probability assigned to each outcome must be $1/N$.

A model with equally likely outcomes is often useful when the experiment consists of tossing a symmetrical object; the geometrical symmetry and the method of tossing would suggest that the correct model—if the toss is "fair" or "ideal"—should treat each landing position the same as every other, and assign equal probabilities to all. Thus, the ideal coin is a mathematical model with probability 1/2 assigned to Heads and also to Tails. The ideal die is a mathematical model in which each of the six faces of the die has probability 1/6. The spin of a roulette wheel and the spin of a revolver's cylinder (Russian roulette) are other examples of this sort.

When the outcomes in a sample space are equally likely, the probability of an event has a simple expression in terms of numbers of outcomes:

$$P(E) = \frac{\text{Number of outcomes in } E}{\text{Number of outcomes in } \Omega}.$$

For, if there are N outcomes in Ω, so that the probability of each outcome is $1/N$, then the probability of E is the sum of as many $1/N$'s as there are outcomes in E.

EXAMPLE 1-n. For the probability space for the toss of a die (outcomes 1, 2, 3, 4, 5, 6) in which the outcomes are equally probable, some sample probability calculations are as follows:

$$P(\text{outcome is even}) = P(\{2, 4, 6\}) = 3/6,$$
$$P(\text{outcome exceeds 2}) = P(\{3, 4, 5, 6\}) = 4/6,$$
$$P(\text{outcome is not a divisor of 6}) = P(\{4, 5\}) = 2/6,$$

and so on.

1.6 A counting principle

As suggested in the preceding section, a convenient way to calculate the probability of an event in a probability model with equally likely outcomes is to enumerate the outcomes in the sample space and in the event. For this process of enumeration, it is useful to have certain techniques at one's command which will be developed in this and in the next section.

In the experiment of tossing a coin, or a die, or some other symmetrical solid, the various faces which might turn up are the elementary "ways," or outcomes. For a coin, which lands so that one face is turned up, the two faces are the outcomes; for a die, the outcomes are the six faces, any one of which can turn up. In the experiment of selecting one object from a group of n objects, the n outcomes are those n objects, any one of which might be drawn.

Often a more complicated experiment can be considered as the consecutive performance of "sub-experiments." In such a case, there is a natural designation of outcomes. *The outcomes of a composite experiment made up of two simpler experiments are taken to be the pairs that can be formed using one outcome from one experiment and one outcome from the other in every possible way.* The extension to any finite number of sub-experiments is obvious.

EXAMPLE 1-o. A coin and die are tossed together. The coin can fall in two ways (H and T) and the die in six (1, 2, 3, 4, 5, 6). The list of possible pairs is as follows:

$$(H, 1) \quad (H, 2) \quad (H, 3) \quad (H, 4) \quad (H, 5) \quad (H, 6)$$
$$(T, 1) \quad (T, 2) \quad (T, 3) \quad (T, 4) \quad (T, 5) \quad (T, 6)$$

The total number of outcomes for the composite experiment, according to this convention of enumeration, is twelve, the product of the two and the six which give, respectively, the numbers of outcomes in the sub-experiments of tossing the coin and tossing the die.

The very convention that defines the (elementary) outcomes in a composite experiment implies the following counting principle:

If an experiment $\mathscr{E}_1$ has exactly n_1 distinct outcomes, and an experiment $\mathscr{E}_2$ has exactly n_2 distinct outcomes, the composite experiment, $\mathscr{E}_1$ and $\mathscr{E}_2$, has exactly $n_1 n_2$ distinct outcomes.

This is obvious at once upon examination of the array in Example 1-o, in which the two rows correspond to the two outcomes of the coin-toss, and the six columns correspond to the six outcomes of the die-toss.

It is to be observed that there is an inherent ordering in the above principle of enumeration. One must keep track of which experiment is which. For example, in counting the outcomes of an experiment which consists of tossing two coins, the outcome H on one coin and T on the other is counted as distinct from the outcome T on the one coin and H on the other; that is, (H, T) is distinct from (T, H), according to this method of enumeration.

The sub-experiments can be performed in any order, or simultaneously, provided that one sub-experiment does not depend on another for its structure, as in the following example, in which case the order of performance does matter.

EXAMPLE 1-p. A bowl contains four beads numbered, respectively, 1, 2, 3, and 4. One bead and then another are drawn. This experiment can be considered as a composite of a first experiment in which the first bead is drawn (four outcomes) followed by a second experiment in which a second bead is drawn from the remaining three beads (three outcomes). The total number of outcomes in the composite experiment is twelve, as follows:

$$(1, 2) \quad (1, 3) \quad (1, 4)$$
$$(2, 1) \quad (2, 3) \quad (2, 4)$$
$$(3, 1) \quad (3, 2) \quad (3, 4)$$
$$(4, 1) \quad (4, 2) \quad (4, 3)$$

Again the systematic listing in a rectangular array makes it clear that the multiplication of 3 by 4 yields the correct number of outcomes in the composite experiment.

The enumeration principle can be used to count the number of ways that n distinct objects can be arranged in a row. This is done by breaking the task of arrangement into subtasks: There are n positions in the row to be filled, and the first can be filled with any one of the n objects—n ways for this subtask. The second position is filled next, and this can be done in $n - 1$ ways for *each* of the n ways of doing the first subtask, and so on. The number of ways in which n things can be arranged in a row is then the product:

$$n(n - 1)(n - 2) \cdots 3 \cdot 2 \cdot 1 = n!$$

These $n!$ arrangements are distinct in that each one differs from any other in some respect; but there are no other possible orderings.

EXAMPLE 1-q.   The four letters A, B, C, D can be arranged in 4! or 24 distinct sequences. These may be enumerated as follows, showing why the product $4 \cdot 3 \cdot 2 \cdot 1$ gives the correct number of arrangements:

$ABCD$	$BACD$	$CABD$	$DABC$
$ABDC$	$BADC$	$CADB$	$DACB$
$ACBD$	$BCAD$	$CBAD$	$DBAC$
$ACDB$	$BCDA$	$CBDA$	$DBCA$
$ADBC$	$BDAC$	$CDAB$	$DCAB$
$ADCB$	$BDCA$	$CDBA$	$DCBA$

EXAMPLE 1-r.   How many different orderings are there of seven names on a ballot, if the names of the three incumbents are listed first?

Here each arrangement is achieved upon ordering the three incumbents' names in the first three positions—in one of 3! ways, and then ordering the remaining names in the remaining four positions—in one of 4! ways. The desired number is then the product $3!4! = 144$.

In another type of arrangement problem some of the objects to be arranged are to be considered as "alike" for the purposes of counting. A simple example of this kind of problem follows.

EXAMPLE 1-s.   Two red flags and one white flag are to be arranged in a row for a signal. How many distinct signals are possible?

Even though the two red flags are not the same flag, and reversing their positions would in a sense yield a different arrangement of the three flags, what is wanted is the number of distinct *signals*. And reversing the positions of the two red flags would not yield a different signal; for if the receiver were close enough to distinguish between the two red flags, such a clumsy mode of communication would hardly be necessary. The distinct signals are easily listed in this case: RRW, RWR, and WRR. That is, the white flag is either first, second, or third in the sequence.

To gain some insight which will show how to count in a more complex situation, suppose that the red flags are labeled R_1 and R_2. The distinct arrangements of the three flags are then:

$$R_1 R_2 W, \qquad R_1 W R_2, \qquad W R_1 R_2,$$
$$R_2 R_1 W, \qquad R_2 W R_1, \qquad W R_2 R_1.$$

Each arrangement in the second row is the same signal as the one above it. Thus, the desired number of possible signals (3) can be thought of as the number of arrangements when the flags are distinct (3!) divided by the number of ways (2!) that the position of the red flags can be arranged without changing the signal.

Let P denote the number of distinct arrangements in a row of n things of which k are alike. The number $n!$ of distinct arrangements of n distinguishable things in a row can be computed as the product of P by the number of ways that the k like objects can be permuted ($k!$):

$$n! = P \cdot k!$$

That is, the task of arranging the n objects, with tags for identification on the k like objects, can be achieved by first arranging the objects without regard for the identification tags, and then arranging the k tagged objects. The result is the useful formula:

$$P = \frac{n!}{k!}.$$

The reasoning is readily extended to the case in which k_1 are alike, k_2 are alike (but different from the k_1), and so on. The number of distinct arrangements is

$$\frac{n!}{k_1! k_2! \cdots}.$$

EXAMPLE 1-t.   Six blocks of which three are red, two are yellow, and one is blue, can be arranged in a row in $6!/(3!2!) = 60$ distinct ways. With moderate patience these could be listed, but the usefulness of the tools developed above is evident.

Problems

1-15.   Count the number of (elementary) outcomes in the following composite experiments:

   (a) a toss of three coins;
   (b) a toss of n coins;

(c) the distribution of five objects among three containers;

(d) the distribution of k objects among m containers;

(e) a toss of n dice.

1-16.   How many three-digit numbers are there whose digits are either 4, 5, 6, or 7?

1-17.   How many numbers with three *distinct* digits are there whose digits are either 4, 5, 6, or 7?

1-18.   How many distinct signals can be made using four flags of different colors in a row?

1-19.   How many distinct signals can be made using four flags in a row, if there are available just three red, one white, and two black flags?

1-20.   In how many ways can a committee of seven be seated along one side of a table, if the chairman must sit in the middle?

1-21.   In how many distinct ways can a committee of seven be seated at a round table (without reference to the location of doors, walls, or air-conditioners)?

1-22.   In a certain experiment it is determined whether observations fall above or below (denoted by A and B, respectively) a certain level. In a series of n observations, how many different sequences of A's and B's could result?

1-23.   Referring to Problem 1-22, suppose that 20 observations are made and that there are as many A's as there are B's. In how many ways can this come about? (That is, how many distinct arrangements are there of ten A's and ten B's?)

1-24.   Of the arrangements counted in Problem 1-23, how many have a string of at least nine A's together?

1-25.   If it is assumed that the sequences of 10 A's and 10 B's in Problem 1-23 are equally likely, what is the probability that there is a run of A's of length at least 9? (Cf. Problem 1-24.)

1-26.   In the toss of a die, what is the probability that the number of points thrown is even or divisible by three?

1-27.   Two dice are tossed. Assuming that the 36 outcomes enumerated according to the principle in Section 1.6 are equally likely, determine the probability that

(a) the sum of the points showing is an even number;

(b) the sum is divisible by three;

(c) the sum is even or divisible by three.

1-28.   Three coins are tossed. Determine the probability that there is at most one "Heads," assuming that the eight outcomes using the enumeration principle of Section 1.6 are equally likely.

1-29.   Four objects are distributed at random among six containers. Assuming the 6^4 ways in which this can be done equally likely, what is the probability that

(a) all objects are in the same container?

(b) no two objects are in the same container?

1.7   Counting combinations

A handy tool for counting elementary outcomes in certain experiments and for later use in computing probabilities is the notion of a *combination*. The basic problem is this: In how many distinct ways can one select k objects from a collection of n objects, without regard to order of selection or to arrangement after selection? One bunch, or combination, or selection of k objects will be considered the same as another selection of k objects if and only if it contains exactly the same k objects.

The symbol $\binom{n}{k}$ is used to denote the answer to the problem just stated, that is, the number of combinations of k things taken from n. (Other symbols for the same quantity are $_nC_k$, C_k^n, $C_{n,k}$.) This number is computed as follows. Consider the auxiliary problem of arranging k A's and $n - k$ B's in a sequence. The arrangement is accomplished as soon as one selects k out of the n sequence positions in which to install the A's, with the B's automatically consigned (one way) to the remaining positions. Thus, there are precisely as many ways of arranging k A's and $n - k$ B's in a row as there are ways of selecting k out of n objects. But this arranging can be done, according to the scheme at the end of the preceding section, in a number of ways obtained by dividing $n!$ by $k!$ and by $(n - k)!$ The desired number of combinations of k from n objects is therefore the quotient:

$$\binom{n}{k} = \frac{n!}{k!(n - k)!}.$$

Cancellation of the $(n - k)!$ in the denominator with corresponding factors in the numerator yields the following form, suited to computation:

$$\binom{n}{k} = \frac{n(n - 1)\cdots(n - k + 1)}{k(k - 1)\cdots 3 \cdot 2 \cdot 1}.$$

Here, there are k factors above the line, beginning with n, and k factors below the line, beginning with k.

Reference to the first formula above shows the following symmetry:

$$\binom{n}{n - k} = \frac{n!}{(n - k)!k!} = \binom{n}{k}.$$

This symmetry becomes evident upon a moment's reflection on the problem: If k objects are selected from n objects, then $n - k$ are also selected at the same time by virtue of being left behind! That is, the selection is really a matter of dividing the pile of n objects into two piles, one with k and the other with $n - k$.

It has been implicit in giving the formulas above that $k = 1, \ldots, n - 1$, for when $k = 0$ or n, there is a zero in the denominator. Of course, selecting n objects from n can be done in just one way—taking all of them, so that $\binom{n}{n} = 1$. This amounts to defining, as is customary in mathematics, 0! to have the value 1; and then to make the symmetry formula valid for $k = 0$, it is convenient to give a value to $\binom{n}{0}$, that is,

$$\binom{n}{0} = \binom{n}{n} = 1.$$

One method of achieving the selection of k objects from n is to select one object at a time until k are selected. This can be exploited to rederive the formula obtained above for the number of selections. In the first drawing of one object there are n available, any one of which can be drawn; in the second drawing, any one of the remaining $n - 1$ can be drawn; and so on. The number of selections with the order of selection preserved is then

$$n(n - 1)\cdots(n - k + 1).$$

This would consider as distinct any selections that contain the same objects but in which those objects were drawn in different orders. To obtain the desired number of selections without regard to order, it is only necessary to divide the above number by the number of different orderings possible for a given selection of k objects:

$$\binom{n}{k} = \frac{n(n - 1)\cdots(n - k + 1)}{k!}.$$

EXAMPLE 1-u.   A group of three men can be selected from five available men in ten ways:

$$\binom{5}{3} = \binom{5}{2} = \frac{5\cdot4}{2\cdot1} = 10.$$

In this case the listing is not tedious; if the five men are $A, B, C, D,$ and E, the ten groups of three are as follows:

ABC, ABD, ABE, ACD, ACE, ADE, BCD, BCE, BDE, CDE.

There are, of course, ten groups of two, not selected, as follows:

DE, CE, CD, BE, BD, BC, AE, AD, AC, AB.

Any one group of three could have been selected, one at a time, in six orders:

ABC, ACB, BAC, BCA, CAB, CBA.

Thus, there are 60 (or $5 \cdot 4 \cdot 3$) ordered selections, which number divided by 3! yields the number 10 of unordered selections.

EXAMPLE 1-v.   A bowl contains three white and two black beads from which three beads are selected. How many combinations are there in which one is black and two are white?

Even though some of the beads are alike in color, the beads are distinct; and the elementary outcomes of this experiment are the $\binom{5}{3}$ selections of three from the five distinct beads. Of these, some have the property that one of the beads is black and the other two are white. It is the number of such selections which is asked for. They can be formed by selecting first one black bead from the two available black beads and then two white beads from the three available white beads. These selections can be accomplished in $\binom{2}{1}$ and $\binom{3}{2}$ ways, respectively. Hence, the desired number is $\binom{2}{1}\binom{3}{2} = 6$. Observe that it is really not necessary to choose the black bead first; one could choose them simultaneously (the black with one hand and the white with the other) without altering the answer.

Perhaps it will be recalled from algebra that the value of $\binom{n}{k}$ as given above is precisely the coefficient of a term of a binomial expansion. To see why this is so, consider $(x + y)^n$. This nth power is the product of the n factors:

$$(x + y)(x + y)(x + y) \cdots (x + y).$$

In this product, one obtains 2^n terms by selecting either the x or the y from each factor. (There are two choices at each of the n selections. Hence, there are 2^n terms.) Each term is made up of n factors, some of them x's and the rest y's—say, k x's and $n - k$ y's:

$$\underbrace{x \cdot x \cdots x}_{k \ x\text{'s}} \cdot \underbrace{y \cdot y \cdots y}_{n-k \ y\text{'s}}.$$

Of these terms, there will be certain ones alike, which may be grouped. That is, there will be as many terms with k x's (and hence $n - k$ y's) as there are ways of selecting k out of the n factors $(x + y)$ from which to use the x. But this number is just $\binom{n}{k}$, and so the coefficient of the term $x^k y^{n-k}$ is $\binom{n}{k}$. Thus,

$$(x + y)^n = \sum_{k=0}^{n} \binom{n}{k} x^k y^{n-k}.$$

For this reason the number $\binom{n}{k}$ is often referred to as a *binomial coefficient*.

EXAMPLE 1-w.   The binomial expansion for $n = 5$ is as follows:

$$(p + q)^5 = \sum_0^5 \binom{5}{k} p^k q^{n-k}$$

$$= \binom{5}{0} q^5 + \binom{5}{1} pq^4 + \binom{5}{2} p^2 q^3 + \binom{5}{3} p^3 q^2 + \binom{5}{4} p^4 q + \binom{5}{5} p^5.$$

1.8   Random selections

The selection of an object from a group of objects will be termed *random* if and only if the correct model is that in which all objects in the group are assigned the same probability—have the same chance of being selected. Thus, the model for the random selection of a card from the 52 cards of a bridge deck is that in which each card has the probability $\frac{1}{52}$ of being drawn. Whether an actual selection process is faithfully represented by such a model cannot be established with certainty. Steps can be taken so that the model would seem to be appropriate; for example, the cards in the deck can be thoroughly shuffled and the selection of a card made without looking at the cards. Or in a lottery the tickets can be (and frequently are) shuffled in a revolving drum. Even so, only experience with the shuffling mechanism being used can determine—and then only with a certain probabilistic degree of assurance—that the selection is truly random.

Selecting persons from a population of people in such a way that the model of equally likely outcomes applies is especially difficult. It would certainly be awkward to put them all into a revolving drum for shuffling; this makes it almost essential to have a listing of the people in the population, and accurate lists are hard to develop—for example, the list of all persons owning television sets in a certain metropolitan area.

In selecting k from n objects, it has been seen that there are $\binom{n}{k}$ outcomes, according to a natural enumeration, and disregarding any ordering among the objects selected. A process represented by the model in which the outcomes are assigned the equal probabilities $1 \big/ \binom{n}{k}$ is referred to as random sampling; one says that k objects are drawn *at random* from n objects. And whenever the phrase "drawn at random" is used, it is to be interpreted as meaning that the $\binom{n}{k}$ selections are equally likely. This definition includes as a special case that given above in the case $k = 1$.

EXAMPLE 1-x. Two articles are drawn at random from a lot containing thirteen articles, five of which are defective. What is the probability that both are good? That one is good and one is bad?

For both questions, the denominator is the same, namely, the number of ways one can select two out of thirteen objects, $\binom{13}{2} = 78$. The phrase "at random" implies that these 78 combinations are to be considered as equally likely. Some of these combinations satisfy the description "both are good (not defective)," and there are as many such combinations as there are ways of selecting two from the eight good articles; the desired probability is then the ratio:

$$P(\text{both good}) = \binom{8}{2} \Big/ \binom{13}{2} = \frac{14}{39}.$$

And some of the 78 combinations satisfy the description "one is good and one is defective." To form such a combination, first select one bad article from five, in one of 5 ways, and then select one good article from the eight, in one of 8 ways. The number of such combinations is therefore 40, and

$$P(\text{one good, one bad}) = 40/78 = 20/39.$$

EXAMPLE 1-y. Five cards are drawn at random from a bridge deck. What is the probability of drawing two pairs? (An example of such a hand would be a pair of 10's, a pair of Aces, and a 4. That is, the pairs are not of the same denomination, and the fifth card is of still a different denomination.)

Since five cards are drawn from the 52 available cards, the denominator of the fraction defining probability is $\binom{52}{5}$, the number of ways in which such selections are possible. These are equally likely. The numerator is the number of ways of selecting the two pairs and the odd card, and the task can be considered in parts. First, select two of the thirteen denominations from which to draw the pairs and a denomination from which to draw the odd card. The number of choices of denominations is $\binom{13}{2}\binom{11}{1}$, where the "11" arises because having selected two of the thirteen denominations for pairs, one has only eleven choices for the denomination of the odd card. Having determined the denominations, pick a pair from each of those groups of four cards having denominations designated for pairs, and pick a single card from the third denomination; the number of ways here is $\binom{4}{2}\binom{4}{2}\binom{4}{1}$. The desired probability is then

$$P(\text{two pairs in a hand of five cards}) = \frac{\binom{13}{2}\binom{11}{1}\binom{4}{2}\binom{4}{2}\binom{4}{1}}{\binom{52}{5}} = \frac{198}{4165}.$$

Notice that the product $\binom{13}{1}\binom{12}{2}$, corresponding to picking first the denomination for the odd card and then the denominations for the pairs, is exactly the same as the product used above, $\binom{13}{2}\binom{11}{1}$. It does not matter which decomposition into subtasks is used.

Problems

1-30. Compute: $\binom{15}{15}$, $\binom{15}{13}$, $\binom{15}{0}$, $\binom{15}{1}$, $\binom{46}{44}$, $\binom{52}{5}$.

1-31. How many connecting cables are needed in order that any two of nine offices in a building can communicate directly?

1-32. If n countries in a bloc exchange ambassadors, how many ambassadors are involved?

1-33. A lot contains fifty articles, six of them defective.

(a) How many selections of five articles can be made from the lot?

(b) How many selections of two defective and four good articles can be made from the lot?

1-34. Show that $k\binom{n}{k} = n\binom{n-1}{k-1}$. Interpret this equality by considering each side as the number of ways of performing certain selections.

1-35. (a) Write the term involving p^8 in the expansion of $(p + q)^{12}$.

(b) Write the term involving x^{20} in the expansion of $(x + 2y)^{35}$.

1-36. One article is drawn at random from a lot consisting of ten good articles, four articles with only minor defects, and two with major defects. Find the probability that the article drawn has

(a) no defects;

(b) no major defects;

(c) either major defects or is good.

1-37. Two articles are selected at random from the lot of Problem 1-36. Determine the probability that

(a) both are good;

(b) both have major defects;

(c) at least one is good;

(d) at most one is good;

(e) exactly one is good;

(f) neither has major defects;

(g) neither is good.

1-38. A committee of four is selected at random from a group consisting of ten labor and five management representatives. What is the probability that the committee selected has on it:

(a) two from labor and two from management?

(b) at least one representative from each group?

(c) the chairman of the labor delegation and the chairman of the management delegation?

1-39. A lot of sixteen articles is to be accepted if three articles selected at random have no major defect. What is the probability that the lot in Problem 1-36 is

   (a) accepted?

   (b) rejected?

1-40. Five cards are drawn at random from a bridge deck, as in Example 1-y. Determine the probability of "three-of-a-kind." (This describes a hand in which there are three of one denomination and one from each of two different denominations—for example, three 8's, a Queen, and an Ace.)

1.9 Conditional probability

It often happens that the sample space for an experiment must be altered to take into account the availability of certain limited information about the outcome of the experiment. Such information may well eliminate certain outcomes as impossible which were otherwise (without the information) possible, and in such a case either the appropriate sample space would omit these impossible outcomes or the probabilities assigned to them would be zero. In the revised model, the probabilities are said to be *conditional* on the occurrence of the event defined by the information. This new model is again a probability space, and the term "conditional" refers only to its origin in a larger probability space.

EXAMPLE 1-z. A standard die is tossed, and before seeing the outcome, one is told by a bystander who does see the result that an even number of points is showing. How should he then bet?

Certainly one would be foolish to place any money on the outcomes 1, 3, or 5—the information that the outcome is an *even* number eliminates these from consideration. The sample space now is effectively just the set of even outcomes {2, 4, 6}, whose occurrence constitutes the information. But, in addition to betting nothing on the odd outcomes, one would find that his probabilities for the even outcomes are increased over what they are in the standard model for the toss of a die (with no information). For, *a priori* considerations would again suggest that there is no reason for any one of the outcomes 2, 4, or 6 to predominate, and each would be assigned probability 1/3. The same conclusion would be reached in considering a long sequence of tosses of the die; in such a sequence the proportions of 1's, 2's, ..., and 6's would be about equal, and the information that the outcome is even would simply eliminate from the sequence those trials that resulted in an odd number of points—leaving a sequence with equal proportions of 2's, 4's, and 6's.

Conditional probabilities, given an event F (or given that F has occurred), are obtained from the unconditional ones in the original sample space by taking F as a new sample space, and distributing a total probability of 1 over this smaller sample space in such a way that the new probabilities are in the same proportions as the old within F. That is, for any event E contained in an event F of positive probability the conditional probability of E given F, written $P(E \mid F)$, is defined to be

$$P(E \mid F) = \frac{P(E)}{P(F)}, \quad \text{(when } E \subset F).$$

Notice that with this definition (for events in F), conditional probabilities are indeed proportional to the unconditional ones, and further, that the assignment of these conditional probabilities to events satisfies the probability axioms. That is, $P(F \mid F) = 1$, $P(E \mid F) \geq 0$, and the additivity axiom holds because it held in the original space.

Thus, conditioning with the information that F has occurred simply introduces a smaller probability space—and yet it is usually desirable to stay in the framework of the original probability space; thus, the adjective "conditional" is used, to refer to the reduced model. Events in the original sample space define events in the smaller space—for instance, the event G in Ω can be interpreted as a condition that characterizes its outcomes, and imposing this condition in the reduced model amounts to imposing *both* conditions G and F. Thus the conditional probability of G given F (again assume $P(F) > 0$) is taken to be

$$P(G \mid F) = P(G \cap F \mid F) = \frac{P(G \cap F)}{P(F)}.$$

This definition includes the earlier one, but it can be used without having to check whether or not G is contained in F. The definition is often useful in the form of a *multiplication law*:

$$P(E \cap F) = P(E \mid F)P(F).$$

[With this, one can compute the probability of $E \cap F$ from what is sometimes an easier determination of the factors $P(E \mid F)$ and $P(F)$.]

EXAMPLE 1-aa. A card is drawn at random from a standard deck of cards. (This wording implies that each card is assigned probability $1/52$.) Given that the card drawn is a face card, the probability that it is a Jack would be computed as follows, since a Jack is a face card:

$$P(\text{Jack} \mid \text{face card}) = \frac{P(\text{Jack})}{P(\text{face card})} = \frac{4/52}{12/52} = \frac{1}{3}.$$

But not all Hearts are face cards, so

$$P(\text{Heart} \mid \text{face card}) = \frac{P(\text{Heart and face card})}{P(\text{face card})} = \frac{3/52}{12/52} = \frac{1}{4}.$$

That is, one-third of the face cards are Jacks, and one-quarter of the face cards are Hearts.

EXAMPLE 1-bb. A bowl contains two white (W) beads and three black (B) beads. One bead is drawn at random, and then another is drawn at random from those remaining. What is the probability that the first is black and the second white?

The phrase "drawn at random" means that the available beads at each drawing are to be assigned equal probabilities. Thus, the probability that the first bead is black is 3/5, the ratio of the number of black beads to the number of beads. At the second drawing the probabilities depend on what happened during the first drawing; if the first bead actually *is* black, then there are two white and two black beads left in the bag. These four remaining beads are assumed equally likely, so that

$$P(\text{2nd white} \mid \text{1st black}) = 2/4.$$

And then,

$$P(\text{1st black and 2nd white}) = P(\text{2nd white} \mid \text{1st black}) \, P(\text{1st black})$$
$$= \frac{2}{4} \cdot \frac{3}{5} = \frac{3}{10}.$$

One can compute the probabilities for each outcome of the composite experiment of selecting the two beads in analogous fashion. The results (including the one just computed) are as follows:

$$P(B, \text{ then } W) = \frac{3}{10},$$

$$P(W, \text{ then } B) = \frac{2}{5} \cdot \frac{3}{4} = \frac{3}{10},$$

$$P(W, \text{ then } W) = \frac{2}{5} \cdot \frac{1}{4} = \frac{1}{10},$$

$$P(B, \text{ then } B) = \frac{3}{5} \cdot \frac{2}{4} = \frac{3}{10}.$$

These total 1, of course, but they are not equal; the equal likelihood occurred in the component parts of the composite experiment. Notice, incidentally, that

$$P(\text{1st white}) = P(W, \text{ then } B) + P(W, \text{ then } W) = 2/5,$$

and

$$P(\text{1st black}) = P(B, \text{ then } W) + P(B, \text{ then } B) = 3/5.$$

That is, the probabilities postulated for the first drawing are recoverable from the model for the composite experiment. Notice also that

$$P(\text{2nd white}) = P(B, \text{ then } W) + P(W, \text{ then } W) = 2/5.$$

That is, the probability of a white bead on the second draw, *without* the knowledge of what happened on the first draw, is the same as though all the beads were still in the bag!

EXAMPLE 1-cc.   A bag contains four white and two black beads, and a second bag contains three of each color. A bag is drawn at random, and a bead is then selected at random from the bag chosen. What is the probability that the bead selected is white?

There are two mutually exclusive ways of selecting a white bead: Either a white bead is drawn from the first bag or a white bead is drawn from the second bag. The probability of a white bead is the sum of the probabilities of these disjoint events. For the first,

$$P(\text{white bead from 1st bag}) = P(\text{white} \mid \text{1st bag}) \, P(\text{1st bag})$$
$$= \frac{4}{6}\cdot\frac{1}{2} = \frac{1}{3},$$

and for the second,

$$P(\text{white bead from 2nd bag}) = P(\text{white} \mid \text{2nd bag}) \, P(\text{2nd bag})$$
$$= \frac{3}{6}\cdot\frac{1}{2} = \frac{1}{4}.$$

The desired probability of a white bead is then $1/3 + 1/4 = 7/12$.

The multiplication rule for dependent events can be written in two ways, for E given or for F given (with E as the condition or F as the condition):

$$P(F \mid E)P(E) = P(E \cap F) = P(E \mid F)P(F).$$

Omitting the middle member of this equality and dividing by $P(E)$, one obtains *Bayes' rule*:

$$P(F \mid E) = P(E \mid F)\frac{P(F)}{P(E)}.$$

EXAMPLE 1-dd.   A certain disease is present in about 1 out of 1000 persons in a given population, and a program of testing is to be carried out using a detection device that gives a positive reading with probability .99 for a diseased person and with probability .05 for a healthy person. It is desired to determine the probability that a person who has a positive reading actually does have the disease.

With obvious notations for diseased, healthy, positive, and negative, the given quantities are as follows:

$$P(D) = .001, \qquad P(+ \mid D) = .99, \qquad P(+ \mid H) = .05.$$

Bayes' theorem permits the computation of $P(D \mid +)$ from these:

$$P(D \mid +) = \frac{P(+ \mid D)P(D)}{P(+)}.$$

The denominator is computed as follows:

$$P(+) = P(+ \mid D)P(D) + P(+ \mid H)P(H) = .99 \times .001 + .05 \times .999$$
$$= .05094.$$

Then the desired conditional probability is the ratio of the first term to the sum:

$$P(D \mid +) = \frac{.00099}{.05094} = 0.0194,$$

or about one chance in 50. This result may seem a bit odd at first, since the characteristics of the detector as given seem rather good; the explanation is that when a positive reading is obtained, it is much more frequently a machine malfunction than a diseased person which gives the reading. For, even with a perfect detection device, only one in 1000 readings would be positive; whereas with the given device and a completely healthy population, five out of every 100 readings would be positive.

Problems

1-41. Determine the probability that a card drawn at random from a standard deck is a face card, given that it is red. Compare this with the probability that the card drawn is a face card.

1-42. Two dice are tossed such that the 36 outcomes (as enumerated according to Section 1.6) can be considered equally likely. Determine the probability that one of the two dice (say the red one) turns up six, given that the other one (say, green) shows an even number of points. Compare this with the probability that the red die turns up six.

1-43. A penny and a nickel are tossed, with equal probabilities assigned to the four outcomes (as enumerated according to the principle of Section 1.6). What is the probability that both are Heads,

    (a) given that at least one is Heads?

    (b) given that the penny falls Heads?

1-44. (a) Determine the probability that two cards from a standard bridge deck are both Aces,

      (i) when two cards are drawn at random from the deck;

      (ii) when first one card is drawn at random from the deck, and then another card is drawn at random from the remaining cards.

    (b) Determine the probability that two cards drawn from a standard deck are one black and the other red, using selection methods (i) and (ii), respectively, of part (a).

1-45. A bag contains three luminous white, five luminous green, four non-luminous white, and six nonluminous green beads. A bead is selected at random from the bag. Determine the probability that the bead selected is

    (a) white;

    (b) luminous, given that it is green;

(c) green, given that it is nonluminous;

(d) green or luminous.

1-46. A box contains ten electron tubes, four bad and six good.

(a) Two are drawn at random from the box, and one of them is tested and found to be good. What is the probability that the other is good also?

(b) Tubes are checked as follows: A tube is drawn at random, tested, and put aside, and this process is repeated until all four bad tubes are located. What is the probability that the last bad tube will be located at the fifth test? At the tenth test? [*Hint:* The fourth bad tube will be found at the fifth test provided that three are found in the first four tests, and then the remaining one is found in the fifth test.]

1-47. A man has two coins, one an ordinary coin and one a two-headed coin. He picks one at random and tosses it. If it falls Heads, what is the probability that it was the two-headed coin that he tossed?

1-48. Machines A and B turn out, respectively, 10 and 90 percent of the total production of a certain type of article. Suppose that the probability that machine A turns out a defective article is .01 and that machine B turns out a defective article is .05. What is the probability that an article taken at random from a day's production was made by machine A, given that it is found to be defective?

1-49. Suppose that experiment 1 has m equally likely outcomes, called $u_1, \ldots, u_m$, and suppose further that experiment 2 has n equally likely outcomes depending on the outcome of experiment 1. If u_i is the result of experiment 1, denote the outcomes of experiment 2 by $v_{i1}, v_{i2}, \ldots, v_{in}$. Count the elementary outcomes of the composite experiment consisting of performing experiment 1 and then experiment 2, and show that these are equally likely.

1.10   Independent events and experiments

Problems 1-41 and 1-42 deal with examples in which certain events are related in a very special way. Perhaps *un*related would be a better description, since in each case information that one event has occurred does not alter the probability of the other event—the conditional and unconditional probabilities are the same. In general, events E and F are said to be *independent events* if either has probability zero or if

$$P(E \mid F) = P(E).$$

This relation appears at first to lack symmetry, although the language is symmetrical; but since if $P(E) \neq 0$,

$$P(F \mid E) = \frac{P(E \text{ and } F)}{P(E)} = \frac{P(E \mid F)P(F)}{P(E)},$$

it follows that if $P(E \mid F) = P(E)$, then $P(F \mid E) = P(F)$. (The converse follows simply by interchanging the roles of E and F.) Moreover, if E and F satisfy this condition, then

$$P(E \text{ and } F) = P(E \mid F)P(E) = P(E)P(F).$$

This, in turn, implies the original condition, for if $P(E \text{ and } F)$ factors into the product $P(E)P(F)$, then

$$P(F \mid E) = \frac{P(E \text{ and } F)}{P(E)} = P(F),$$

and similarly, $P(E \mid F) = P(E)$. In summary, then, any of the following three equivalent conditions can be taken as defining independence of E and F (if $P(E) \neq 0$ and $P(F) \neq 0$):

  (i) $P(E \mid F) = P(E)$,
  (ii) $P(F \mid E) = P(F)$,
  (iii) $P(E \text{ and } F) = P(E)P(F)$.

(Notice that the condition (iii) is fulfilled if either $P(E) = 0$ or $P(F) = 0$.)

The notion of independent events is extended inductively to several events $E_1, \ldots, E_n$. These are said to be independent if (1) they are such that every subset of fewer than n of them form an independent set of events, and (2) $P(E_1 \text{ and } E_2 \cdots \text{ and } E_n) = P(E_1)P(E_2) \cdots P(E_n)$. Thus, three events are independent if every two of them are independent and if $P(E_1 \text{ and } E_2 \text{ and } E_3) = P(E_1)P(E_2)P(E_3)$, and so on.

EXAMPLE 1-ee.   In Problem 1-41, it was seen that the event "red" and the event "face card" in the random selection of a card are such that

$$P(\text{red} \mid \text{face card}) = P(\text{red}) = 1/2.$$

These are then independent events. The information that the card drawn is a face card does not alter how one should bet concerning the color. Notice that also

$$P(\text{face card} \mid \text{red}) = P(\text{face card}) = 3/13,$$

and

$$P(\text{red face card}) = 6/52 = \frac{1}{2} \cdot \frac{3}{13} = P(\text{red})P(\text{face card}).$$

EXAMPLE 1-ff.   There are twelve outcomes in the simultaneous toss of a coin and a die, using the enumeration principle of Section 1.6. Consider the probability model that weights these twelve outcomes equally, assigning probability $1/12$ to each. This assignment implies, for example,

$$P(\text{coin } H \mid \text{die } 6) = \frac{P(H \text{ and } 6)}{P(6)} = \frac{1/12}{1/6} = \frac{1}{2} = P(\text{coin } H).$$

(Observe that from the way probability is assigned, $P(6)$ must be computed as the sum of the probabilities assigned to the outcomes $(H, 6)$ and $(T, 6)$, and the value of $P(H)$, as the sum of the probabilities of $(H, 1), \ldots, (H, 6)$.) So the event H for the coin and 6 for the die are independent.

It is easily checked, in similar fashion, that if E is an event relating only to the toss of the coin and F an event relating only to the toss of the die, these events E and F are independent. The sub-experiments, tossing the coin and tossing the die, are said to be *independent experiments*.

In general, if a composite experiment has components such that events relating to the separate components are always independent, one says that those component *experiments* are *independent*. This notion is frequently used in constructing probability models for composite experiments when it is desired to incorporate independence into the model. Often it is clear from the way in which an experiment is conducted that the outcome of one component of the experiment cannot alter the chances relating to another component; it is then assumed that they are independent, this assumption being incorporated into the model by using the multiplication rule for independent events.

EXAMPLE 1-gg.   Suppose that the probability that a night lookout on a blacked-out ship detects a periscope under certain weather conditions is .7. What is the probability that a combination of two such lookouts, A and B, would make the detection?

The assumption of independence again calls into play the multiplication rule for independent events:

$$P(\text{detection}) = 1 - P(\text{both } A \text{ and } B \text{ fail to detect})$$
$$= 1 - P(A \text{ fails to detect})P(B \text{ fails to detect})$$
$$= 1 - (.3)(.3) = .91 .$$

Thus, whether or not .7 is really correct for a single lookout, it is at least clear that the extra lookout increases considerably the probability of a detection.

EXAMPLE 1-hh.   A coin and die are tossed together, and it is agreed that the toss of the coin and the toss of the die are independent. Assuming models with equally likely outcomes for the coin and for the die tossed separately, the probabilities for H and T are each 1/2, and the probabilities for 1, 2, 3, 4, 5, and 6 on the die are each 1/6. The probability of the joint occurrence of an H on the coin and a 6 on the die is then defined using the multiplication formula:

$$P(H, 6) = P(H)P(6) = \frac{1}{2} \cdot \frac{1}{6} = \frac{1}{12} .$$

It can be seen, similarly, that the probability for *each* of the elementary outcomes of the composite experiment is 1/12, so that the model for this composite experiment turns out to be the same as that used in Example 1-ff.

Example 1-hh is readily generalized to show that the outcomes formed using the principle of Section 1.6 from equally likely outcomes in independent component experiments are again equally likely. Thus, the 8 outcomes in the independent tosses of three fair coins are equally likely, and the 6^n outcomes in the independent tosses of n fair dice are equally likely, and so on.

An important type of problem in which probabilities are formed with the aid of the multiplication law for independent experiments is that leading to the *binomial* model. The following characteristics identify this problem:

(1) An experiment with two outcomes, say E and E^c, is conducted a given, finite number of times.
(2) The trials are independent.
(3) The probability p that E occurs in a single trial is the *same for each trial.*
(4) The quantity of interest is the number of times among the sequence of trials that E occurs, without regard to the location of those occurrences in the sequence.

The method of solution of this type of problem will be seen in working out the answer for a specific example.

EXAMPLE 1-ii.   What is the probability that exactly three 6's show when eight dice are tossed together?

Whether the dice are tossed simultaneously or not is immaterial, and the toss of eight dice can be considered equivalent to eight successive tosses of one die. Let these trials be deemed independent, and let E denote the outcome "6" in one toss. ("Not E" is then the event made up of the outcomes 1, 2, 3, 4, 5.) To determine the desired probability, compute first the probability that three particular dice among the eight show "6" and that the remaining five do not. According to the multiplication rule for independent events, this probability is

$$\frac{1}{6}\cdot\frac{1}{6}\cdot\frac{1}{6}\cdot\frac{5}{6}\cdot\frac{5}{6}\cdot\frac{5}{6}\cdot\frac{5}{6}\cdot\frac{5}{6} = \left(\frac{1}{6}\right)^3\left(\frac{5}{6}\right)^5.$$

This same product is the probability that any other specified set of three of the eight dice show a 6 (and the rest something other than 6). These various sets of three of the eight dice correspond to the mutually exclusive ways in which the result of the toss of the eight dice is that exactly three show a 6; the probability of the latter event is then the sum of the probabilities for these various choices of three particular dice:

$$P(\text{exactly three 6's}) = \left(\frac{1}{6}\right)^3\left(\frac{5}{6}\right)^5 + \left(\frac{1}{6}\right)^3\left(\frac{5}{6}\right)^5 + \cdots.$$

There are as many (identical) terms in this sum as there are ways of selecting three of the eight dice to show the 6's. Hence,

$$P(\text{exactly three 6's}) = \binom{8}{3}\left(\frac{1}{6}\right)^3\left(\frac{5}{6}\right)^5.$$

In the general case, there is a constant probability p that E occurs in a given trial, and therefore a probability $1 - p$ that E does not occur in a given trial. Reasoning as in Example 1-ii, but with n trials and with $1/6$ replaced by p and $5/6$ by q, one obtains the following *binomial formula* (occurrence of E is termed "success"):

$$P(k \text{ successes in } n \text{ trials}) = \binom{n}{k} p^k q^{n-k}.$$

EXAMPLE 1-jj. The same reasoning yields the solution to a somewhat more complicated problem, in which there are several outcomes possible in each trial. For example, the probability that among n independent tosses of a die there are f_1 ones, f_2 twos, ..., and f_6 sixes is

$$\frac{n!}{f_1! f_2! \cdots f_6!} \left(\frac{1}{6}\right)^{f_1} \left(\frac{1}{6}\right)^{f_2} \cdots \left(\frac{1}{6}\right)^{f_6}.$$

The coefficient—the ratio of factorials multiplying the powers of $1/6$ in this expression—is called a *multinomial coefficient* and appears in the expansion of a power of a multinomial, corresponding to the role of the binomial coefficient in the expansion of a power of a binomial.

Problems

1-50. Two coins and a die are tossed. What is the probability that both coins fall Heads and the die shows a 3 or a 6? (In this and in the following problems involving "tossing," assume independence of the tosses.)

1-51. Two dice are thrown three times in succession.

(a) What is the probability that an 8, 5, and 7 are thrown in that order?

(b) What is the probability that the third throw results in a 7, given that the first two throws were an 8 and a 5, in that order?

(c) What is the probability of throwing exactly one 7 and exactly one 11 in the first three throws?

1-52. A bag contains four white and two black beads, and a second bag contains three of each color. A bead is drawn from each bag. What is the probability that one bead is white and one is black?

1-53. What is the probability that if four coins are tossed,

(a) exactly three show Heads?

(b) at least three show Heads?

(c) at most one shows Heads?

1-54. Six dice are tossed. What is the probability that

(a) at most two 1's show?

(b) at least five 2's or 3's show?

1-55. A sample of twenty is chosen from a collection of 45 white and 55 black beads as follows: A bead is chosen at random, the color noted, and *replaced.* After thorough mixing another bead is chosen, and so on. What is the probability that the sample of twenty shows a majority (more than half) of white beads? (This is called "sampling with replacement.")

1-56. Referring to Problem 1-55, if the twenty beads are drawn together, at random, what is then the probability of a majority of white beads in the sample? ("Sampling without replacement.")

1-57. A fire control system consists of a radar and a computer, so connected that the system fails if either of these components fails. If the probability that the radar operates 100 hours without failure is .9 and that the computer operates 100 hours without failure is .7, what is the probability that the combined system operates 100 hours without failure? (Assume failures of the components to be independent.)

1-58. Three alarm devices are so arranged that any one of them will give alarm when something undesirable occurs. If each device has probability .9 of working properly, what is the probability that an alarm is sounded when warranted? (Assume independent operation.)

1-59. The probability that a part produced by a certain machine is defective is .05. What is the probability that out of ten parts made by this machine, exactly one is defective? (Assume independence.)

1-60. The probability that an interceptor can make a successful attack is .6 if he has been "vectored" into position in a certain region with respect to the target. The probability that he is properly directed into position is .8. What is the probability of a successful interception? Suppose that the figure .6 includes a reliability (probability of successful operation) of .7 of the electronic computation system. What would be the probability of successful interception if the electronic system had a reliability of .95 instead? (Assume independence.)

Review Problems

1-61. In how many ways can eight objects be drawn from eleven?

1-62. How many distinct code groups of four symbols in a row can be formed, where each symbol is either a dot or a dash?

1-63. What is the probability that if four dice are tossed, exactly one is a 6?

1-64. A tester smokes cigarettes of each of three different brands, *A*, *B*, and *C*. He then assigns the name *A* to one cigarette, *B* to another, and *C* to the remaining one. If he does this purely by chance, what is the probability that he correctly identifies just one brand?

1-65. Suppose that 10,000 tickets are sold in a lottery, and 5000 in another lottery, each lottery having just one winner. A man has 100 tickets in each. What is the probability that

(a) he wins exactly one prize?

(b) he wins something?

1-66. What is the probability that five cards drawn together from a standard deck of fifty-two cards are from the same suit and could form a "run" of five? (For example: 9, King, Queen, 10, Jack of clubs.) Ace counts only high.

1-67. A child has five blocks, three with the letter A and two with the letter B. How many distinct arrangements of four of these blocks can he make?

1-68. It is found that in manufacturing a certain article, defects of one type occur with probability .1, and of another type with probability .05. What is the probability that

(a) an article does not have both kinds of defect?
(b) an article is defective?
(c) an article has only one type of defect, given that it is defective?

1-69. A coin is tossed ten times. What is the probability that the tenth toss results in heads, given that the first nine tosses are heads?

1-70. Each of eight members of a committee flips a coin to decide whether he should attend a certain meeting of the committee.

(a) What is the probability that a majority will show up?
(b) How many different combinations might show up?

1-71. A man has $7000 to invest in recovering his vacation expenses of $1000. He does this by playing a gambling game in which he is given even odds, but in which his probability of winning is only .4, at a given play. He bets $1000 on the first play and doubles his bet on successive trials if he loses.

(a) What is the probability that he wins (net) the $1000 before going broke?
(b) What is the probability that he wins before going broke on each of eight out of ten annual trips to the casino?

1-72. What is the probability that at least two people in a room of twenty people will be found to have the same birthday?

1-73. A bag contains four beads. One is red, luminescent, and has a hole; another is green, luminescent, and solid (no hole); a third is red, nonluminescent, and solid; and a fourth is green, nonluminescent and has a hole. A bead is drawn at random from the bag. Consider the events: R, the bead is red; H, the bead has a hole; L, the bead is luminescent. Show that any two of these three events are independent, but that the three events are not independent.

1-74. In a certain series of games, the probability that A wins the first game is $1/2$; in any subsequent game, the odds are 2 to 1 in favor of the previous winner. The first player who wins four games wins the series. What is the probability that A wins in four games? In five games?

2

DISCRETE RANDOM
VARIABLES

Having performed a given experiment of chance, obtaining thereby one of the outcomes of the experiment, one is often concerned with some numerical characteristic of that outcome. When the value of this characteristic is determined for a given outcome, the number so obtained certainly depends on the outcome of the experiment and has the element of chance in it even as the outcome itself has. Such a *function* of the outcome is called a *random variable*. To introduce some convenient notation, suppose that the outcomes of the experiment are called generically ω, and specifically $\omega_1, \omega_2, \ldots$. The measured characteristic of the outcome ω is then a function of ω to be denoted, say, by $X(\omega)$. More generally, one might be concerned about *several* numerical characteristics of ω, say $X(\omega)$, $Y(\omega)$, and $Z(\omega)$. Such a triple—or in general, n-tuple—of functions of the outcome ω is called a *random vector*. In summary then:

Definition A *random variable* is a numerical-valued function of the outcomes of an experiment of chance. A *random vector* is an n-tuple of numerical-valued functions of the outcomes of an experiment of chance.

EXAMPLE 2-a. A person is drawn at random from a certain population of N people. These N people, $\omega_1, \omega_2, \ldots, \omega_N$, are the outcomes of the experiment. The height of the person drawn is then an example of a random variable:

$$X(\omega) = \text{height of the person } \omega.$$

37

A random vector of interest might be $(X(\omega), Y(\omega), Z(\omega))$, where $Y(\omega)$ is the weight of ω, and $Z(\omega)$ is the age of ω.

It is often the case, when there is no natural numerical characteristic, that it is convenient to *assign* numbers to outcomes, arbitrarily, just to have available a numerical coding for purposes of identification. The die manufacturer, for instance, builds into the die such a coding, marking each of the six faces with a certain number of dots; this number is then a random variable.

EXAMPLE 2-b.   In the toss of a coin, let 1 be assigned to Heads and 0 to Tails. That is,

$$X(\omega) = \begin{cases} 1, & \text{if } \omega = \text{Heads}, \\ 0, & \text{if } \omega = \text{Tails}. \end{cases}$$

With this same coding, one obtains a random vector upon tossing the coin, say, five times. If the outcomes are H, H, T, H, T, for instance, then the corresponding "value" of the random vector of coded outcomes is $(1, 1, 0, 1, 0)$.

A condition on a random variable defines an event in the sample space on which it is defined, namely, the set of outcomes having values assigned which satisfy that condition. The probability that the condition is satisfied is then just the probability of that event defined by the condition. To be sure, one can consider the values of a random variable as elementary outcomes in a sample space, and the various sets of values as events; probabilities for these events are induced by an assignment of probabilities to the original ω's, but in constructing a model one could start in this sample space of numbers and assign probabilities there. When this is done, a random variable of interest might be the outcomes themselves: $X(\omega) = \omega$.

EXAMPLE 2-c.   In tossing a die with the usual dots marked on it, one can consider the sample space to be the six *numbers* 1, 2, 3, 4, 5, 6 (rather than the six faces themselves). For a fair toss the obvious model is that in which these six numbers are all assigned probability 1/6. The random variable $X(\omega) \equiv \omega$ is just the outcome itself, but one might be interested in still other aspects of the outcome. For instance, let

$$Y(\omega) = \begin{cases} 1, & \text{if } \omega \text{ is even}, \\ 0, & \text{if } \omega \text{ is odd}. \end{cases}$$

The condition $Y(\omega) = 1$ defines the event $(2, 4, 6)$ in the sample space of numbers of dots, and is then assigned the probability of that event, 3/6:

$$P(Y(\omega) = 1) = P(2, 4, \text{ or } 6) = 1/2.$$

The value $Y(\omega) = 0$ is similarly seen to have the probability 1/2, and the numbers 0 and 1, with probabilities 1/2 and 1/2, respectively, could be considered as a new space.

2.1 Describing a distribution

It should now be clear that the function defining a random variable induces an assignment of probabilities in the space of values of the function; this is referred to as a *probability distribution* in that space of values, and is completely defined by the *probability function*:

$$p(x_i) = P(X(\omega) = x_i).$$

It is occasionally convenient to shorten $p(x_i)$ further to p_i, or if necessary to distinguish the probability function for one random variable from that of a second random variable, to lengthen the notation to $p_X(x_i)$. The function may be specified by a formula or by a tabulation of its values.

It is often the case that even though there is an underlying sample space in which probability is naturally defined, the values of the random variable of interest and its probability distribution in this set of values are all that matter. Because of this focus of attention on the value space, the reference to the original ω's is often dropped, and one writes simply X in place of $X(\omega)$. (This is perhaps especially appropriate when the ω's are themselves numbers and the random variable being studied is $X(\omega) = \omega$.) Similarly, in the case of a random vector, the notation would be (X, Y, Z), for example.

EXAMPLE 2-d.   The random variable X in Example 2-b and the random variable Y in Example 2-c define the same distribution in the space of values of these variables; that is, the same "induced" distribution, which puts probability 1/2 at each of the values 0 and 1. The probability function in each case is then

$$p(x) = \begin{cases} 1/2, & \text{if } x = 0 \\ 1/2, & \text{if } x = 1. \end{cases}$$

EXAMPLE 2-e.   The probability function of Z, the number of points showing when a die is tossed, assigns probability 1/6 to each of the possible values $1, 2, \ldots, 6$:

$$p(1) = p(2) = \cdots = p(6) = 1/6.$$

EXAMPLE 2-f.   A function on a sample space that is constant defines a "constant random variable": $X(\omega) = k$, for all ω. That is, no matter what outcome ω results from performing the basic experiment, the value k is assigned to it. (This notion of "constant variable" is consistent with the mathematical practice of considering a function that is constant to be a particular case of a "function," even though its value does not really depend on the independent variable.) The probability distribution of X assigns probability 1 to the value k, and so $p(k) = 1$, with $p(x) = 0$ for $x \neq k$.

EXAMPLE 2-g.   Consider n identical, independent trials of an experiment, and let p denote the probability that a certain event E occurs at a given trial. Let X

denote the number of times E occurs among the n trials. This number X is a random variable, with possible values $0, 1, \ldots, n$, and its probability distribution is defined by

$$p(k) = P(X = k) = P(k \text{ successes in } n \text{ trials})$$
$$= \binom{n}{k} p^k (1 - p)^{n-k}.$$

One could consider the various sequences of E's and *not* E's to be the outcomes ω in a sample space for this experiment; the probability assigned to these outcomes would be $p^k(1 - p)^{n-k}$, for a sequence having exactly k E's. All of the $\binom{n}{k}$ sequences having exactly k E's would be assigned the value k by the random variable $X(\omega)$, and the probability of that value k is the sum of the $\binom{n}{k}$ terms $p^k(1 - p)^{n-k}$ corresponding to those sequences.

EXAMPLE 2-h.   Consider an infinite sequence of independent tosses of a coin, and let X denote the number of the toss in which Heads first appears. The values of X are the integers $1, 2, 3, \ldots$, and probability function values are as follows:

$$p(1) = P(\text{Heads in 1st toss}) = \frac{1}{2},$$

$$p(2) = P(\text{Tails in 1st, Heads in 2nd}) = \frac{1}{2} \cdot \frac{1}{2},$$

$$\vdots$$

$$p(k) = P(\text{Tails in first } k - 1, \text{ Heads in } k\text{th}) = \left(\frac{1}{2}\right)^k,$$

and so on. Note that the series $\sum p(k)$ is a geometric series and converges to 1.

Although the probability function is one device, and a commonly used one, for describing the distribution of probability in the set of values of a discrete random variable, it does not carry over to an analogue in the continuous case to be taken up in Chapter 4. The *cumulative distribution function* (often referred to as the *c.d.f.*) or, more simply, the *distribution function* of a distribution, gives another way of describing a distribution and is defined to be

$$F(x) = P(X \le x) = P[X(\omega) \le x].$$

For a given x, the distribution function specifies the probability assigned to all values of the random variable that do not exceed x, and this probability is a sum of probabilities of those values:

$$F(x) = P(X \le x) = \sum_{\text{all } x_i \le x} p(x_i).$$

Thus, in moving from left to right on the *x*-axis, the probabilities found at the values x_i are accumulated as they are encountered, and $F(x)$ keeps track of how much has accumulated by the time the value x is reached. In this "motion," the amount accumulated jumps by an amount $p(x_i)$ when the value x_i is passed. Thus, the distribution function is just a step function, starting with the value 0 at $x = -\infty$, jumping an amount $p(x_i)$ at x_i, and remaining constant between successive possible values of X. The final height at the right is of course 1, the total of all of the assigned probabilities.

EXAMPLE 2-i.   The distribution function for the random variable Z in Example 2-e, the number of points showing when a die is tossed, is a step function that jumps an amount 1/6 at $x = 1, 2, \ldots, 6$, reaching a height of 1 at 6 and maintaining that height from there on (see Figure 2-1).

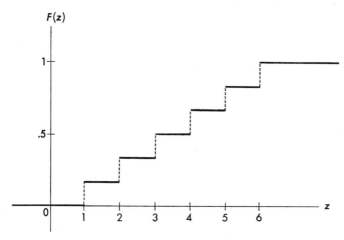

Figure 2-1   Distribution function for the toss of a die.

EXAMPLE 2-j.   Table XII (page 283) gives a family of probability distributions in terms of the (cumulative) distribution function. For example, in the column headed $c = .50$, one finds this table:

c	0	1	2	3	4
$F(c)$	.607	.910	.986	.998	1.000

(These entries happen to be rounded off to three decimal places, and there should be entries given for $5, 6, \ldots$—which are all 1.000, rounded off; this does not concern us at this point.) The probability function values can easily be read as differences:

$$F(k) - F(k - 1) = p(k), \quad \text{for } k = 1, 2, 3, 4.$$

The table of these values would be as follows:

c	0	1	2	3	4
$p(c)$	.607	.303	.076	.012	.002

The reason that this particular distribution is given as it is in Table XII is that, in what is perhaps the most common use of the distribution, it is cumulative probabilities that are needed.

The "values" of a random vector (X, Y) are pairs of numbers (x, y), and the distribution of probability in the set of possible pairs is described by a probability function of two arguments:

$$p(x, y) = P(X = x \text{ and } Y = y).$$

Tabulation of such a function is often convenient in a two-way table, the possible values of X across one margin and the possible values of Y down the other margin, the quantity $p(x, y)$ then being entered opposite x in one margin and y in the other:

	x_1	x_2	$\cdots$
y_1	$p(x_1, y_1)$	$p(x_2, y_1)$	$\cdots$
y_2	$p(x_1, y_2)$	$p(x_2, y_2)$	
$\vdots$	$\vdots$		

Problems

2-1. Let X be the total number of dots which turn up in a toss of two dice. Construct a table giving the probability function.

2-2. Compare the probability distributions of the following random variables: $X = 1$ or 0 according as a coin falls Heads or Tails; $Y = 1$ or 0 according as an odd or an even number of points show when a die is tossed; $Z = 1$ or 0 according as a black or a white bead is drawn when a bead is selected at random from a bag containing three white and three black beads.

2-3. A lot contains ten good and three defective articles. Four articles are selected at random from the lot. Construct the probability function for X, the number of defective articles among those selected.

2-4. Four articles are taken from a production line in which good articles are being produced with probability $1 - p$, defective articles with probability p. Determine the probability function for the number of defectives among those selected. (Assume independence.)

2-5.   A box of articles contains four good and one defective articles. To locate the defective article, one at a time is drawn at random from the box and tested (and not replaced). Let X denote the number of the test in which the defective article is located. Determine the probability function of X.

2-6.   Consider an infinite sequence of independent tosses of two dice. Let X be the number of the toss in which a seven is first thrown. Determine the probability function of X.

2-7.   A bowl contains five beads numbered 1, 2, 3, 4, 5, respectively. A bead is selected at random; let X denote the number on the bead selected. From the remaining beads another is selected at random; let Y denote the number on this bead. Construct the probability function:

$$p(j, k) = P(X = j \text{ and } Y = k)$$

for the random vector (X, Y). (It can be conveniently represented in a table with values of X on one margin and values of Y on the other.)

2-8.   Let there be conducted three independent trials of an experiment on which a random variable X is defined. Let the value of this variable obtained on the first trial be X_1, the value on the second trial X_2, and the value on the third trial X_3. Let $p(x) = P(X = x)$, where x is one of the values of X, and determine the probability function for the random vector (X_1, X_2, X_3), that is,

$$p(x_1, x_2, x_3) = P(X_1 = x_1, X_2 = x_2, \text{ and } X_3 = x_3).$$

(The result will be an expression involving x_1, x_2, x_3, and the function $p(x)$.)

2-9.   Sketch distribution functions (c.d.f.'s) for each of the random variables given in Problems 2-1 through 2-6.

2.2   Expected value

The following example will show how the stability of long-run frequencies leads naturally to the concept of *expectation*.

EXAMPLE 2-k.   In a certain (unusual) gambling house, a game consists of a toss of a coin, with a one dollar payoff for Heads and a two dollar payoff for Tails. If the game is to be exactly fair (this is the unusual part), how much should customers be charged to play the game?

In a large number of tosses, say N tosses, it will happen that the number of Heads is about $N/2$ and the number of Tails about $N/2$. In those N plays of the game the house will pay out approximately $N/2$ dollars for the $N/2$ Heads and N dollars for the $N/2$ Tails:

$$\text{Total paid out} \doteq \$1 \cdot \frac{N}{2} + \$2 \cdot \frac{N}{2} = \$3 \cdot \frac{N}{2},$$

If this is exactly the total paid out, the house should collect $3N/2 from the N players in order to break even. Charging all players the same amount, the house should collect $1.50 from each. This is an "average" amount won, distributed over all N players:

$$\text{Average payment} = \$1 \cdot \frac{1}{2} + \$2 \cdot \frac{1}{2} = \frac{\$3}{2}.$$

It is called the *expectation*, or sometimes *mathematical expectation*, the adjective "mathematical" implying that the expectation is an idealization as N becomes large without limit, and the proportions converge to probabilities.

If an experiment has mutually exclusive outcomes $E_1, E_2, \ldots$ with probabilities $p_1, p_2, \ldots$, respectively, and corresponding rewards $R_1, R_2, \ldots$ (that is, there is a payment or reward in the amount R_i when E_i occurs), the *expectation* is defined to be

$$R_1 p_1 + R_2 p_2 + \cdots = \sum_i R_i p_i.$$

It is a kind of average, and can be interpreted as approximately the average reward per trial over a large number of trials of the experiment.

A reward or payment attached to the various outcomes of an experiment of chance is a special instance of a random variable; the number of dollars paid is a function of the outcome. The notion of expectation is carried over to the more general function, as follows.

Let X be a random variable with values $x_1, x_2, \ldots$, and corresponding probabilities $p(x_1), p(x_2), \ldots$. The *expected value* or *expectation* of X is defined to be the following weighted sum of its values:

$$E(X) = x_1 p(x_1) + x_2 p(x_2) + \cdots = \sum_j x_j p(x_j).$$

This is also called the *mean value* of X or the *average value* of X.

Because the expectation is determined by the distribution of X in its space of values—that is, by the probability function $p(x)$—it will be the same for all random variables having the same probability functions. Thus, one often speaks of the *mean of the distribution* defined by $p(x)$, meaning the above weighted sum, or the expected value of any random variable having $p(x)$ as its probability function.

The notation $E(\ )$ or $E[\ ]$ will mean that the expected value is to be computed for whatever random variable appears between the parentheses or brackets, and this random variable may be specified in complicated symbolism; when the random variable is simple and there can be no question of ambiguity, the expected value operation may be indicated without parentheses, for example, $E(X)$ may be written as EX.

The term "average" is appropriate, since the weights used in the defining sum have the property that they add up to 1, and can be interpreted as *relative* weights. For instance, if there are n values with equal weights $1/n$, the above average reduces to the ordinary arithmetic mean of those n values. The more general, unequal weighting simply recognizes that some values are more likely than others and should be counted more heavily in the averaging process.

EXAMPLE 2-l.   A man wins a dollar for Heads and loses a dollar for Tails when a coin is tossed. Suppose that he tosses once and quits if he wins, but tries once more if he loses on the first toss. What are his expected winnings?

He can win one dollar, by getting Heads on the first toss; he can lose two dollars, by getting Tails both times; or he can come out even, by getting Tails the first time and Heads the second. The number of dollars he wins is a random variable with possible values 1, -2, and 0. These have probabilities 1/2, 1/4, and 1/4, respectively. The expected number of dollars won is then

$$1 \cdot \frac{1}{2} + (-2) \cdot \frac{1}{4} + 0 \cdot \frac{1}{4} = 0.$$

EXAMPLE 2-m.   A die is cast; let X be the number of points thrown. The possible values of X are 1, 2, 3, 4, 5, and 6. Each of these has probability 1/6, and hence the expected number of points thrown is

$$E(X) = \frac{1}{6}(1 + 2 + 3 + 4 + 5 + 6) = \frac{7}{2}.$$

It is often convenient to arrange this computation in tabular form.

x_i	$p(x_i)$	$x_i p(x_i)$
1	1/6	1/6
2	1/6	2/6
3	1/6	3/6
4	1/6	4/6
5	1/6	5/6
6	1/6	6/6
	$\sum p(x_i) = 1$	$\sum x_i p(x_i) = 21/6 = 7/2.$

Observe that, in this instance, the average or "expected" number of points would never actually be thrown in a single trial—it is *not* one of the possible values.

EXAMPLE 2-n.   As in Example 2-h, page 40, let X be the number of tosses of a coin it takes to produce the first Heads. The possible values are the integers,

1, 2, ..., and the probability function is $p(k) = 2^{-k}$. The expected number of tosses required is then

$$E(X) = 1 \cdot \frac{1}{2} + 2 \cdot \left(\frac{1}{2}\right)^2 + 3 \cdot \left(\frac{1}{2}\right)^3 + \cdots = 2.$$

[This sum was computed using the following trick: Differentiation of the identity (valid for $|a| < 1$)

$$(1 - a)^{-1} = 1 + a + a^2 + a^3 + \cdots$$

with respect to a yields

$$(1 - a)^{-2} = 1 + 2a + 3a^2 + \cdots ;$$

and then upon multiplying by a:

$$a(1 - a)^{-2} = a + 2a^2 + 3a^3 + \cdots$$

one obtains the desired sum by substituting $a = 1/2$.]

The expected value of the random variable X, or to use the more complete notation $X(\omega)$, can be computed from the probability distribution in the underlying sample space of outcomes ω:

$$E[X(\omega)] = \sum_j x_j p(x_j)$$
$$= \sum_j x_j P(X = x_j) = \sum_i X(\omega_i) P(\omega_i),$$

where $P(\omega)$ is the probability assigned to the outcome ω. These last two sums are equal because each term of the form $x_j P(X = x_j)$ comes from those terms in the last sum which correspond to ω's that have been assigned the value x_j; and the probability $P(X = x_j)$ is simply the sum of the probabilities of those ω's. This will become clear upon examining the particular situation in the following example.

EXAMPLE 2-o. A bag contains four beads, ①, ②, ③, ④. Two beads are drawn at random from the bag—which means that the six combinations of the four beads taken two at a time are equally likely. Now, let $X(\omega)$ denote the sum of the

ω_i	$P(\omega_i)$	$X(\omega_i)$	$X(\omega_i)P(\omega_i)$	x_j	$p(x_j)$	$x_j p(x_j)$
① ②	1/6	3	3/6	3	1/6	3/6
① ③	1/6	4	4/6	4	1/6	4/6
① ④	1/6	5	5/6	5	2/6	10/6
② ③	1/6	5	5/6	6	1/6	6/6
② ④	1/6	6	6/6	7	1/6	7/6
③ ④	1/6	7	7/6			
			$E(X) = 30/6 = 5$		$E(X) = 30/6 = 5.$	

numbers on the beads drawn. The accompanying tables show how the expected value $E(X)$ can be computed in two ways.

A discrete distribution of probability is quite analogous to a discrete distribution of *mass*. Suppose that a mass $m(x_1)$ is placed at the point x_1 (on an axis of x-values), a mass $m(x_2)$ is placed at x_2, and so on. The sum of these quantities $m(x_j)$ is the total mass, M:

$$\text{Total mass, } M = \sum_j m(x_j),$$

and then the *relative masses*, $m(x_j)/M$, have the property that their sum is 1:

$$\sum_j \frac{m(x_j)}{M} = \frac{1}{M} \sum_j m(x_j) = \frac{M}{M} = 1.$$

Thus, the relative masses are analogous to probabilities; indeed, given a distribution of mass, one could define a probability distribution by

$$p(x_j) = \frac{m(x_j)}{M},$$

and conversely, a given probability model could be realized by any number of mass distributions having masses in proportion to the probabilities.

In this analogy between mass and probability distributions, the *center of gravity* of the mass system corresponds to the *expected value* of the distribution:

$$\text{center of gravity} = \frac{\sum_j x_j m(x_j)}{\sum_j m(x_j)} = \sum_j x_j \frac{m(x_j)}{M} = \sum_j x_j p(x_j).$$

The expected value can then be interpreted as a measure of location, or "center" (in a special sense) of the probability distribution.

Problems

2-10. Compute the expected number of dots showing in a toss of two dice. (See Problem 2-1.)

2-11. Compute the mean of the common distribution of X, Y, and Z in Problem 2-2.

2-12. Compute the expected number of defectives in a random selection of four from a lot containing ten good and three defective articles. (See Problem 2-3.)

2-13. Compute the expected number of defectives among four articles produced by a production process which is turning out articles such that the probability of a defective is p. (See Problem 2-4.)

2-14. Compute the expected value of X in Problem 2-5.

2-15. Compute the expected number of tosses of two dice needed to get a seven. (See Problem 2-6, and for the method of summing the infinite series that arises see Example 2-n.)

2-16. Show that the expected value of a constant is that constant. That is, determine the expected value of the random varible X in Example 2-f.

2-17. Calculate the center of gravity of these five point masses: 2 grams at $x = 0$, 3 grams at $x = 1$, 1 gram at $x = 4$, 2 grams at $x = 6$, and 2 grams at $x = 7$.

2.3   Functions of random variables and random vectors

After conducting an experiment of chance and evaluating a certain random variable or function on the outcomes, it is frequently necessary to perform certain operations on the value obtained to determine yet another number. That is, if the random variable is $X(\omega)$, and the operations to be performed on its values are embodied in the function $g(x)$, it is desired to consider $g(X(\omega))$. This is again a function of ω, and so it is a new random variable. Denoting it by $Y(\omega)$ or more simply by Y, one often writes $Y = g(X)$. This new random variable has a probability distribution which can be thought of as induced either by the original probabilities on the outcomes, through $Y(\omega)$, or more directly by the probabilities on the values of X, through $g(x)$. The equations

$$P(Y = y_k) = P(g(X) = y_k) = P(g(X(\omega)) = y_k)$$

show how to compute the probabilities of Y-values from the probabilities of X-values or from the probabilities assigned to the outcomes ω.

Actually, the relationship of $g(X)$ to X is of exactly the same type as the relationship of X to the original sample space. That is, one can think of the values $x_1, x_2, \ldots$ and their probabilities as constituting a new sample space and can treat this space just as the ω's and other probabilities are treated. From this it follows, as in Section 2.2 (page 46) that the expected value of Y can be computed either from the probability distribution of Y or from the probability distribution in the (new) sample space of X-values:

$$E(Y) = \sum_k y_k P(Y = y_k) = \sum_j g(x_j)P(X = x_j).$$

Moreover, thinking of Y as a function $Y(\omega)$ on the *original* sample space (bypassing the intermediate X-distribution), it follows, also from Section 2.2, that

$$E(Y) = \sum_i Y(\omega_i)P(\omega_i) = \sum_i g(X(\omega_i))P(\omega_i).$$

So there are three levels on which the computation of $E(Y)$ can be carried out, with the same result; the simplest of these is usually in terms of the distribution of X:

$$E(g(X)) = \sum_j g(x_j)P(X = x_j).$$

EXAMPLE 2-p.   Let X denote the number of dots on the face which turns up in the case of an ordinary die, and suppose that the faces are equally likely. Let $Y = 0$ if X is even and $Y = 1$ if X is odd. That is,

$$g(x) = \begin{cases} 0, & \text{if } x \text{ is even,} \\ 1, & \text{if } x \text{ is odd,} \end{cases}$$

and $Y = g(X)$. Then probabilities for the values 0 and 1 which Y can assume are computed from the distribution on the X-values as follows:

$$P(Y = 0) = P(X = 2, 4, \text{ or } 6) = 3/6,$$
$$P(Y = 1) = P(X = 1, 3, \text{ or } 5) = 3/6.$$

The expected value of Y can be computed (a) from the distribution on the Y-values or (b) from the distribution on the X-values:

(a) $E(Y) = \sum_k y_k P(Y = y_k) = 1 \cdot P(Y = 1) + 0 \cdot P(Y = 0) = 1/2$;

(b) $E(Y) = \sum_j g(x_j) P(X = x_j)$

$\qquad = 1 \cdot P(X = 1) + 1 \cdot P(X = 3) + 1 \cdot P(X = 5)$
$\qquad\quad + 0 \cdot P(X = 2) + 0 \cdot P(X = 4) + 0 \cdot P(X = 6)$
$\qquad = 1/2.$

It may seem that (a) is "simpler," but observe that a preliminary computation of probabilities of Y-values was required.

A random variable is also defined when a function of several variables is applied to the components of a random vector: $(X_1(\omega), X_2(\omega), \ldots, X_n(\omega))$. If the value of $g(x_1, \ldots, x_n)$ is computed when the random vector results in $(x_1, \ldots, x_n)$, then

$$Y(\omega) \equiv g(X_1(\omega), \ldots, X_n(\omega))$$

is a function on the outcomes ω and so defines the random variable Y. The distribution of Y can be thought of as induced from the assignment of probabilities to the outcomes ω, or as induced from the probabilities in the (new) sample space of vectors $(x_1, \ldots, x_n)$, whose probabilities, of course, come in turn from the probabilities of the ω's. A study of Example 2-q below will make this more clear, as well as the equivalent formulas for the expected value of Y:

$$E(Y) = \begin{cases} \sum_k y_k P(Y = y_k), \\ \sum_i g(X_1(\omega_i), \ldots, X_n(\omega_i)) P(\omega_i), \\ \sum g(x_1, \ldots, x_n) P(X_1 = x_1, \ldots, \text{ and } X_n = x_n). \end{cases}$$

(The last summation extends over all vectors $(x_1, \ldots, x_n)$ which occur as particular values of the random vector $(X_1, \ldots, X_n)$.)

The summation over all "values" $(x_1, \ldots, x_n)$ of a random vector is often best accomplished by summing systematically, first over the values of X_1, then over the values of X_2, and so on. In the case of two variables, for instance, one can sum first on x for each fixed y and then on y, or the other way around:

$$E[g(X, Y)] = \sum_{(x,y)} g(x, y)p(x, y) = \sum_x \left\{ \sum_y g(x, y)p(x, y) \right\}$$
$$= \sum_y \left\{ \sum_x g(x, y)p(x, y) \right\}.$$

The braces are shown to indicate the steps in a certain order, but are usually omitted in writing double sums.

By using the particular case of two variables, and the particular function $g(x, y) = x + y$, an important property of the expectation operator $E(\ )$ can now be derived, namely, *additivity*:

$$E(X + Y) = E(X) + E(Y).$$

To verify this property, work with the expected value of $Z = X + Y$ expressed as a sum in the sample space of ω's:

$$E(X + Y) = \sum_i [X(\omega_i) + Y(\omega_i)]P(\omega_i)$$
$$= \sum_i X(\omega_i)P(\omega_i) + \sum_i Y(\omega_i)P(\omega_i)$$
$$= E(X) + E(Y).$$

EXAMPLE 2-q. A coin is tossed twice, the four outcomes (H, H), (H, T), (T, H), and (T, T) being assigned equal probabilities. (That is, the tosses are assumed to be independent.) Let $X(\omega)$ be 1 or 0 according as the *first* of the two tosses in ω is Heads or Tails; and let $Y(\omega)$ be 1 or 0 according as the *second* of the two tosses in ω is Heads or Tails. For example, $X(H, T) = 1$ and $Y(H, T) = 0$. The random vector (X, Y) has the possible values $(1, 1)$, $(1, 0)$, $(0, 1)$, and $(0, 0)$, corresponding to the ω's as listed above, and each is then assigned the probability $1/4$:

$$p(x, y) = P(X = x \text{ and } Y = y) = 1/4, \quad \text{for } x = 0, 1 \text{ and } y = 0, 1.$$

The following table shows the values of $X(\omega)$, $Y(\omega)$, and $Z(\omega) = X(\omega) + Y(\omega)$, and a computation of $E(X)$, $E(Y)$, and $E(X + Y)$.

	$P(\omega)$	$X(\omega)$	$Y(\omega)$	$X(\omega) + Y(\omega)$	$X(\omega)P(\omega)$	$Y(\omega)P(\omega)$	$[X(\omega) + Y(\omega)]P(\omega)$
(H, H)	1/4	1	1	2	1/4	1/4	2/4
(H, T)	1/4	1	0	1	1/4	0	1/4
(T, H)	1/4	0	1	1	0	1/4	1/4
(T, T)	1/4	0	0	0	0	0	0

$$E(X) = 2/4 \quad E(Y) = 2/4 \quad E(X + Y) = 4/4.$$

Tables showing computations in the sample space of vectors (x, y) and in the space of Z-values are as follows:

(x, y)	$p(x, y)$	$x + y$	$(x + y)p(x, y)$
(1, 1)	1/4	2	2/4
(1, 0)	1/4	1	1/4
(0, 1)	1/4	1	1/4
(0, 0)	1/4	0	0

$$E(X + Y) = 4/4.$$

z_k	$P(Z = z_k)$	$z_k P(Z = z_k)$
2	1/4	2/4
1	2/4	2/4
0	0	0

$$E(Z) = 4/4.$$

The operation of taking expected values also satisfies a property of *homogeneity*; multiplication of a random variable by a constant multiplies its expected value by that constant:

$$E(kX) = kE(X).$$

This is seen as follows:

$$E(kX) = \sum_i kX(\omega_i)P(\omega_i) = k \sum_i X(\omega_i)P(\omega_i) = kE(X).$$

Combining the properties of additivity and homogeneity, one obtains the following property, referred to as *linearity*:

$$E(aX + bY) = aE(X) + bE(Y),$$

for any constants a and b.

Problems

2-18. Show that if X has only the two values 0 and 1, then $E(X^2 - X) = 0$.

2-19. Let ω denote the number of points showing when a standard die is tossed. Let $X(\omega) = \omega^2 - 7\omega + 11$, and let $Y = |X|$. Determine probabilities for X and Y, and compute $E(Y)$ in three ways.

2-20. Make up tables like those in Example 2-q for *three* independent tosses of a thumbtack, such that the probability of "point up" is p at each toss, and the coding is 1 for "point up" and 0 for "point down." From each table compute the value of $E(X + Y + Z)$, where X, Y, and Z are the coded results of the three tosses.

2-21.† The average $E(t^X)$ depends on what number is used for t, as well as on the probability distribution of X, and so for a given random variable X it is a function of t: $\eta(t) = E(t^X)$. Write out a formula for this expected value, and show that $\eta'(1) = E(X)$ and $\eta''(1) = E(X^2) - E(X)$, where each ' denotes a differentiation with respect to t.

† Requires calculus.

2-22. Compute $E(X - EX)$.

2-23. Show the following:

(a) $E(X - EX)^2 = EX^2 - (EX)^2$;

(b) $E(XY) - (EX)(EY) = E[(X - EX)(Y - EY)]$.

2.4 Independent random variables

Consider random variables $X(\omega)$ and $Y(\omega)$ defined on a sample space of outcomes ω, with values denoted generically by x and y, respectively. Let $p_X(x) = P(X = x)$ and $p_Y(y) = P(Y = y)$, and let

$$p(x, y) = P(X = x \text{ and } Y = y),$$

the "joint probability function" of X and Y. The events $X = x$ and $Y = y$ are independent (according to the definition of independent events) if and only if

$$P(X = x \text{ and } Y = y) = P(X = x) \cdot P(Y = y),$$

or in terms of probability function notation,

$$p(x, y) = p_X(x)p_Y(y).$$

When this holds for *every* pair of possible values (x, y), the random variables X and Y are said to be *independent random variables*.

EXAMPLE 2-r. Let X and Y denote, respectively, the numbers of points on a red and a green die, tossed together. If equal likelihood is *assumed* for the 36 outcomes of this composite experiment, then for each particular choice of x and y,

$$P(X = x \text{ and } Y = y) = 1/36.$$

From this it follows that

$$P(X = x) = P(X = x \text{ and } Y = 1) + \cdots + P(X = x \text{ and } Y = 6)$$
$$= \frac{1}{36} + \cdots + \frac{1}{36} = \frac{6}{36} = \frac{1}{6},$$

and similarly,

$$P(Y = y) = P(Y = y \text{ and } X = 1) + \cdots + P(Y = y \text{ and } X = 6) = 1/6.$$

So for each choice of x and y,

$$P(X = x \text{ and } Y = y) = \frac{1}{36} = \frac{1}{6} \cdot \frac{1}{6} = P(X = x) \cdot P(Y = y).$$

In this model, therefore, X and Y are independent random variables.

The multiplication relation $p(x, y) = p_X(x)p_Y(y)$ is often used to construct a model in which X and Y are to be independent. That is, given the probability functions $p_X(x)$ and $p_Y(y)$, their product is used to define the probability function of the random vector (X, Y) in making a model in which X and Y are to be independent random variables

More generally, random variables $X_1, X_2, \ldots, X_n$ are independent if and only if for every choice of $x_1, x_2, \ldots, x_n$ the joint probability function factors:

$$p(x_1, \ldots, x_n) = p_{X_1}(x_1)p_{X_2}(x_2)\cdots p_{X_n}(x_n).$$

This condition implies, in particular, that any subset of the variables $X_1, \ldots, X_n$ is a set of independent variables.

EXAMPLE 2-s.   A coin is tossed five times, with results (in that order) X_1, X_2, X_3, X_4, X_5, where each X_i is 0 or 1 according as the ith toss results in Tails or Heads. Assuming a (possibly biased) coin with probability p of Heads on each toss and probability $q = 1 - p$ of Tails, one constructs a model for independent tosses by using the multiplication condition. For example, the probability assigned to the sequence of results $(1, 1, 0, 1, 0)$, corresponding to the sequence of outcomes H, H, T, H, T, is the product:

$$p(1, 1, 0, 1, 0) = P(X_1 = 1)P(X_2 = 1)\cdots P(X_5 = 0) = p \cdot p \cdot q \cdot p \cdot q.$$

More generally, for the sequence $(x_1, \ldots, x_5)$, where each x_i is a 0 or a 1, the probability is

$$p(x_1, \ldots, x_5) = p^{x_1 + \cdots + x_5} q^{5 - x_1 - \cdots - x_5}.$$

An important consequence of independence of X and Y is that if $g(X)$ and $h(Y)$ denote any functions of X alone and Y alone, respectively, then from the factorization of the joint probability function for independent X and Y there follows:

$$\begin{aligned}
E[g(X)h(Y)] &= \sum \sum g(x)h(y)p(x, y) \\
&= \sum \sum g(x)h(y)p_X(x)p_Y(y) \\
&= \sum g(x)p_X(x) \sum h(y)p_Y(y) \\
&= E[g(X)]E[h(Y)].
\end{aligned}$$

In particular, again if X and Y are independent,

$$E(XY) = E(X)E(Y).$$

This is a very special result of independence and does not, conversely, imply independence, as seen in the following example.

EXAMPLE 2-t.   Let (X, Y) have five values, $(0, 0)$, $(1, 1)$, $(-1, 1)$, $(1, -1)$, and $(-1, -1)$, each with probability 1/5. This can be summarized in the following table of values of $p(x, y)$:

X \\ Y	−1	0	1
−1	1/5	0	1/5
0	0	1/5	0
1	1/5	0	1/5

From this, one can compute

$$p_X(-1) = p(-1, -1) + p(-1, 0) + p(-1, 1) = 2/5,$$

and similarly,

$$p_X(0) = 1/5, \qquad p_X(1) = 2/5.$$

Then

$$EX = -1 \cdot \frac{2}{5} + 0 \cdot \frac{1}{5} + 1 \cdot \frac{2}{5} = 0,$$

and since Y has exactly the same distribution as X, $EY = 0$. Further,

$$E(XY) = (-1)(-1)\frac{1}{5} + (-1)(1)\frac{1}{5} + 1 \cdot 1 \cdot \frac{1}{5} + 1 \cdot (-1) \cdot \frac{1}{5} + 0 \cdot 0 \cdot \frac{1}{5} = 0.$$

Therefore, $E(XY) = (EX)(EY)$, whereas, for instance,

$$p(0, -1) = 0 \neq \frac{1}{5} \cdot \frac{2}{5} = p_X(0) \cdot p_Y(-1),$$

so that X and Y are *not* independent.

Random variables so related that $E(XY) = (EX)(EY)$ are called *uncorrelated*; it has been shown in Example 2-t that independence of X and Y does not follow from the fact that they are uncorrelated. Notice that if X and Y are uncorrelated and if either one has expectation zero, then $E(XY)=0$.

Problems

2-24. A coin and a die are tossed together; let $X = 0$ or 1 according as the coin falls Tails or Heads, and let Y denote the number of points showing on the face of the die. Assuming the values of X to be equally likely and the values of Y to be equally likely, show that the twelve outcomes of the composite experiment are equally likely when independence is postulated. Show also that if the twelve outcomes are assumed equally likely, independence follows, as well as the equal likelihood of the values of X and of the values of Y.

2-25. Let X_1, X_2, X_3 denote the successive outcomes of three tosses of a coin with the usual coding (0 for Tails, 1 for Heads). Determine the probability function of (X_1, X_2, X_3) assuming independence of the three tosses and a probability p for Heads on each toss. Then working with that result as an *assumption,* show that the independence and probabilities for the individual tosses follow as a consequence.

2-26. A bowl contains four chips, one marked "$X = -1$, $Y = 0$," one marked "$X = 0$, $Y = -1$," one marked "$X = 0$, $Y = 1$," and one marked "$X = 1$, $Y = 0$." A chip is drawn at random from the bowl. Construct $p(x, y)$, giving its values in a table such as that in Example 2-t. Compute the probability functions $p_X(x)$ and $p_Y(y)$, and show that X and Y are not independent. Show that $E(XY) = E(X)E(Y)$.

2-27.† For any random variable X let $\eta_X(t) = E(t^X)$, as in Problem 2-21. Show that if X and Y are independent and $Z = X + Y$, then $\eta_Z(t) = \eta_X(t)\eta_Y(t)$.

2-28.† Use the results of Problems 2-21 and 2-27 to calculate the expected value and the expected square of $Y = X_1 + X_2 + X_3$, where X_1, X_2, and X_3 are the results of three successive, independent tosses of a fair coin, coded 0 for Tails and 1 for Heads.

2.5 Moments

In continuing the analogy of a probability distribution with a distribution of mass, the terminology of "moments" is carried over. In the case of a discrete distribution of mass with $m(x_i)$ at x_i $(i = 1, 2, \ldots)$ the quantity $x_i m(x_i)$ is called the *first moment* of the point mass at x_i, and the sum of these for all mass points is the *total first moment*. Division of this by the total mass, $M = \sum m(x_i)$, yields the center of gravity (c.g.), which can then be thought of as an *average first moment*:

$$\text{c.g.} = \text{average first moment} = \frac{1}{M} \sum_i x_i m(x_i).$$

Since this formula gives the expected value of a random variable X whose probability function is $p(x_i) = m(x_i)/M$, the expected value EX is often called the first moment of X, or the first moment of the distribution of X.

The quantity $(x_i - a)m(x_i)$ is called the first moment of the mass $m(x_i)$ about $x = a$, in which terminology the first moment above is about $x = 0$. Continuing the analogy, the quantity $E(X - a)$ is called the first moment of X (or of its distribution) about $x = a$. An important property of distributions (mass or probability) is that the first moment about the mean (or center of gravity) is zero:

$$E(X - EX) = EX - E(EX) = EX - EX = 0.$$

† Requires calculus.

In terms of mass this is the balance property of the center of gravity—the total moment of masses on one side of the center of gravity exactly balances the total moment of those on the other side.

When the number of values of a random variable is infinite, it is possible that the weighted sum of those values which defines the expected value may not exist as a finite number; in such a case the random variable simply does not have an expected value, and so when making statements involving expected values it is to be assumed that the random variables are such as to possess expectations.

EXAMPLE 2-u.   Consider the distribution given by the probability function

$$p_X(k) = 1/2^k, \qquad k = 1, 2, 3, \ldots,$$

and consider the random variable $Y = 2^X$. The values of Y are $2, 2^2, 2^3, \ldots$, and weighting these with the corresponding probabilities, one obtains the sum used to define expected value:

$$2 \cdot \frac{1}{2} + 2^2 \cdot \frac{1}{2^2} + 2^3 \cdot \frac{1}{2^3} + \cdots.$$

This series is just $1 + 1 + 1 + \cdots$, whose partial sums can be made as large as one pleases; it diverges to infinity—does not have a finite number as a value. The random variable Y does not have an expected value. (The random variable X does, however, as seen in Example 2-n.)

The first moment of a distribution is a property of the distribution which describes one aspect of the distribution—its location or center. Of course, different distributions can have the same first moment without being identical distributions, so other descriptive means are needed for a more complete characterization of a distribution. The quantity $E(X - a)^k$ is called the kth moment of X about $x = a$, and frequently the complete family of such moments ($k = 0, 1, 2, \ldots$) for any given a does characterize the distribution of X. The second moment of a probability distribution is of particular importance, as also in the case of a mass distribution. The second moment about the mean is called the *variance* of X:

$$\text{var } X \equiv E(X - EX)^2.$$

According to Problem 2-23(a) the variance can also be expressed as the difference between the average square and the square of the average:

$$\text{var } X = E(X^2) - (EX)^2.$$

It is useful to know what happens to the variance under a linear change in the random variable: $Y = aX + b$. Since $EY = aEX + b$, and $Y - EY = a[X - EX]$, it follows that

$$\text{var } (aX + b) = a^2 \text{ var } X.$$

This should not be surprising; the variance is based on differences from the center of gravity, and a shift in origin does not affect differences. But multiplication by a constant, a change in scale, introduces that constant squared as a factor, since the variance is a second moment.

The variance of a distribution is the analogue of the average moment of inertia of a mass distribution about the center of gravity. The "parallel axis theorem" of mechanics is obtained by setting $X = Y - a$ in the second formula for variance above:

$$\text{var } Y = \text{var } (Y - a) = E(Y - a)^2 - (EY - a)^2,$$

which can also be written in the form (now reverting to X):

$$E(X - a)^2 = \text{var } X + (EX - a)^2.$$

In words: The second moment about $x = a$ is equal to the variance plus the square of the distance from $x = a$ to the mean. This shows, incidentally, that the mean or expected value of X is that value about which the second moment is smallest.

The positive square root of the variance is called the *standard deviation*, often denoted by σ, or by σ_X when it is helpful to make specific reference to the random variable:

$$\sigma_X \equiv \sqrt{\text{var } X}.$$

It might seem that one does not know any more about a distribution in knowing its standard deviation than in knowing its variance, but the point is that the units of σ are the same as the units of X itself, and σ can be marked on the x-axis, from EX, as a kind of average deviation. More precisely, it is a "root-mean-square" deviation, and is a convenient measure of variability or dispersion of the distribution.

It will be convenient to have an expression for the variance of a sum of random variables. Consider first two random variables X and Y, and let $X' = X - EX$ and $Y' = Y - EY$. Then $EX' = 0$ and $EY' = 0$, whence $E(X' + Y') = 0$, so that

$$\begin{aligned}
\text{var } (X + Y) = \text{var } (X' + Y') &= E(X' + Y')^2 \\
&= EX'^2 + EY'^2 + 2E(X'Y') \\
&= \text{var } X + \text{var } Y + 2 \text{ cov } (X, Y).
\end{aligned}$$

The quantity

$$\text{cov } (X, Y) \equiv E(X - EX)(Y - EY) = EXY - (EX)(EY)$$

is called the *covariance* of X and Y. The condition $\text{cov } (X, Y) = 0$ was described in the preceding section by saying that X and Y are uncorrelated.

When X and Y are independent, they are automatically uncorrelated, and then

$$\text{var}\,(X + Y) = \text{var}\,X + \text{var}\,Y \qquad (X \text{ and } Y \text{ uncorrelated}).$$

More generally, it follows in similar fashion that if every pair of a set of random variables $X_1, X_2, \ldots$ are uncorrelated (and surely, then, if these variables are independent),

$$\text{var}\,(X_1 + \cdots + X_n) = \text{var}\,X_1 + \cdots + \text{var}\,X_n.$$

Problems

2-29. Compute the variance of the number of dots showing in a toss of two dice. (See Problems 2-1 and 2-10.)

2-30. Compute the variance of the distribution in Problem 2-2.

2-31. Compute the variance of the number of defectives in a random selection of four from a lot containing ten good and three defective articles. (See Problems 2-12 and 2-3.)

2-32. Compute the variance of the number of defectives among four articles produced by a production process that is turning out articles such that the probability of a defective is p. (See Problems 2-13 and 2-4.)

2-33. Compute the variance of X in Problem 2-5.

2-34. Show that the variance of a constant random variable is zero. (See Example 2-f and Problem 2-16.)

2-35. Compute the (total) moment of inertia about the center of gravity for the five point masses in Problem 2-17. Determine also the second moment around $x = 0$.

2-36. Referring to the distribution of (X, Y) in Problem 2-7, determine EX, EY, EXY, var X, var Y, cov (X, Y), and var $(X + Y)$. Check the last computation by determining the probability function for $Z \equiv X + Y$ and computing the variance directly from the distribution of Z.

2-37. Compute var $(X + Y)$ for the distribution in Example 2-t.

2-38. Compute var $(X + Y)$ for the distribution of Problem 2-26.

2.6   The Bernoulli distribution

A random variable that can take on only two values is sometimes said to have a *Bernoulli distribution*. The two values are usually 0 and 1; but when they are, say, a and b, a simple linear transformation produces a variable with values 0 and 1. For, if Y has values a and b, the random variable

$$X = \frac{Y - a}{b - a}$$

has the value 0 when $Y = a$ and the value 1 when $Y = b$.

Indeed, the values 0 and 1 are usually artificial, a coding convenient for counting, assigned to some event E and its complement (*not E*), respectively. One important kind of problem of this kind is that in which E denotes some quality of an object drawn at random from a "population" of objects— either the object drawn has this quality or it does not have it. Other examples of E and *not E* are Heads and Tails, defective and nondefective articles, yes and no votes, success and failure of a mission, rain and no rain on a certain date, hit and miss in firing at a target, red and black in a spin of a roulette wheel, and so on.

The probability distribution for a Bernoulli variable with values 0 and 1 is completely described by the value of the "parameter" p:

$$p = P(X = 1),$$

or alternatively by

$$q = P(X = 0) = 1 - p.$$

The probability function is then quite simple, and may be indicated as in the following table, in which certain calculations are also given for determining the first two moments of the distribution.

x_i	$p(x_i)$	$x_i p(x_i)$	$x_i^2 p(x_i)$
1	p	p	p
0	q	0	0
Sums:	1	$p = E(X)$	$p = E(X^2)$

The parameter p is seen to be the expected value, EX, and the variance is computed as follows:

$$\text{var } X = E(X^2) - (EX)^2 = p - p^2 = pq.$$

It is occasionally useful to have the following formula for the probability function:

$$P(X = x) = p^x(1 - p)^{1-x}, \qquad x = 0, 1,$$

which clearly has the value p when $x = 1$ and the value q when $x = 0$, thus representing, as claimed, the probability function of the Bernoulli distribution.

2.7 The binomial distribution

The distribution called *binomial* arises naturally in sampling from a Bernoulli distribution. Suppose that $X_1, X_2, \ldots, X_n$ are the successive results of independent performances or "trials" of a Bernoulli experiment, the probability function for the ith observation in the sequence being

$$p_{X_i}(x) = p^x(1 - p)^{1-x}, \qquad x = 0, 1.$$

The joint probability function for the n results of the independent trials is a product:

$$
\begin{aligned}
p(x_1, \ldots, x_n) &= P(X_1 = x_1, \ldots, \text{and } X_n = x_n) \\
&= p_{X_1}(x_1) \cdots p_{X_n}(x_n) \\
&= p^{x_1 + \cdots + x_n}(1 - p)^{n - x_1 - \cdots - x_n},
\end{aligned}
$$

where of course each x_i is either a zero or a one. Notice that this probability is the same for all sequences $(x_1, \ldots, x_n)$ having the same sum.

It is to be observed that the sum of the 0's and 1's in the sequence of results is just the *number* of 1's, or if 1 corresponds to a certain event E, is the number of E's:

$$Y \equiv X_1 + X_2 + \cdots + X_n = \text{number of } E\text{'s}.$$

For instance, if the sequence of results of eight trials is 1, 0, 0, 1, 1, 1, 0, 1, the sum is $1 + 0 + 0 + 1 + 1 + 1 + 0 + 1 = 5$, corresponding to the five E's in the eight trials. Adding the results, or equivalently counting the number of E's, loses track of the original order of the sequence of results, but the number of E's is usually as informative for purposes of inference as the original sequence.

The distribution of Y, the number of E's in n trials, is defined by the probability function

$$p_Y(k) = P(Y = k) = P(X_1 + \cdots + X_n = k).$$

This can be computed as the sum of the probabilities assigned to all sequences $(x_1, \ldots, x_n)$ whose sum is k, and there are as many of these as there are sequences of k 1's and $n - k$ 0's, namely, $\binom{n}{k}$. The probability for each particular sequence of this type is $p^k q^{n-k}$, and so the desired probability is

$$p_Y(k) = P(Y = k) = \binom{n}{k} p^k q^{n-k}, \qquad k = 0, 1, 2, \ldots, n.$$

This was derived also in Chapter 1 and called there the "binomial formula." A random variable Y having this probability function is said to have a *binomial distribution* or to be a *binomial random variable*.

The mean value of Y is easily computed as the sum of the expected values of the terms in the sum defining Y:

$$\begin{aligned} EY &= E(X_1) + E(X_2) + \cdots + E(X_n) \\ &= p + p + \cdots + p = np, \end{aligned}$$

since each X_i is Bernoulli with mean p. Similarly, the variance of the sum of the X_i's, since these are assumed to be independent, is the sum of the variances, each pq:

$$\mathrm{var}\ Y = \mathrm{var}\ X_1 + \mathrm{var}\ X_2 + \cdots + \mathrm{var}\ X_n = npq.$$

EXAMPLE 2-v. Five cards are selected from a standard deck of cards, one at a time, each card drawn being replaced and the deck thoroughly shuffled before the next card is drawn. Let X denote the number of spades among the five cards drawn. At each drawing the probability that a spade is drawn is $1/4$. Replacement and shuffling are intended to ensure that conditions are identical each time and that the results of the five draws are independent. The random variable X has a binomial distribution with

$$n = 5, \qquad p = 1/4, \qquad \text{and} \qquad q = 3/4.$$

A table giving the values of the probability function, multiplied by 4^5 for convenience, is given below, computed from the binomial formula:

$$p(k) = \binom{5}{k} \left(\frac{1}{4}\right)^k \left(\frac{3}{4}\right)^{5-k}$$

k	$4^5 p(k)$	$k 4^5 p(k)$	$k^2 4^5 p(k)$
0	243	0	0
1	405	405	405
2	270	540	1080
3	90	270	810
4	15	60	240
5	1	5	25
Totals:	$1024 = 4^5$	1280	2560

From the computations of the last two columns of this table, one can compute the mean and variance:

$$EX = \sum kp(k) = \frac{1280}{1024} = \frac{5}{4},$$

$$EX^2 = \sum k^2 p(k) = \frac{2560}{1024} = \frac{40}{16},$$

and

$$\text{var } X = EX^2 - (EX)^2 = \frac{40}{16} - \left(\frac{5}{4}\right)^2 = \frac{15}{16}.$$

The same results can be obtained with less effort from the formulas for the mean and variance of a binomial distribution, but it is pleasant to see that the formulas do work properly, at least in this one example.

Problems

2-39. A die is tossed; let X have the value 1 if a "six" shows, and the value -1 if any other number of points shows. Determine the expected value and variance of X.

2-40. If X is a Bernoulli variable with values 0 and 1, determine (for a given t) the quantity $\eta(t) = E(t^X)$ in terms of $p = P(X = 1)$.

2-41. A machine produces articles in such a way that there is a probability .01 that a given article has a defect.

(a) What is the probability that out of four articles none has a defect? At most one has a defect?
(b) What is the average number of defects in lots of fifty of these articles?

2-42. Four hundred nickels are tossed on a table. What are the expected value and standard deviation of the number of coins which fall Heads?

2-43. Compute the mean and standard deviation of the number of sixes thrown in 1620 tosses of a die.

2-44. Let X denote the number of 1's and 2's thrown in four tosses of a die. Compute the mean and variance of X directly from a table of probabilities, and then verify the computations using the formulas.

2-45. In each of ten sets of twins, one is given diet A and the other diet B. After a certain period their gains in weight are to be compared. What is the probability that if diet A is really no more nor less effective than diet B, the twin with diet A gains more in eight or more of the ten sets of twins? (Treat each set of twins as a trial, with probability $1/2$ that the one given diet A gains more than the one given diet B.)

2-46.† Let $X_1, \ldots, X_n$ denote the results of n independent Bernoulli trials, and let $Y = X_1 + \cdots + X_n$, the number of 1's in the n trials. Use the result of Problem 2-27 to determine $E(t^Y) = \eta_Y(t)$ from the function in Problem 2-40 above. From this compute $E(Y)$ and $E(Y^2)$ using the relations derived in Problem 2-21.

2.8   The hypergeometric distribution

A situation that was seen in the preceding section to give rise to the binomial distribution was that in which objects, say beads, are drawn one at a time at random from a "population" of beads of two types, say black and white, with replacement and mixing between draws. The number of black beads among those drawn is the random variable that is binomially distributed. When the beads are *not* replaced between draws, however, this number is no longer a binomial variable but has a distribution that will be called *hypergeometric*.

The phrase *at random* in the description of the selection process implies that at each drawing the available beads are assigned equal probabilities, and this assumption determines the probability model. The following example will illustrate how the probability function can be computed.

EXAMPLE 2-w.   Five beads are drawn one at a time, at random and without replacement, from a bowl containing six black and four white beads. Let Y denote the number of black beads among the five beads drawn. The event $Y = 3$ occurs if any one of the $\binom{5}{3} = 10$ sequences of three black and two white beads is the result of the experiment. Consider in particular the sequence B, B, B, W, W:

$$P(B, B, B, W, W) = \frac{6}{10}\frac{5}{9}\frac{4}{8}\frac{4}{7}\frac{3}{6}.$$

In this product the second fraction, 5/9, is the *conditional* probability that the second bead is black, given that the first is black; the third fraction, 4/8, is the conditional probability that the third bead is black, given that the first is black and the second is black; and so on. (Each fraction is the ratio of the number of beads of the specified color for that point in the sequence to the total number of beads that remain.) Similarly,

$$P(B, W, B, B, W) = \frac{6}{10}\frac{4}{9}\frac{5}{8}\frac{4}{7}\frac{3}{6}.$$

† Requires calculus.

Observe that the same numerator and denominator factors are involved, as would be the case for all ten of the sequences of three blacks and two whites. Hence,

$$P(3 \text{ black}, 2 \text{ white}) = 10 \cdot P(\text{a particular sequence})$$

$$= \binom{5}{3} \frac{6 \cdot 5 \cdot 4 \cdot 4 \cdot 3}{10 \cdot 9 \cdot 8 \cdot 7 \cdot 6}$$

$$= \frac{5!}{3!2!} \frac{\frac{6!}{3!} \frac{4!}{2!}}{\frac{10!}{5!}} = \frac{\binom{6}{3}\binom{4}{2}}{\binom{10}{5}}.$$

Having reached this last form of the desired probability, one observes immediately that it is precisely the same as the probability that a random selection of five beads from the bowl contains three black beads!

This example illustrates a general fact, derivable in the same fashion as in the computation of the special case, namely, that as far as the number of black beads is concerned, the same distribution is obtained from the assumption that the individual beads, when selected one at a time, are drawn at random from those remaining, as from the assumption that the beads are drawn in a bunch, with each bunch assigned the same probability. The probability function of Y, the number of black beads included among n beads drawn without replacement, is then the following:

$$p(k) \equiv P(Y = k) = \frac{\binom{M}{k}\binom{N - M}{n - k}}{\binom{N}{n}}.$$

This is the probability function of the hypergeometric distribution. The values that Y can take on are certainly limited by definition to the list $0, 1, 2, \ldots, n$, but not all of these need be possible values. For instance, if six beads are drawn from a bowl containing four white and four black beads, the number of black beads among the six can only be 2, 3, or 4; for, if there are at most four of each color, then each selection of six must contain at least two of each color. The formula given above for the probability function can be used for $k = 0, 1, \ldots, n$ if the quantity $\binom{m}{j}$ is defined to be zero when j exceeds m.

To compute the mean of the hypergeometric distribution it is convenient to refer to the model for the random selection of beads one at a time, in which the result of the ith drawing is X_i, with values 1 and 0 according as the result is black or white. The notation is thus the same as that for the binomial model, but the X's are now not independent. However, whether independent or not, it is true that

$$EY = E(X_1 + X_2 + \cdots + X_n) = EX_1 + EX_2 + \cdots + EX_n.$$

And it is still true that each X_i is a Bernoulli random variable, with $p = M/N$, the ratio of the number of black beads to the number of beads; for, lacking information about the other draws, each bead by itself may be thought of as being drawn at random from the original bowl of beads. (Cf. Example 1-bb.) Hence,

$$EY = EX_1 + \cdots + EX_n = p + p + \cdots + p = np,$$

where $p = M/N$. The variance computation is more complicated because of the interdependence of the X's, but it can be shown, by using the formula for the variance of a sum derived in Section 2.5, that

$$\text{var } Y = npq \, \frac{N - n}{N - 1},$$

where again $p = M/N$ and $q = 1 - p$.

EXAMPLE 2-X.   For the bowl of Example 2-w, containing six black and four white beads, the number of blacks among five beads drawn at random from the bowl has a hypergeometric distribution with probability function

$$p(k) = \frac{\binom{6}{k}\binom{4}{5 - k}}{\binom{10}{5}}.$$

The mean number of blacks in the selection of five is $np = 5 \cdot \dfrac{6}{10} = 3$, and the variance is

$$5 \cdot \frac{6}{10} \cdot \frac{4}{10} \cdot \frac{10 - 5}{10 - 1} = \frac{2}{3}.$$

It is perhaps of interest to verify in part the claim made above concerning the distribution of the X's. Consider X_3, for instance; this variable is 1 for sequences that start out one of these ways: BBB, BWB, WBB, WWB, and each of these contingencies has a probability easily computed from the specification that each selection of a bead is to be done at random from those remaining. Thus,

$$P(\text{1st } B, \text{ 2nd } W, \text{ and 3rd } B) = \frac{6}{10} \frac{4}{9} \frac{5}{8} = \frac{120}{720}.$$

The others are similarly computed, with the result

$$P(X_3 = 1) = P(BBB \text{ or } BWB \text{ or } WBB \text{ or } WWB)$$
$$= \frac{6}{10}\frac{5}{9}\frac{4}{8} + \frac{6}{10}\frac{4}{9}\frac{5}{8} + \frac{4}{10}\frac{6}{9}\frac{5}{8} + \frac{4}{10}\frac{3\cdot6}{9\cdot8} = \frac{6}{10} = p.$$

It can be verified that the other X's have this distribution also.

Problems

2-47. Make a table giving the values of the probability function in Example 2-x, and from this table compute directly the mean and variance of the distribution, thereby verifying the results obtained using the formulas.

2-48. Compute the distribution of X_4 in the same way the distribution of X_3 was computed in Example 2-x, thereby verifying that X_4 is Bernoulli.

2-49. A lot of ten articles contains two that are defective.

(a) What is the probability that one drawn at random is defective?

(b) What is the probability that k are defective in a sample of four drawn at random from the lot?

(c) Determine the mean and variance of the number of defective articles in a sample of four drawn from the lot.

2-50. Determine the mean and variance of the number of spades in a hand of thirteen cards drawn at random (no replacement) from a standard bridge deck.

2-51. Determine the mean and variance of the number of Aces in a hand of thirteen cards drawn at random from a standard bridge deck. What is the probability that a hand contains three or four Aces?

2-52. A group of 60 students, 20 girls and 40 boys, is divided into two equal sections at random (by selecting, say, 30 students from the 60 to put in Section A, the rest in Section B). What is the mean number of boys in Section A? What is the mean number of girls in Section A? (How are these two means related?) Write an expression whose value would be the probability that at most five girls are in Section A.

2.9   The Poisson distribution

The Poisson distribution is a probability model that exploits the expansion (derived in calculus):

$$e^m = 1 + m + m^2/2! + m^3/3! + \cdots = \sum_0^\infty \frac{m^k}{k!}.$$

The series on the right converges (that is, the partial sums of finitely many terms tend to a limit as more and more terms are added on) for all values of

m to the function e^m, where e is the base of the "natural" logarithm system. Dividing the above relation by e^m one obtains

$$1 = e^{-m} + me^{-m} + m^2e^{-m}/2! + m^3e^{-m}/3! + \cdots$$

Since each term of the series on the right is nonnegative and since their sum is 1, a proper probability model is obtained by using each term in the series as a probability; a random variable X is said to have a *Poisson distribution* with parameter m if and only if

$$P(X = k) = m^k e^{-m}/k!, \qquad k = 0, 1, 2, \ldots.$$

The mean of this distribution is

$$EX = \sum_0^\infty kp(k) = \sum_1^\infty km^k e^{-m}/k!$$
$$= me^{-m}(1 + m + m^2/2! + \cdots) = m.$$

Similarly,

$$EX(X - 1) = \sum_0^\infty k(k - 1)m^k e^{-m}/k! = \sum_2^\infty m^k e^{-m}/(k - 2)!$$
$$= m^2 e^{-m}(1 + m + m^2/2! + \cdots) = m^2.$$

And so

$$\text{var } X = EX(X - 1) + EX - (EX)^2 = m^2 + m - m^2 = m.$$

The parameter m happens then to be the value of both the mean and the variance of the distribution.

Values of the Poisson probability function are easily computable from Table XI, a table of values of the negative exponential e^{-m}; but the probabilities themselves are frequently tabled, as in Table XII, page 283. That table gives the values of

$$F(c) \equiv P(X \le c) = p(0) + p(1) + \cdots + p(c)$$

for several values of c and m. From these "cumulative" probabilities one can easily obtain the probabilities of individual values:

$$P(X = c) = P(X \le c) - P(X \le c - 1) = F(c) - F(c - 1).$$

The Poisson model finds application in a wide variety of situations in which some kind of "event" occurs repeatedly, but haphazardly, such as is indicated in Figure 2-2 (each $\times$ represents an occurrence of the event):

Figure 2-2

These events may occur at points in time, or at points along a wire, or at points in a plane region, and so on. The figure above would suggest points in time or along a wire. Typical situations are those in which the "event" is the arrival of a telephone call in an exchange, the breakdown of a piece of equipment, the emission of a radioactive particle, the completion of a repair job by a steadily working repairman, a defect along a long tape or wire or chain, a defect in a sheet of manufactured material, a typing error, a bacterial colony on a Petri plate, and so on.

The random variable of interest, the random variable that is to have the Poisson distribution, is the *number of events in a given region*—in a time interval, or in a certain plane region, depending on the application. This number of events can have the values $0, 1, 2, 3, \ldots$, and under certain circumstances it is found that the Poisson probabilities usefully describe the phenomenon. In particular, the Poisson model applies whenever it may be assumed that the following postulates hold:

(a) The numbers of events in nonoverlapping regions are independent.
(b) The probability of an event in a region of size h is approximately proportional to h for small h, independent of the location of the region.
(c) The probability of more than one event in a region of size h is negligible in comparison with the probability of one event, for small h.

The imprecise terms "approximately proportional" and "negligible" can be avoided by using the more precise mathematical formulation as follows:

(b') $P(\text{one event in } h) = \lambda h + o(h)$,
(c') $P(\text{two or more events in } h) = o(h)$,

where λ is a constant which characterizes the particular process, and the quantity $o(h)$ (read: "some function of smaller order than h") denotes an unspecified function having the property that

$$\lim_{h \to 0} \frac{o(h)}{h} = 0.$$

(For example, the functions h^2, h^3, $\sin^2 h$, $1 - e^{-h^2}$ are all $o(h)$.)

These postulates can be shown to imply that the number of events in a given time interval of width t has the Poisson distribution with parameter $m = \lambda t$:

$$P(n \text{ events in time } t) = e^{-\lambda t} \frac{(\lambda t)^n}{n!}, \qquad n = 0, 1, 2, \ldots.$$

Showing this to be the case requires calculus and will be deferred to the end of the section.

Since the mean of the Poisson distribution has been shown to be m, it follows that

$$\lambda t = \text{Expected number of events in time } t$$

and, with $t = 1$, that

$$\lambda = \text{Expected number of events per unit time.}$$

That is, the average number of events in an interval is directly proportional to the width of the interval—doubling the interval doubles the expected number of events, for instance. The expected number of events per unit time depends on the time units chosen in a problem, but it is always the combination λt that is used in computations, and this is the same for any choice of units.

EXAMPLE 2-y.   Suppose that customers arrive at a service station according to a Poisson distribution, and that the arrivals average 24 per hour. What is the probability of no arrivals in a given five-minute interval?

The expected number of arrivals in a five-minute interval is five sixtieths of the expected number in an hour:

$$\lambda t = \frac{5}{60} \cdot 24 = 2.$$

The desired probability is then

$$P(0 \text{ arrivals in 5-minute period}) = e^{-\lambda t} = e^{-2} \doteq .135.$$

If the basic unit is one minute, then $t = 5$ and $\lambda = .4$; if the basic unit is taken to be one hour, then $t = 1/12$ and $\lambda = 24$.

One can also compute, for instance, the probability that more than two arrivals occur in a one-minute period; in this case λt is $2/5$, the expected number of arrivals per minute:

$$
\begin{aligned}
P(\text{more than 2 arrivals in one minute}) &= 1 - P(0, 1, \text{ or } 2 \text{ arrivals in one minute}) \\
&= 1 - e^{-\lambda t}(1 + (\lambda t) + (\lambda t)^2/2!) \\
&= 1 - e^{-.4}(1 + .4 + (.4)^2/2) = .008.
\end{aligned}
$$

As promised earlier, there will now be given a sketch of the derivation of the Poisson formula from the Poisson postulates. It is based on an approach commonly employed in setting up differential equations and, of course, requires a knowledge of calculus for its appreciation.

Because the distribution of X, the number of events occurring in a region of given size, depends on that size, it will be convenient to have a notation for the probability function which indicates that size:

$$P_n(t) = P(n \text{ events in region of size } t) = P(X = n).$$

The Poisson postulates given above can be used to determine $P_n(t)$ as a Poisson probability. Consider first $P_0(t)$, and an increment in t from t to $t + h$ (let t denote the length of a time interval):

$$
\begin{aligned}
P_0(t + h) &= P(\text{no events in } t + h) \\
&= P(\text{no events up to } t \text{ } and \text{ no events from } t \text{ to } t + h) \\
&= P(\text{no events in } t)P(\text{no events in } h) \\
&= P_0(t)P_0(h).
\end{aligned}
$$

But according to Postulates (b) and (c), the probability of no events is

$$
\begin{aligned}
P(\text{no events in } h) &= 1 - P(\text{at least one event in } h) \\
&= 1 - \lambda h + o(h).
\end{aligned}
$$

Hence,

$$
\frac{P_0(t + h) - P_0(t)}{h} = -\lambda P_0(t) + \frac{o(h)}{h},
$$

and passing to the limit, one obtains the derivative:

$$
P_0'(t) = -\lambda P_0(t),
$$

which implies (since $P_0(0) = 1$) that

$$
P_0(t) = e^{-\lambda t}.
$$

To compute $P_1(t)$ it is observed that "one event in time $t + h$" is equivalent to "one event in time t and none in h, or one event in h and none in t." Exploiting this one obtains

$$
P_1'(t) = -\lambda P_1(t) + \lambda P_0(t),
$$

from which it follows, with the initial condition $P_1(0) = 0$, that

$$
P_1(t) = \lambda t e^{-\lambda t}.
$$

Proceeding in similar fashion one obtains the equation

$$
P_n'(t) = -\lambda P_n(t) + \lambda P_{n-1}(t),
$$

for $n = 2, 3, \ldots$. This family of equations is seen to be satisfied by

$$
P_n(t) = \frac{(\lambda t)^n}{n!} e^{-\lambda t},
$$

which can also be derived (by induction) by solving the differential equations.

Problems

2-53. Calls come in to a telephone exchange at random but at a rate of 300 per hour (when taken over a long period). Assume that the number of calls coming in during a given period is a random variable with a Poisson distribution and determine the probability that

(a) one call comes in during a given one-minute period;
(b) at least two calls come in during a given one-minute period;
(c) no calls arrive in an interval of length T minutes.

2-54. A random variable X has a Poisson distribution with variance 1. Calculate $P(X = 2)$.

2-55. Splices in a certain manufactured tape occur at random, but on the average of one per 2000 feet. Assuming a Poisson distribution, what is the probability that a 5000-foot roll of tape has

(a) no splices?
(b) at most two splices?
(c) at least two splices?

2-56. Flaws in the plating of large sheets of metal occur at random, on the average of one in each section of area 10 square feet. What is the probability that a sheet 5 by 8 will have no flaws? At most one flaw?

2-57. Failures of electron tubes in airborne applications have been found to follow closely the Poisson postulates. A receiver with sixteen tubes suffers a tube failure on the average of once every 50 hours of operating time.

(a) What is the probability of more than one failure on an 8-hour mission?

(b) What is the expected number of failures in 1000 hours of operating time?

2-58.† Let X have the Poisson distribution with parameter $EX = m$. Compute the value of $\eta(t) = E(t^X)$. [Hint: $t^k m^k = (tm)^k$.] From this determine EX and var X, using the results of Problem 2-21.

2.10 Relationships among the models

The four discrete models considered above happen to be quite closely related. Indeed, the binomial random variable was essentially defined as the sum of a finite number of independent, identical Bernoulli variables. It will be shown now that the binomial distribution is approximately Poisson under certain conditions, and that the hypergeometric distribution tends to the binomial as the population size becomes infinite.

It is intuitively clear that if the size of the population or collection of objects from which a given number of objects are selected is large, relative to the number drawn, the proportion of the two kinds of objects does not change appreciably as the selection proceeds. Sampling without replacement becomes equivalent to sampling with replacement and mixing. Thus, it would be expected that as the population size N becomes infinite with a fixed ratio M/N

† Requires calculus.

(the proportion of black beads, say), the probabilities in the hypergeometric distribution of the number of black beads among those drawn approaches the probabilities in a binomial distribution with $p = M/N$. This is the case, for, as N and M become infinite in a fixed ratio,

$$\frac{M - a}{N - b} \to p \quad \text{and} \quad \frac{N - M - a}{N - b} \to q = 1 - p,$$

for any constants a and b. It follows that

$$\frac{\binom{M}{k}\binom{N - M}{n - k}}{\binom{N}{n}}$$

$$= \frac{M(M - 1)\cdots(M - k + 1)(N - M)\cdots(N - M - n + k + 1)n!}{N(N - 1)\cdots(N - k + 1)(N - k)\cdots(N - n + 1)k!(n - k)!}$$

$$\to p \cdot p \cdots p \cdot p \cdot q \cdots q\binom{n}{k} = \binom{n}{k}p^k q^{n-k}.$$

EXAMPLE 2-z. Let X denote the number of black beads among three beads drawn from a bowl with an equal number of black and white beads. The probability function values are as follows:

$$p(0) = p(3) = \frac{\binom{N/2}{0}\binom{N/2}{3}}{\binom{N}{3}},$$

$$p(1) = p(2) = \frac{\binom{N/2}{1}\binom{N/2}{2}}{\binom{N}{3}}.$$

The values of these probabilities are given in the table below for several population sizes, N.

N	$p(0) = p(3)$	$p(1) = p(2)$
20	.105	.395
50	.117	.383
100	.121	.379
1000	.1246	.3754
∞ (binomial)	.125	.375

The above example gives some idea of the degree of success in approximating hypergeometric probabilities with the more easily computed binomial probabilities. It is not easy to give a rule of thumb since the desired accuracy of a result will determine whether or not the approximation is successful. A ratio of 100 to 1 (population size to sample size) would usually be sufficient to permit the approximation.

The relation between the binomial and Poisson distributions will be demonstrated next, by using the binomial formula and the Poisson postulates to derive the formula for Poisson probabilities. Let X be the number of events in an interval of time t, and let λ denote the constant of proportionality in Poisson postulate (b), which then also has the interpretation of the expected number of events in a unit interval. Subdivide the time interval of length t into n parts each of length t/n. Each of these subintervals is to be thought of as a "trial," and "success" is defined as the occurrence of an event in that trial or subinterval. Either an event does not occur in a given subinterval (failure $= 0$), or an event does occur (success $= 1$), or more than one event does occur; this last is quite unlikely, according to Postulate (c), and is neglected as the number of subintervals increases so that their size decreases to 0. Then with $p = P(1 \text{ event in } t/n)$,

$$P(X = k) = P(k \text{ successes in } n \text{ trials})$$

$$= P(k \text{ subintervals contain an event}) = \binom{n}{k} p^k (1 - p)^{n-k}.$$

The value of p is approximately proportional to the time length t/n, and so

$$P(X = k) \doteq \binom{n}{k} \left(\frac{\lambda t}{n}\right)^k \left(1 - \frac{\lambda t}{n}\right)^{n-k},$$

in which the approximation becomes better and better as n becomes infinite. The expression on the right can be rewritten as follows:

$$\frac{n}{n} \cdot \frac{n-1}{n} \cdot \cdots \cdot \frac{n-k+1}{n} \cdot \frac{(\lambda t)^k}{k!} \left(1 - \frac{\lambda t}{n}\right)^{-k} \left(1 - \frac{\lambda t}{n}\right)^{n}.$$

As n becomes infinite the first k factors tend to 1, the next factor is fixed (independent of n), the next factor tends to 1, and the last factor is

$$\lim_{n \to \infty} \left[\left(1 - \frac{\lambda t}{n}\right)^{-n/\lambda t}\right]^{-\lambda t}.$$

With $-\lambda t/n = h$, this becomes

$$\left[\lim_{h \to 0} (1 + h)^{1/h}\right]^{-\lambda t} = e^{-\lambda t},$$

the quantity in brackets being the usual definition of the number e. So as claimed, the binomial approximation to the probability that $X = k$ approaches

$$e^{-\lambda t}\frac{(\lambda t)^k}{k!},$$

as the approximation becomes exact with n going to infinity.

Although this is a way of deriving the Poisson formula from the binomial formula, the practical significance of what has been done lies in the fact that the approximate equality

$$e^{-\lambda t}\frac{(\lambda t)^k}{k!} \doteq \binom{n}{k}\left(\frac{\lambda t}{n}\right)^k\left(1 - \frac{\lambda t}{n}\right)^{n-k}$$

can be read both ways, and gives a method for approximating binomial probabilities with the Poisson limit. That is, setting $p = \lambda t/n$, one obtains

$$\binom{n}{k}p^k(1 - p)^{n-k} \doteq e^{-np}\frac{(np)^k}{k!},$$

which is useful for large n and small p. The following example gives an idea of the success of this approximation.

EXAMPLE 2-aa.   In the table below are given values of the probability function for each of two binomial distributions, one in which $n = 10$ and $p = .1$, and the other in which $n = 20$ and $p = .05$. In each case $np = 1$, and the Poisson approximations using $m = 1$ are also given. (The table is clearly not quite complete—it should go to $k = 10$ in one column, to $k = 20$ in another, and to $k = \infty$ in the other.)

k	Poisson, $m = 1$	Binomial (10, .1)	Binomial (20, .05)
0	.368	.349	.358
1	.368	.387	.377
2	.184	.194	.187
3	.061	.057	.060
4	.015	.011	.013
5	.0031	.0015	.0022

It is difficult to give a universal rule which would say when to use and when not to use the Poisson approximation to the binomial, since the rule would necessarily depend on the desired accuracy in computing a probability. It is usually considered that the approximation is applicable when $p < .1$, when for n even as small as 10 the results are fairly close.

Perhaps it should be pointed out that the approximation is also useful for values of p close to 1 if one simply reverses the coding and calls "p" what was $q = 1 - p$. For, if p is close to 1, then q is small.

EXAMPLE 2-bb. Suppose that the probability that a certain type of inoculation takes effect is .995. What is the probability that at most two out of 400 people given the inoculation find that it has not taken effect?

Here let p denote the probability that the inoculation does *not* take effect, namely, $p = .005$. The number of people among the 400 for whom the inoculation does not take effect is binomial, with

$$p(k) = \binom{400}{k}(.005)^k(.995)^{400-k}.$$

Rather than carry out this computation (for $k = 0, 1, 2$), it is simpler to compute the Poisson approximation, using $m = np = 400 \times (.005) = 2$:

$$p(k) \doteq e^{-2}\frac{2^k}{k!}.$$

The desired probability is then

$$p(0) + p(1) + p(2) = e^{-2}(1 + 2 + 2^2/2) = 5e^{-2} = .677.$$

(This can be read directly in Table XII, incidentally, with $m = 2$ and $c = 2$.)

Problems

2-59. Let X be the number of defectives in a box of fifty articles taken from the output of a machine which produces articles that are defective with probability .01. Determine approximately the probability that $X = 0, 1,$ or 2, that is, that the box of fifty contains no more than two defectives.

2-60. An electric light sign is constructed using 10,000 15-watt bulbs. The probability that a new 15-watt bulb will operate for ten hours is given to be .9995. If all the bulbs are new, determine the probability that

  (a) the sign will operate the first ten hours without any bulbs burning out;
  (b) exactly x bulbs will burn out in the first ten hours;
  (c) at least two bulbs will burn out in the first ten hours.

2-61. As an acceptance procedure, a company will buy a shipment of 500 items according to the following plan. The inspector will take a sample of 75 and will pass the shipment if at most two defectives are found in the sample. If a shipment which is 20 percent defective is submitted by a vendor, what is the probability that the company will accept these items?

2-62. A poll is taken to determine the number of people in a town of population 10,000 who have never left their state. In place of questioning the entire population, a sample of 100 people is selected from the population. Of these, 3 have never left the state. What is the approximate probability of such a result, when in fact 5 percent of the population have never left the state?

2-63. A sampling plan calls for taking 100 items from a very large lot which is 3 percent defective. Let X be the number of defectives found in the sample of 100. Construct a table of probabilities $P(X = x)$, for $x = 0, 1, 2, 3, 4$, using first the binomial probability distribution and then the Poisson approximation.

Review Problems

2-64. A random vector (X, Y) has the discrete distribution given in the following table:

Y \ X	2	3	4
0	.1	0	.1
1	.3	.2	.3

Compute each of the following:

(a) $P(X = 3 \mid Y = 1)$ (c) cov (X, Y)

(b) $E(XY)$ (d) $P(X + Y = 4)$

2-65. If $Y = 2X - 4$ and $E(Y) = 8$ and var $Y = 4$, what are the mean and variance of X?

2-66. A discrete random variable X has mean 12 and variance 8. Compute $E(X^2 + 2X)$.

2-67. Referring to Problem 1-64, let X denote the number of cigarettes correctly identified as to brand. Determine the probability function and the mean and variance of X.

2-68. A box contains four defective and six good articles. Articles are drawn and tested, one at a time, without replacing any that are drawn. Determine the expected number of tests necessary to locate the defective articles.

2-69. A "signal" consists of a series of pulses of magnitude X having the values 1, 0, and -1, each with probability 1/3. A "noise" consists of a series of pulses of magnitude Y, having the values 2, 0, and -2 with probabilities 1/6, 2/3, and 1/6, respectively. If noise and signal are mixed with the pulses synchronized, the sum consists of pulses of magnitude $Z = X + Y$. Construct the probability function for Z and compute its mean and variance, assuming independence of noise and signal.

2-70. Are the random variables X and Y in Problem 2-7 independent?

2-71. A coin is tossed repeatedly until two Heads in a row or two Tails in a row turn up. Assuming a fair coin and independent tosses, determine the probability distribution of X, the number of tosses required. Compute also EX.

2-72. A bowl contains five beads numbered 1, 2, 3, 4, 5, respectively. Three beads are drawn at random from the bowl. Let X denote the largest of the numbers on the beads drawn, and Y the smallest of those numbers. Let $Z = X - Y$. Determine the probability distributions, the means, and the variances of X, Y, and Z. Verify the appropriate relations connecting the mean and variance of Z with the means and variances of X and Y.

2-73. The probability that a certain cut-off device functions properly is 11/12. What is the probability that the function will be performed when necessary if four such devices are arranged so that it will be performed if any one or more of the devices operate properly? (Assume independent operation.)

2-74. Of twenty cups of coffee, fifteen are brewed starting with cold water and five starting with hot water. After tasting all twenty cups, a taster selects five he thinks are the ones made starting with hot water. What is the probability that if his selection of five is made purely by chance, he selects a group containing four or five that actually were made with hot water?

2-75. The number X of defects per foot of a long cable is assumed to have a Poisson distribution. If there are, on the average, ten defects per hundred feet of cable, what is the probability that a one-foot length of cable will have at least one defect?

2-76. A lot contains ten articles, and a sample of four is drawn without replacement from the lot. Let X be the number of defective articles in the sample of four. Suppose that in a particular case X turns out to have the value 1. What number of defectives in the *lot* would give the largest probability of getting one defective in the sample of four?

2-77. Given that X is binomial with mean 12 and variance 8, determine n.

2-78. Determine approximately the probability of drawing a card at random from a standard bridge deck twenty times (replacing and shuffling between draws) and never getting an Ace.

2-79. Compute the probability that a hand of thirteen cards from a bridge deck of cards contains no face cards or Aces. Referring to such a hand as a "bust," what is the probability that in 100 hands a bridge player gets no "bust" hands.

2-80. A machine manufactures bolts so that an average of one per 200 is defective. What is the probability that a box of fifty has at most one defective? What is the probability that of 100 boxes of fifty in a carton, no box has more than one defective bolt?

3

INTRODUCTION

TO INFERENCE

It would appear that when the true probability model governing an experiment of chance is not known, or known only in part, the way to get more information about the model is to perform the experiment one or more times. Because of the nature of an experiment of chance, such data ordinarily will not define the model with complete accuracy. If the purpose is to be able to announce certain characteristics of the model, the announcement can only be made as an "estimate," with a certain inherent degree of inaccuracy depending on the amount of data at hand.

Sometimes the purpose of gathering data and so learning about the true model is to furnish a guide for action. Thus, one may be faced with making a choice between two or more actions, which choice would be obvious if the true model of a certain experiment of chance were known completely. By using data, one can make a more intelligent choice among the available actions, even though (because the data do not give the complete story) it may turn out that the choice is wrong.

This chapter will introduce the basic problems of inference, those of estimation and of "testing of hypotheses" (in which one is faced with a choice between two actions), in the relatively simple case in which the probability model is of the Bernoulli type. The data for such inferences will be the results of a sequence of independent Bernoulli trials; and at the possible risk† of losing pertinent information, the data will be summarized in a single number; that is, the number of "successes" in the given number of trials.

3.1   Estimating *p*

Consider now an experiment for which the true probability model is of the Bernoulli type with probability of "success" given by *p*, an unknown number on the range $0 \leq p \leq 1$. This Bernoulli distribution for the basic experiment is referred to as the *population distribution*, and the number *p* as a *population parameter*.

It will be assumed first that *n* independent trials of the experiment have been performed and that *Y* trials resulted in success and $n - Y$ in failure. The number *Y* is a random variable, and its distribution is *binomial* with parameters (n, p). Inasmuch as the number *p* is intended to be the ideal or long-run limit of relative frequencies of success, it is certainly natural to think of the relative frequency of success in *n* trials, that is Y/n, as a reasonable estimate of *p*. One must then face the question: How good an estimate is Y/n likely to be? That is, how close to the true value will it come, or how confident can one be that it will lie close enough for one's purposes?

There is no unique way of measuring how close an estimator comes to the true value of the parameter it is estimating, because the estimator is based on random variables (the results of individual trials) and is itself a random variable. In one sequence of trials, the estimator may come close and in another it may not come close, and one will never really know unless he knows *p*, in which case he would not be experimenting to estimate *p*. A common criterion for "closeness" is the average or mean square difference between the estimator and the actual or true parameter value. Thus, if *p* is the true value and $\tilde{p}$ is an estimator of *p*, the measure of closeness is

$$E[(\tilde{p} - p)^2],$$

where the average is taken with respect to the distribution of the estimator $\tilde{p}$, which is a random variable (based on the results of the several trials).

To come back to the particular estimator Y/n, it is observed first that because *Y* is binomial (n, p), its mean and variance are $E(Y) = np$ and var $Y = np(1 - p)$, respectively. Hence, $E(Y/n) = p$ and

$$E[(Y/n - p)]^2 = E[(Y/n - E(Y/n))^2] = \text{var}\,(Y/n)$$

$$= \frac{1}{n^2} \text{var } Y = \frac{p(1 - p)}{n}.$$

† There is actually no such risk, a fact that will not be demonstrated here. It is a consequence of the "sufficiency" of the number of successes. Cf. B. W. Lindgren, *Statistical Theory* (2nd ed.), p. 246ff.

Thus, if $p = 0$ or $p = 1$, the estimator Y/n will be very close indeed to p, which should not be too surprising after a moment's reflection (for, if $p = 0$, Y will be 0 with probability 1). The largest the mean squared error will ever be, for the estimator Y/n, is $1/(4n)$, obtained when $p = 1/2$. Observe that, in any case, the larger the n the smaller the mean squared error.

It is common practice to use the square root of the mean squared error (root-mean-square or r.m.s. error) since the unit of measurement of this square root is the same as that of the estimator and can be measured on the same scale. For the above estimator, Y/n, whose mean squared error is its variance, the square root is its standard deviation:

$$\sigma_{Y/n} = \sqrt{E[(Y/n - p)^2]} = \sqrt{\frac{p(1 - p)}{n}}.$$

This is plotted in Figure 3-1 for the case $n = 9$.

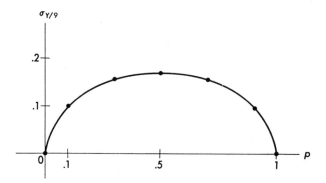

Figure 3-1 Standard deviation of relative frequency, $n = 9$.

The r.m.s. error depends on p, the unknown parameter being estimated; and so it cannot be calculated exactly, although one can obtain a bound for the error by setting $p = 1/2$, for which value $p(1 - p)$ is largest:

$$\sigma_{Y/n} \leq \sqrt{\frac{1/2(1 - 1/2)}{n}} = \frac{1}{2\sqrt{n}}.$$

Moreover, if the sample is of at least moderate size, Y/n tends to be close enough to p so that $(Y/n)(1 - Y/n)$ is a fairly good approximation to $p(1 - p)$. The term *standard error of estimate* is applied to the approximation to the r.m.s. error obtained by replacing the parameter p by its sample version Y/n:

$$\text{Standard error of estimate} = \sqrt{\frac{(Y/n)(1 - Y/n)}{n}}.$$

EXAMPLE 3-a.   The 50 thumbtacks in a box of identical tacks are tossed onto a flat surface, with the result that 35 land with points up. If p denotes the probability of U in a single trial, the estimate of p is announced as

$$p = .70 \pm \sqrt{\frac{.70 \times .30}{50}} = .70 \pm .065.$$

The significance of the standard error .065 is simply in whatever one's intuition tells him about the standard deviation as a measure of dispersion or repeatability. The $\pm$ is simply a matter of tradition, implying only that the error in the estimate could be either positive or negative. It might be noted that, if 70 percent of the tacks in a box of 500 had landed U, the standard error would be smaller by a factor $1/\sqrt{10}$, that is,

$$\sqrt{\frac{.70 \times .30}{500}} = 0.0205.$$

The increased number of observations permits what is thought of as a more precise or reliable estimate of p.

One feature of the estimator Y/n which is a little disconcerting is that when $Y = 0$ or $Y = n$, the estimate is 0 or 1, respectively—values that are not likely to be correct. The point is that the results $Y = 0$ and $Y = n$ are not at all unreasonable even when p is different from 0 or 1, particularly if n is only moderately large. Of the host of estimators other than Y/n which might be tried, the estimate $(Y + 1)/(n + 2)$ works rather well.†

The mean or expected value of this random variable is

$$E\left(\frac{Y + 1}{n + 2}\right) = \frac{E(Y) + 1}{n + 2} = \frac{np + 1}{n + 2} = p + \frac{1 - 2p}{n + 2}.$$

Unless $p = 1/2$, this expected value is not equal to p, so the mean squared error is not just the variance. By means of the parallel axis theorem‡ one obtains

$$E\left[\left(\frac{Y + 1}{n + 2} - p\right)^2\right] = \operatorname{var}\left(\frac{Y + 1}{n + 2}\right) + \left(\frac{1 - 2p}{n + 2}\right)^2$$

$$= \frac{1}{(n + 2)^2}\left[\operatorname{var} Y + (1 - 2p)^2\right]$$

$$= \frac{1}{(n + 2)^2}\left[np(1 - p) + (1 - 2p)^2\right].$$

† A method and set of assumptions leading to this estimator will be given later, in Section 8.6, Example 8-t.

‡ Cf. page 57. Use $a = \dfrac{1 - 2p}{n + 2}$.

This mean squared error, although not zero at $p = 0$ or 1, as in the case of Y/n, is actually smaller at $p = 1/2$ than the mean squared error using Y/n.

EXAMPLE 3-b.   Suppose that a coin is tossed five times, resulting in a sequence of five Heads. The relative frequency estimator, $Y/5$, would have the value 1, and of course there is always the possibility that the coin has two Heads! The other estimator proposed above would have the value

$$\frac{5 + 1}{5 + 2} = 6/7.$$

For other values of Y, the number of Heads in five tosses, the estimates using the two estimators would be as follows:

Y	0	1	2	3	4	5
Y/n	0	1/5	2/5	3/5	4/5	1
$(Y + 1)/(n + 2)$	1/7	2/7	3/7	4/7	5/7	6/7

Plots of the expected squared error for the two estimators are given in Figure 3-2.

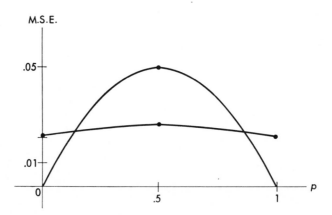

Figure 3-2   Mean squared error for estimators in Example 3-b.

Two other methods of "sampling" (obtaining data) are sometimes employed when the population is of the Bernoulli type. One is called *inverse sampling*, and differs from the sampling employed in the preceding discussion in that the number of successes rather than the number of trials is fixed. That is, one performs the basic experiment until a fixed number of successes, say k, of them, is observed. If this takes N trials to accomplish, the number N is a random variable; its probability function is

$$
\begin{aligned}
p_N(n) = P(N = n) &= P(n \text{ trials required for } k \text{ successes}) \\
&= P(k - 1 \text{ success in } n - 1 \text{ trials})P(\text{success in } n\text{th}) \\
&= \binom{n - 1}{k - 1} p^{k-1}(1 - p)^{n-k} p \\
&= \binom{n - 1}{k - 1} p^k (1 - p)^{n-k}, \qquad n = k, k + 1, \ldots .
\end{aligned}
$$

The estimator k/N is here again frequently used to estimate p for essentially the same intuitive reasons as in the case in which n is fixed. However, since the random variable appears now in the denominator, the mean and variance, and so the expected mean square, are not so easy to compute—at least, not in general.

Sampling without replacement can be used when the basic Bernoulli experiment consists of drawing an object at random from a group of say, N objects, M of which are of one type and the rest of another type. If objects are drawn one at a time and in succession *with* replacement and mixing between drawings, the number of objects drawn of the first type (success) is again binomial with parameters (n, p) where $p = M/N$. But if they are *not* replaced between drawings, the number of successes has the hypergeometric distribution. Denoting this number again by Y, one has

$$
E(Y) = nM/N, \quad \text{and} \quad \text{var } Y = n(M/N)(1 - M/N)\frac{N - n}{N - 1}.
$$

Thus, if one estimates $p = M/N$ by Y/n, as was done in the case of sampling with replacement, the mean squared error is the variance:

$$
E[(Y/n - M/N)^2] = \text{var}(Y/n) = \frac{(M/N)(1 - M/N)}{n} \frac{N - n}{N - 1}.
$$

EXAMPLE 3-c.   Five persons are selected at random from a group of 50 persons, M of whom are Democrats and the remaining $50 - M$ are Republicans. Denoting by Y the number of Democrats among the five drawn, one might consider $Y/5$ as an estimator of $M/50$, or $10Y$ as an estimator of M. Since $E(Y/5) = M/50 \equiv p$, the mean squared error in estimating p by $Y/5$ is

$$
E(Y/5 - p)^2 = \text{var}(Y/5) = \frac{45}{49}\frac{p(1 - p)}{5}.
$$

Notice that this is little different (just a factor of 45/49) from the mean squared error if $Y/5$ were used to estimate p in sampling *with* replacement. On the other hand, if Z denotes the number of Democrats in a random selection of 25 from the 50 persons, the mean squared error in the estimator $Z/25$ for p is

$$
\text{var}(Z/25) = \frac{25}{49}\frac{p(1 - p)}{25},
$$

approximately half of what it would be if the sampling were done with replacement. In the extreme case $n = 50$, of course, the variance of the natural estimator of p would be zero—*no* variability, since the whole group is selected.

Problems

3-1. If a certain treatment is found to be effective in 120 out of 200 cases, estimate the probability that it is effective in a single case, and give the standard error of estimate.

3-2. Let Y denote the number of black beads among the beads in a random selection of 10 beads from a container with M black and $25 - M$ white beads. Determine the mean squared error as a function of M (and plot) for each of the estimators

(a) $Y/10$, (b) $(Y + 1)/12$.

3-3. Compute the mean squared error for the estimator $\tilde{p} \equiv 1/2$ (i.e., one announces that p is $1/2$ no matter what the sample result is). Compare this with the mean squared error for the estimator $Y/5$ where Y is the number of successes in a sequence of five independent trials. (Are there *any* values of p for which the estimator $\tilde{p} \equiv 1/2$ is better than $Y/5$?)

3-4. Compute the mean squared error for the estimator $\hat{p} \equiv aY$, where Y is the number of successes in 5 independent trials, and determine the value of a that makes this m.s.e. smallest when $p = 1/2$. [Hint: the minimum of a quadratic function $ca^2 + da + e$ is achieved for $a = -d/2c$.]

3-5. Toss a coin until 21 Heads have been obtained, and estimate the probability of Heads from that experiment.

3-6. For inverse sampling with $K = 1$ (i.e., repeat the basic experiment until one success is obtained), calculate the expected value of the estimator $1/N$, where N is the number of trials required. [Use the fact that $\sum_1^\infty X^n/n = -\log(1 - X)$.] Carry out such a process 10 times using a coin ($p = 1/2$) and average your $1/N$'s for these 10 experiments; how does it compare with $E(1/N)$?

3-7. A sample of 1000 is drawn at random without replacement from a population of 10,000 voters. If 480 are found to favor candidate A and the remaining to favor candidate B, determine an estimate of the proportion of the population in favor of A, and give (approximately) the standard deviation of the estimator used.

3.2 A problem of testing

Mr. A feels that he has the unusual power of seeing into the future, and in particular claims to be able to predict the outcome of the toss of a coin before it is tossed. Mr. B, a skeptic, asks him for some evidence, and the two conduct an experiment: Mr. B tosses a coin five times, and before each toss

Mr. A announces the outcome. It turns out that he is right four times out of five. The question to be answered is whether this means anything, since four out of five correct pronouncements could be achieved by one who has no occult powers and only guesses.

It might be asserted that since Mr. A was wrong once, he does not have occult powers, but in response Mr. A would insist that he only meant, in the first place, that he could announce the result correctly more often than an ordinary person, that is, that his probability of being right is greater than that of an ordinary person. This statement introduces a probability model: In a given trial, Mr. A is correct with a certain probability, say p, and wrong with probability $1 - p$. The number of successes in five independent trials is then binomially distributed with parameters $(5, p)$. The positions of Mr. A and Mr. B are *hypotheses* about the correct model; that is, about the correct or true value of p. Mr. B, assuming that Mr. A is an ordinary person, would insist that $p = 1/2$, whereas Mr. A claims that p is a number greater than $1/2$.

After the sequence of trials, Mr. B can either accept Mr. A's claim or reject it. In either case he might be wrong, because the evidence is based on only a finite number of trials and is not really conclusive. Mr. B's hypothesis that $p = 1/2$ is called his *null hypothesis*, and the hypothesis that $p > 1/2$ is called the *alternative hypothesis*. The random variable Y, the number of successes in the five trials, which is to be used as the basis of the decision to accept or to reject the null hypothesis, is called the *test statistic*.

Before the experiment is conducted, Mr. B would realize that the test statistic can have one of six values, 0, 1, 2, 3, 4, 5, and that he must be prepared to make his decision according to the particular value of Y that is then observed. Thus, he would be prepared to reject the null hypothesis if Y has certain values, and to accept it if Y has any other value. The *test* he uses is essentially the rule he will follow, and is defined by the list of Y-values that he will consider sufficiently "significant" to warrant rejection of the null hypothesis.

For instance, Mr. B may decide that he will reject his null hypothesis that $p = 1/2$ (Mr. A is an ordinary person) only if $Y = 5$—if Mr. A guesses right all five times. Now, even with this test or rule, Mr. B may err—he may be led to agree that Mr. A has occult powers when this is not true; that is, he may reject $p = 1/2$ even when p is actually equal to $1/2$. For, when $p = 1/2$ it is still possible for five successes in five trials. Indeed,†

$$P(Y = 5 \mid p = 1/2) = (1/2)^5 = 1/32.$$

† It will be convenient to use the notation in which the specified value of a parameter appears as a "condition." Thus, $P(E \mid p_0)$ means the probability of E calculated in the model defined by $p = p_0$.

This error, rejecting the null hypothesis when it is true, is called a *type I error*, and the above probability is called the *size* of the type I error, denoted by α:

$\alpha = P$(rule results in rejecting null hypothesis given that the null hypothesis is true).

The quantity α is also called the *significance level* of the test; one considers the value $Y = 5$ to be "significant at the level 1/32."

The basic idea in this language is that because it is uncommon, in five trials with $p = 1/2$, for five successes in a row to turn up, the occurrence of five successive successes can be taken as evidence that p is really greater than 1/2.

Other tests could be used. For example, one might reject $p = 1/2$ if $Y = 4$ or 5, and accept $p = 1/2$ if $Y = 0, 1, 2,$ or 3. The significance level or type I error size of this test would be

$$\alpha = P(Y = 4 \text{ or } 5 \mid p = 1/2) = (1/2)^5 + 5(1/2)^4 1/2 = 6/32.$$

Clearly, there now is a greater risk of rejecting the null hypothesis when it is true than there was with the test that rejected it for $Y = 5$.

The set of values of a statistic that are taken as calling for rejection of a null hypothesis according to a given test or rule is called the *critical set* or *critical region* of the test. A test is defined by a specified critical region and vice versa. In a problem of the type under discussion, in which the number of possible values of the test statistic is finite, there is at most a finite number of distinct rules possible—indeed, just the number of distinct subsets of the set of possible values. In the present problem, in which Y has one of six values, the number of possible tests or critical regions is $2^6 = 64$. Some of these make sense and some are clearly ridiculous.

Consider the critical set $Y = 0$. This defines the test that says to reject $p = 1/2$ if there are no successes in five trials, and otherwise accept $p = 1/2$. The significance level of this test is

$$\alpha = P(Y = 0 \mid p = 1/2) = (1/2)^5 = 1/32,$$

which is precisely the same as the α for the critical region $Y = 5$. That is, the value $Y = 0$ is just as unusual as $Y = 5$, when $p = 1/2$. And yet when Mr. A is wrong five times out of five, would it be reasonable to conclude that his probability of success exceeds 1/2? Surely the test with critical region $Y = 5$ (which we shorten frequently to "the test $Y = 5$") is intuitively better than the test $Y = 0$; but the comparison is not based on what happens when $p = 1/2$, that is, on the size of the type I error. Instead, it is based on a conscious or unconscious consideration of the fact that the alternatives to

$p = 1/2$ are values of p *larger* than $1/2$, together with a presumption that large numbers of successes are suggestive of large values of p.

The latter point, that large Y-values make large p-values reasonable, is fundamental to inference, but (at this point, at least) it is purely an intuitive notion. What *is* true is that large p-values make large Y-values more likely than do small p-values, but what is needed for inference is the reverse of this.

3.3   The power function

Selecting a critical region to satisfy the intuition must take into account the alternatives to the null hypothesis. The *power function* of a test is a device designed to aid in judging the performance of various competing tests in terms of what happens when the alternative is true (as well as in terms of significance levels). It is defined as the probability that the test rejects the null hypothesis when the actual probability of success is p, expressed as a function of the value of the parameter p. For a test with given critical region C, the power function is simply the probability assigned to C when p is the true value of the parameter; it is denoted and defined as follows:

$$\pi_C(p) = P(C \mid p) = P(\text{test statistic falls in } C \mid p \text{ is the true value})$$
$$= P(\text{test rejects null hypothesis when } p \text{ is the true value}).$$

Ideally, one would want this power to be 0 when p has a value satisfying the null hypothesis, because in this case he would not want to reject the null hypothesis. And he would want it to be 1 when p has a value satisfying the alternative hypothesis, since he then would want to reject the null hypothesis. However, the power function of an actual test based on a finite amount of data will not have these ideal characteristics, as seen in the following example.

EXAMPLE 3-d.   In the context of the example of the preceding section, the test statistic is Y, the number of successes in five independent trials, the null hypothesis is that $p = 1/2$, and the alternative hypothesis is that $p > 1/2$. Consider again the three tests introduced there, given by corresponding critical regions:

$$C_1: Y = 5,$$
$$C_2: Y = 4 \text{ or } 5,$$
$$C_3: Y = 0.$$

The power functions are as follows:

$$\pi_{C_1}(p) = P(Y = 5 \mid p) = P(5 \text{ successes in 5 trials}) = p^5,$$
$$\pi_{C_2}(p) = P(Y = 4 \text{ or } 5 \mid p) = p^5 + 5p^4(1 - p) = p^4(5 - 4p),$$
$$\pi_{C_3}(p) = P(Y = 0 \mid p) = P(0 \text{ successes in 5 trials}) = (1 - p)^5.$$

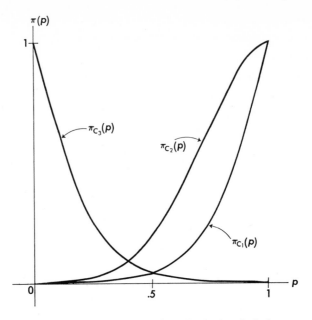

Figure 3-3   Power functions for Example 3-d.

These are sketched as functions of p (for $0 \le p \le 1$) in Figure 3-3. Observe that the power function for C_3 is doing just the opposite of what would be ideal: it is small for $p > 1/2$ and largest (when $p \ge 1/2$) at $p = 1/2$. It is said to have small "detecting power"; there is a very small chance that when $p > 1/2$ this test will discover it to be so. On the other hand, both C_1 and C_2 are trying to do what is right—to be large for the alternative values of p ($p > 1/2$) and small for the null hypothesis ($p = 1/2$). Between C_1 and C_2, one would have to think a while to come up with a preference, because although C_2 is "more powerful" for the alternatives, the α or size of type I error is greater.

The power of a test on the alternatives is closely related to the notion of *type II error*. This is the mistake of accepting the null hypothesis when it is false, which can also happen. Indeed, the probability of *accepting* the null hypothesis when one of the alternatives, say p_1, is true, is just $1 - \pi(p_1)$, since $\pi(p_1)$ is the probability of *rejecting* the null hypothesis when p_1 is true—when using a given test. In the particular situation that has been used above to introduce the concepts of hypothesis testing, the null and alternative hypotheses are different in that a single value $p = 1/2$ makes up the null hypothesis, while a host of p-values (all those exceeding 1/2) make up the alternative. The former is called a *simple* hypothesis and the latter a *composite* hypothesis. Thus, whereas the type I error has a uniquely defined size α, the type II error's size depends on which p makes the alternative true.

In the very special (and perhaps unrealistic) case of testing $p = p_0$ against $p = p_1$, a number greater (say) than p_0, the type I error and the type II error *both* have unique "sizes":

$$\alpha \equiv P(\text{test rejects } p_0 \mid p_0) = \pi(p_0)$$
$$\beta \equiv P(\text{test accepts } p_0 \mid p_1) = 1 - \pi(p_1).$$

EXAMPLE 3-e. As in the preceding example, consider the test statistic Y, the number of successes in five trials, for testing $p = 1/2$ against $p = 3/4$. The critical set called C_2: $\{4, 5\}$ defines a test (reject $p = 1/2$ if $Y = 4$ or 5) whose error sizes are

$$\alpha_2 = P(Y = 4, 5 \mid p = 1/2) = 5(1/2)^5 + (1/2)^5 = 24/128$$
$$\beta_2 = P(Y = 0, 1, 2, 3 \mid p = 3/4)$$
$$= 1 - [5(3/4)^4(1/4) + (3/4)^5] = 47/128.$$

The critical region C_1: $\{5\}$ has smaller α but larger β:

$$\alpha_1 = P(Y = 5 \mid p = 1/2) = 4/128$$
$$\beta_1 = 1 - P(Y = 5 \mid p = 3/4) = 1 - (3/4)^5 \doteq 97/128.$$

The phenomenon observed in Examples 3-d and 3-e is unfortunately rather general. In choosing among the various critical regions that are intuitively of the proper type, an attempt to increase the power on the alternatives (or decrease the type II error sizes) results in an increase in the size of the type I error. And conversely, making the size of the type I error smaller serves to decrease the power on the alternatives (or increase the type II error sizes).

Although the test of Mr. A's occult powers, introduced in Section 3.2, seemed to lead naturally to testing the null hypothesis $p = 1/2$ against the alternative that $p > 1/2$, one might argue that even if p were *less* than 1/2 there would be some basis to the claim that Mr. A is unusual. His predictions could be taken advantage of by a gambler, knowing that $p < 1/2$, simply by betting on the opposite of what Mr. A predicts. This would mean that really to test whether or not Mr. A is normal in terms of predicting powers one should test $p = 1/2$ against the alternative that $p \neq 1/2$. This alternative is said to be *two-sided*, as opposed to the *one-sided* alternative $p > 1/2$.

For the case of a two-sided alternative, a critical region including extreme values of the test statistic on both ends of the scale would seem appropriate, if (as before) one presumes to infer that large values of the test statistic imply a large p-value and small values of the test statistic imply a small p-value. The following computations show (at least in the example being discussed) that a two-sided critical region has a power function that is essentially large for p in the alternative set $(p \neq 1/2)$ and small for the null hypothesis $(p = 1/2)$.

EXAMPLE 3-f.   If it is decided to reject $p = 1/2$ and accept $p \neq 1/2$ if the number of successes in five independent trials is either $Y = 0$ or $Y = 5$, this is a statistical test or rule with power function

$$\pi(p) = P(Y = 0 \text{ or } 5 \mid p) = (1 - p)^5 + p^5$$
$$= 1 - 5p + 10p^2 - 10p^3 + 5p^4.$$

The plot of this fourth-degree polynomial in p, over the range $0 \leq p \leq 1$, is shown in Figure 3-4. Notice that the significance level is the value of $\pi(p)$ at $p = 1/2$:

$$\alpha = \pi(1/2) = 1/2^5 + 1/2^5 = 1/16.$$

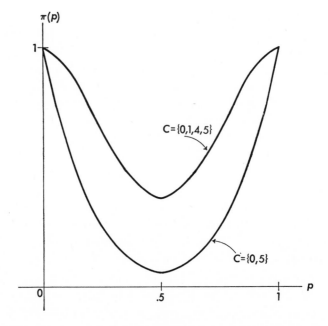

Figure 3-4   Power functions for two-sided tests (Example 3-f).

The power of this test, with critical region $\{0, 5\}$, is not very great for p even a moderate distance from $p = 1/2$, and to increase the power one can put more Y-values into the critical region. For instance, the test that rejects the null hypothesis if $Y = 0, 1, 4,$ or 5, has the power function

$$\pi(p) = p^5 + 5p^4(1 - p) + 5p(1 - p)^4 + (1 - p)^5,$$

a fourth-degree polynomial which is horizontal at $p = 0$, $1/2$, and 1. It is also shown in Figure 3-4. Notice that although the power is indeed greater for $p \neq 1/2$, the size of the type I error is greater:

$$\alpha = \pi(1/2) = 1/32 + 5/32 + 5/32 + 1/32 = 12/32.$$

Again one has the struggle between the two types of error—decreasing the size of one increases the size of the other.

Problems

3-8. Suppose that a test is to be based on the number of successes in three independent trials of a Bernoulli experiment. Make a list of all eight of the possible critical regions that could be adopted and sketch the corresponding power functions.

3-9. Referring to the tests listed in Problem 3-8, which ones would you deem appropriate to test (a) $p = 1/2$ against $p > 1/2$? (b) $p = 1/2$ against $p \neq 1/2$? (c) $p = 1/2$ against $p < 1/2$?

3-10. Two of the tests listed in Problem 3-8 essentially ignore the data. One of them has $\alpha = 0$ and the other $\alpha = 1$. What would be good about the test with $\alpha = 1$, and what would be wrong with the test having $\alpha = 0$?

3-11. A drug intended to lower blood pressure is to be administered to ten patients. What critical region of values of Y, the number of patients among the ten whose blood pressure is lowered, would be used to test the null hypothesis that the drug is ineffective against the alternative that the probability of lowering the blood pressure is greater than $1/2$, if a significance level of approximately .05 is desired? If Y turns out to have the value 9, would you reject the null hypothesis using this test?

3-12. Compute the power of the test in Problem 3-11 for detecting the alternative $p = 2/3$. (That is, what is the probability that the test will reject $p = 1/2$ when p is actually $2/3$?)

3-13. Show that the test with critical region $Y = 0, 1, 2$ has the same significance level as the test in Problem 3-11 and compare their powers at $p = 2/3$ (see Problem 3-12).

3-14. Determine and sketch the power functions of all symmetrical, two-sided tests of $p = 1/2$ against $p \neq 1/2$ based on Y, the number of successes in six independent trials. (Symmetrical here means that the power function is to be symmetric about $p = 1/2$; this can be accomplished by making the critical region symmetrical about $Y = 3$.)

3.4   Acceptance sampling

Suppose that a certain article is manufactured in quantity and can be judged as either good or defective; suppose further that the over-all quality of a lot of these articles would determine whether the lot is to be forwarded to a consumer or withheld, or whether a consumer will accept the lot or reject it. One would naturally prefer lots containing no defectives, but perhaps a few can be endured if this would save a complete testing of all articles in the lot. Not only is a 100 percent inspection costly, it does not really guarantee perfect lots owing to weaknesses in actual inspection procedures; and certainly if testing damages the articles (flash bulbs, ammunition, for example), a complete inspection would not leave much for the consumer.

A sampling inspection procedure is one that calls for inspecting each article in a sample drawn from a given lot, the lot then being either accepted or rejected on the basis of the results of the sample. This is essentially a problem of testing of hypotheses, the "null hypothesis" being the hypothesis that the quality of the lot is good enough so that the lot should be accepted—a hypothesis of the form $p \leq p_0$, where p is the proportion defective in the lot. The problem is one-sided in that a large p would call for rejection of the lot and a small p for acceptance of the lot. The sampling will be assumed to be done by a random selection without replacement, and the test statistic will be taken to be the number of defectives in the sample—a hypergeometric random variable. The following notation will be used:

N = lot size.

n = sample size.

Y = number of defectives in the sample.

c = acceptance number for a given rule. (The lot will be accepted if no more than c defectives turn up in a sample.)

M = actual number of defectives in the lot.

p = M/N, proportion of defectives in the lot.

As suggested in the above definition of c, the only rules to be considered will be those whose critical set (values calling for rejection of the lot) consists of the *largest* values of Y; the number c defines a particular rule of this type.

In describing the performance characteristics of a given rule, it is traditional to use the probability that the rule accepts the lot as a function of the number of defectives in the lot, or equivalently as a function of the parameter $p = M/N$. Taking the "null hypothesis" to be the hypothesis that the lot quality is acceptable, so that rejecting the null hypothesis amounts to rejecting the lot, the probability that the lot is accepted is 1 minus the power function for the rule or test being used. This probability of acceptance is called the *operating characteristic* of the plan:

$$OC(p) = OC(M/N) = P(\text{lot is passed} \mid p)$$
$$= P(Y \leq c \mid p) = \sum_{k=0}^{c} P(Y = k \mid p),$$

where the probability function $P(Y = k \mid p)$ is hypergeometric:

$$P(Y = k \mid p) = \frac{\binom{M}{k}\binom{N-M}{n-k}}{\binom{N}{n}}.$$

When the lot size is much greater than the sample size, so that in effect sampling without replacement is approximately the same as sampling with replacement and mixing, the above hypergeometric probability can be approximated using the binomial formula with $p = M/N$:

$$P(Y = k \mid p) \doteq \binom{n}{k}p^k(1 - p)^{n-k}, \qquad (N \gg n).$$

If p is small and n large but still much smaller than N, this binomial probability can be approximated by a Poisson probability:

$$P(Y = k \mid p) \doteq e^{-np}\frac{(np)^k}{k!}.$$

EXAMPLE 3-g.   Consider a lot of size eight, and the plan defined by an acceptance number $c = 1$ in a sample of size four. The operating characteristic function is then

$$OC(p) = \sum_{k=0}^{1} P(Y = k \mid p) = \frac{\binom{M}{0}\binom{8-M}{4}}{\binom{8}{4}} + \frac{\binom{M}{1}\binom{8-M}{3}}{\binom{8}{4}}$$

where $p = M/8$. This is defined for $M = 0, 1, \ldots, 8$, and its values are given in the following table:

M	0	1	2	3	4	5	6	7	8
OC	1	1	$\frac{55}{70}$	$\frac{35}{70}$	$\frac{17}{70}$	$\frac{5}{70}$	0	0	0

EXAMPLE 3-h.   Consider the more realistic situation in which $N = 1000$, $n = 50$, and $c = 2$. In this case the binomial approximation is fairly good, and for small p the Poisson approximation applies:

$$OC(p) = \sum_{k=0}^{2} \frac{\binom{M}{k}\binom{1000-M}{50-k}}{\binom{1000}{50}} \doteq \sum_{k=0}^{2} \binom{50}{k}p^k(1 - p)^{50-k}$$

$$\doteq e^{-50p}(1 + 50p + 1250p^2).$$

This is plotted in Figure 3-5 (as though p varied continuously on the interval from 0 to 1, whereas actually $p = M/1000$). It is perhaps worth noting that so long as the lot size N is much larger than the sample size n, the actual lot size really does not matter much—it does not enter the binomial approximation. The same operating characteristic would be obtained, for practical purposes, if the lot size had been 10,000, with the same sample size of $n = 50$.

Specifying numbers p_1 and p_2 such that acceptance is strongly preferred for $p \leq p_1$, and rejection is strongly preferred for $p \geq p_2$, one defines a kind of "α" and "β" with special names for this application:

$$\text{Producer's risk} = \max_{p \leq p_1} [1 - OC(p)] = 1 - OC(p_1),$$

$$\text{Consumer's risk} = \max_{p \geq p_2} OC(p) = OC(p_2).$$

It is seen that in the examples above the operating characteristic functions are *decreasing* so that the largest "α" on $0 \leq p \leq p_1$ occurs at $p = p_1$ and the largest "β" on $p_2 \leq p \leq 1$ occurs at $p = p_2$; it can be shown that this occurs generally.

An acceptance sampling plan is not completely specified without some rules for the disposition of rejected lots and for the treatment of lots that are passed. One scheme is as follows: In lots that are "accepted" replace articles found to be defective with ones known to be good, thereby bringing the lot size back up to N. In lots that are "rejected" inspect every article and replace defectives with good ones, and then send the lot on to the consumer. Following this plan one would be sending out lots having either $0, M, M - 1, \ldots$, or $M - c$ defectives; the expected number of defectives in shipped lots is therefore

$$0 + M \cdot P(Y = 0 \mid M) + \cdots + (M - c) \cdot P(Y = c \mid M),$$

and the expected *proportion* of defectives in shipped lots is

$$\sum_{k=0}^{c} \frac{M - k}{N} P(Y = k \mid M).$$

This is called the *average outgoing quality* or *AOQ*. It is small when M is small, since lots are then good before inspection, and it is small when M is large, since lots are then often inspected completely; between these extremes it has a maximum value, called the *average outgoing quality limit*, or *AOQL*. When this is low, the quality is high.

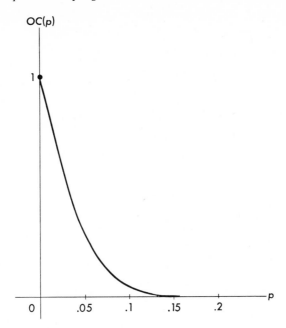

Figure 3-5   Operating characteristic for Example 3-h.

Problems

3-15.   Let $N = 8$ and $n = 3$. Determine the operating characteristic functions for the two rules $c = 0$ and $c = 1$.

3-16.   Determine the AOQ function for each of the plans in Problem 3-15, assuming that each defective located is replaced with an article known to be good. Determine also the $AOQL$ in each case.

3-17.   Compute the producer's and consumer's risks for each of the plans in Problem 3-15, using $p_1 = 1/8$ and $p_2 = 4/8$.

3-18.   Determine the operating characteristic function for the cases

   (a) $N = 2000$, $n = 100$,   and $c = 4$;
   (b) $N = 2000$, $n = 50$, $c = 2$;
   (c) $N = 2000$, $n = 25$, $c = 1$,

and sketch on the same axes. How does (b) compare with that given in Example 3-f? [Use Table XII in computing functional values.]

3-19.   Compare operating characteristics of these situations:

   (a) $N = 8$, $n = 3$, $c = 0$;
   (b) $N = 100$, $n = 3$, $c = 0$.

3-20.   Compute the AOQ and $AOQL$ for plan (c) in Problem 3-18.

4

CONTINUOUS

RANDOM VARIABLES

Having thus far studied only models for experiments with a finite or at most countably infinite number of outcomes, we turn to the more sophisticated *continuous* models—designed for experiments whose outcomes are so numerous, or dense, that a simplification of the model is achieved by assuming a continuum of possible outcomes.

EXAMPLE 4-a.   A machine makes "one-pound" packages of butter by cutting rectangular parallelepipeds. Owing to the irregularities in texture and density, the actual amount of butter by weight varies from package to package. The weight of a package is a random variable. In considering the possible values of this random variable, there is no reason to exclude any values in some interval about the nominal weight of one pound; but the number of values in an interval is not finite, and not even countable, so the discrete models studied so far are not adequate.

If one is to make observations on a continuous random variable, a measurement is ordinarily required; and a reading of any measuring device is necessarily recorded only after rounding off—to the nearest tenth of a gram, or nearest millimeter, and so on. Thus, the measured weight or length is actually a discrete variable, having a finite number of possible values. But even so, the idealization which permits any of the continuum of values in an interval as a measured value is in many respects simpler than the model which includes only the finitely many values that would result from round-off.

The points in the sample space can be taken to be the objects measured (packages of butter, in the above example), the measurement $X(\omega)$ of the object ω then defining a random variable. But it is usually convenient to think of the space of values or measurements as the sample space, so that ω is an ordinary number and the random variable of interest is $X(\omega) = \omega$. In constructing a probability model, one then assigns probability directly to events in this space of values.

4.1 Distributions defined by densities

A *density function* can be used to define a probability distribution in the space of values of a continuous random variable. This can be any† function $f(x)$ that is nonnegative and has the property that the area between its graph and the x-axis is 1 (see Figure 4-1). In terms of a specified density function, probability is assigned to events or sets of values of the random variable X by the relation:

$$P(E) = P(X \text{ takes on a value in } E)$$
$$= \text{Area under the graph of } f(x) \text{ above the set } E.$$

An interval is the simplest kind of set of numbers (that is, simplest event) for purposes of illustration; Figure 4-2 shows the region whose area is the

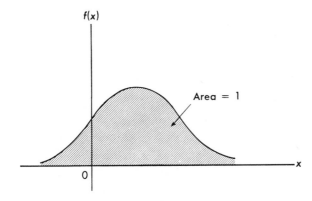

Figure 4-1 A density function.

† Some restriction, such as a condition of piece-wise continuity, is ordinarily imposed (and satisfied in practice) to ensure integrability.

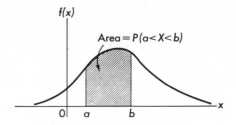

Figure 4-2   Probability as area.

probability assigned to the interval from $x = a$ to $x = b$. Intervals are not only simple but also important in that events of interest can be composed of intervals. The interval $a < x < b$ will often be denoted by (a, b).

Without a study of area and its properties one cannot give a rigorous development of probability based on an area-definition. However, the concept of area is close enough to the intuition that it does not lead one astray. The following properties are evident intuitively, can be proved mathematically, and will be assumed:

(i) $0 \le P(E) \le 1$, for any event E.
(ii) $P(\text{whole sample space}) = 1$.
(iii) $P(E \text{ or } F) = P(E) + P(F)$, for disjoint E, F.
(iv) $P(X = a) = 0$, for any number a.

Property (i) reflects the fact that the area of a part of the region between $f(x)$ and the x-axis is no larger than that of the whole region, and is non-negative. Property (iii) says that the area of a region consisting of two non-overlapping parts is the sum of the areas of those parts. It can also be shown that

(iii)' $P(E_1 \text{ or } E_2 \text{ or } \cdots) = P(E_1) + P(E_2) + \cdots,$ $\{E_i\}$ disjoint.

Property (iv) can be shown to follow from (iii)' and says that the area of a region of zero thickness is zero.

The term "density" means, here, about the same as it does in physics—in the case of *mass* density. Indeed, just as a discrete probability distribution is analogous to a discrete mass distribution, so a continuous probability distribution is analogous to a continuous mass distribution along a line.

Let h denote a tiny interval along the x-axis, an increment from x to $x + h$. The probability that X falls in that interval can be approximated, as seen in Figure 4-3, as the area of a rectangle:

$$P(x < X < x + h) = \text{Area under } f(x) \text{ between } x \text{ and } x + h$$
$$\doteq f(x)h.$$

Thus, $f(x)$ is approximately the ratio of the probability in the interval x to $x + h$ to the length of the interval; and since the approximation becomes an exact value as h tends to zero, $f(x)$ is the limit of that ratio, written as follows:

$$f(x) = \lim_{h \to 0} \frac{1}{h} P(x < X < x + h).$$

This has been written for $h > 0$, but a similar expression would be valid for $h < 0$. It is also true that for $h > 0$,

$$f(x) = \lim_{h \to 0} \frac{1}{h} P(x - h/2 < X < x + h/2).$$

(The reader should construct a graph corresponding to this similar to Figure 4-3.) The notion of the limiting ratio of the amount of something in an interval to the length of the interval, as that length tends to zero, is *density*; if the "something" is mass, the result is a mass density, and if it is probability, the result is a probability density. Density is large at points where the "something" is highly concentrated, and small where it is sparsely distributed.

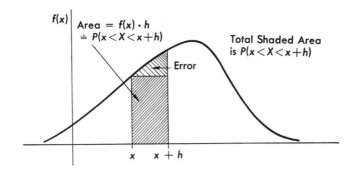

Figure 4-3 The probability element.

A density function can be specified in some instances by means of a formula, or by several formulas corresponding to different regions of x-values. Calculation of probability then involves calculation of the area under a graph whose equation is given by the formula. And although in nice cases methods of calculus can be used to carry out such computations exactly (in terms of familiar functions), the only technique available in general is that of numerical approximation. This is based on subdivision of the region in question and approximation of the pieces by simple geometric figures such as rectangles or trapezoids.

EXAMPLE 4-b.   Consider the density function defined by the formula

$$f(x) = \begin{cases} 2x, & \text{for } 0 < x < 1, \\ 0, & \text{for other values of } x. \end{cases}$$

This is graphed in Figure 4-4; the graph of $y = 2x$ is a straight line that rises two units for every horizontal unit. The region between the density function and the x-axis is a triangle, whose area is

$$A = \frac{1}{2} \text{ base} \times \text{height} = \frac{1}{2} \cdot 1 \cdot 2 = 1.$$

The probability that a random variable X having this density function takes on a value between $x = a$ and $x = b$, where a and b are two numbers between 0 and 1 ($a < b$), is the area of the trapezoid shown in Figure 4-4. The ordinates at $x = a$ and $x = b$ are the "bases." Then

$$P(a < X < b) = \text{Area of trapezoid of height } b - a \text{ and bases } 2a \text{ and } 2b$$
$$= \text{height} \times \text{average of bases}$$

$$= (b - a)\frac{2a + 2b}{2} = b^2 - a^2.$$

Notice then that the area between x and $x + h$ is (for $0 < x < 1$, and h small)

$$P(x < X < x + h) = (x + h)^2 - x^2$$
$$= (2x)h + h^2 \doteq f(x)h.$$

The approximation improves as h becomes small.

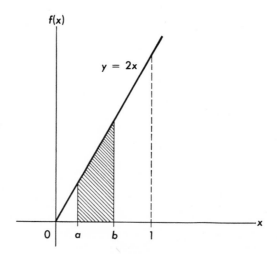

Figure 4-4

As stated above, the computation of probabilities from density functions generally requires numerical approximation. This has been carried out once and for all for most of the commonly occurring continuous distributions, and the results are given in tables. These tables give the probabilities for events of the type $X \leq x$, for a sequence of convenient and evenly spaced values of x. That is, what is tabled is a set of values of the function

$$F(x) = P(X \leq x) = \text{Area under } f(x) \text{ to the left of } x,$$

called the *distribution function* of the random variable X. From this one can compute probabilities of other kinds of events, using the additivity property. For instance, since

$$P(X \leq a) + P(a < X \leq b) = P(X \leq b)$$

(why is this so?), it follows that

$$P(a < X \leq b) = P(X \leq b) - P(X \leq a)$$
$$= F(b) - F(a).$$

That is, the probability assigned to an interval is the amount of increase in the distribution function over that interval. (In the continuous case under discussion the probability that $X = b$ is zero, so the intervals $a < X < b$ and $a < X \leq b$ have the same probability. The above formula is actually valid even in noncontinuous cases.)

EXAMPLE 4-c. Table I gives the value of $\Phi(x)$, the area (above the x-axis) to the left of x underneath the density function

$$\phi(x) = \frac{1}{\sqrt{2\pi}} e^{-x^2/2},$$

called the *standard normal density*. The graph of this density function is shown in Figure 4-5. The table entries are rounded to four decimal places and are given for values of x from -3 to $+3$ at intervals of .01. Interpolating between these entries one can read, for example,

$$P(X < -1.143) = \Phi(-1.143) = .1265.$$

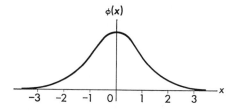

Figure 4-5 The standard normal density.

The probability of an interval, say $-2.37 < X < 1.29$, can be computed:

$$P(-2.37 < X < 1.29) = \Phi(1.29) - \Phi(-2.37)$$
$$= .9015 - .0089 = .8926.$$

Consider now a pair of random variables, $X(\omega)$ and $Y(\omega)$, or (X, Y), each of which has values in a continuum so that a continuous model for the joint distribution is required. Such a model is defined by a two-dimensional density function—a nonnegative function $f(x, y)$ having the property that the *volume* under its graph (which is a surface above the xy-plane) is 1. The probability that the random point (X, Y) falls in a given two-dimensional set E (that is, a set in the plane of possible values (x, y)) is defined to be the volume under the surface representing the density function, above the xy-plane, and within the right cylinder having E as its base.

A joint distribution for the n random variables $(X_1, X_2, \ldots, X_n)$ can also be defined in terms of a density function $f(x_1, \ldots, x_n)$, but the "volumes" involved are in spaces of dimension greater than three, and our elementary means of computation are insufficient. Let it suffice to say that probability is defined in terms of integral calculus; such computations will not be required in what follows.

Problems

4-1. A continuous random variable X has a distribution defined by the following density function:

$$f(x) = \begin{cases} 1/2, & \text{if } 0 < x < 2, \\ 0, & \text{for other values of } x. \end{cases}$$

(A distribution whose density is constant over an interval and zero outside that interval is called *uniform*.) Sketch this density function, verify that the total area under its graph is 1, and show that the probability of an interval contained within the limits 0 and 2 is proportional to the width of the interval. Calculate also $P(|X - 1| > .5)$. [Note: $|a|$ denotes the absolute value of the number a, equal to a if $a \geq 0$ and equal to $-a$ if $a < 0$. Thus, the inequality $|a| < b$ is equivalent to the inequality $-b < a < b$.]

4-2. For the density of Example 4-b compute the probability assigned to the event $X > .2$. Determine also a formula (or formulas) for $F(x)$, the distribution function corresponding to the given density.

4-3. A density is defined as follows:

$$f(x) = \begin{cases} 1 - x, & \text{for } 0 < x < 1, \\ 1 + x, & \text{for } -1 < x < 0, \\ 0, & \text{for other values of } x. \end{cases}$$

Sketch the graph of this function and determine the following (by area computations):

(a) $P(|X| > .5)$,   (b) $P(X < -2)$,
(c) $P(X = 0)$,   (d) $P(X < x)$

(Give the answer to (d) as a function of x; different formulas will be required for different regions of x-values).

4-4.   Use Table I to determine the following, for a random variable X having a distribution given by that table:

(a) $P(X < 1.136)$,   (b) $P(X > -.42)$,   (c) $P(-1.1 < X < 2)$,
(d) $P(|X - 1| > 1)$,   (e) $P(|X| > 2)$,   (f) $P(|X| < 3)$.

4.2   Expected value

The formula used for computing the mean or expected value of a discrete random variable does not apply to continuous cases, since the sum would have to extend over an uncountable set of values—an operation that is not defined. What is required is the notion of *integral* from calculus (see Section 4.4), according to the following development.

It will be convenient to suppose first that the random variable X has a probability distribution restricted to a finite interval from say $x = a$ to $x = b$. That is, the density $f(x)$ of its distribution is zero outside that interval. Let the interval (a, b) be divided into n equal parts, of width $h = (b - a)/n$. Let x_i denote the left endpoint of the ith subinterval (counting from left to right) and round off all values of X in that ith subinterval to x_i, for $i = 1, 2, \ldots, n$. The rounded-off values $x_1, \ldots, x_n$ are values of a new random variable X^*. This new variable is discrete, inasmuch as it can take on only n values. The probability that this variable X^* takes on say the value x_2 is the probability that X takes on a value that would be rounded off to x_2, that is, a value in the second subinterval:

$$P(X^* = x_2) = P(x_2 < X < x_2 + h),$$

where of course $x_2 + h = x_3$. When h is small this probability can be approximated by the area of a rectangle, as in Figure 4-3:

$$P(X^* = x_2) \doteq f(x_2)h.$$

The approximation improves as h tends to zero—as n becomes infinite.

The expected value of the discrete variable X^* (which approximates the continuous variable X) is the weighted average of its values:

$$EX^* = \sum_{k=1}^{n} x_k P(X^* = x_k) \doteq \sum_{k=1}^{n} x_k f(x_k)h.$$

The expected value of X is then defined to be the limit of such sums as n becomes infinite, and this is precisely the concept of the definite integral in calculus. (For a random variable whose distribution is not confined to a finite interval one approximates it with a variable $X_{A,B}$ equal to X on the interval $(-A, B)$ and equal to zero outside that interval, and then passes to a limit as A and B become infinite.)

The technique (from calculus) for computing such quantities in certain cases is discussed in Section 4.4; these are special cases in which the density function is expressible in terms of "elementary" functions. In general, however, it is necessary to carry out a numerical approximation; this is done by choosing a large value of n and computing the finite sum that is given above as an approximation for EX^*, or by some refinement of this process (such as using trapezoids in place of rectangles).

The expected value of a continuous probability distribution, as in the case of discrete distributions, is the center of gravity of the analogous continuous mass distribution. That is, if one thinks of the distribution as describing a long thin rod of variable density, the mean or expected value is the location of the point at which the rod balances.

The following useful properties, shown to hold for discrete distributions in Chapter 2, hold also for continuous distributions; this will not be demonstrated here, but the proofs depend on the fact that expectation in the continuous case is defined in terms of approximating discrete distributions:

(a) $E(aX + b) = aEX + b$
(b) $E(X - EX) = 0$
(c) $E(X + Y) = EX + EY$
(d) If $f(a + x) \equiv f(a - x)$ for fixed a, then $EX = a$.

According to Property (a), a linear change in the coordinate system in which X is measured (that is, a combination of shift in origin and change of scale) produces the same linear change in the expected value. Property (b), stating that the first moment of a distribution about its center of gravity is zero, is the balance property of the center of gravity; in other words, the expected value of a distribution is the point at which the corresponding mass system would balance. Additivity-Property (c) extends, of course, to any finite number of variables. Property (d) is a very useful fact about symmetrical distributions, stating that such a distribution balances at its point of symmetry; this is because, roughly speaking, each moment of a little piece on one side of the center is canceled by a moment of equal magnitude and opposite sign from a little piece symmetrically located on the other side of the center.

Moments of higher order are defined for continuous distributions by exactly the same formulas in terms of expectation that were used for discrete distributions. In particular, the *variance* of a continuous distribution is again given by the formulas

$$\text{var } X = E(X - EX)^2 = EX^2 - (EX)^2,$$

and the *standard deviation* is again the positive square root of the variance. As in the case of the expectation, the variance (which is also an expected value) can sometimes be calculated using integral calculus; but in general a numerical computation of the average that defines it may be required. The variance has an analogue in mass distributions—it is the average moment of inertia about the center of gravity; the standard deviation is the radius of gyration.

EXAMPLE 4-d. Consider again the uniform distribution introduced in Problem 4-1, defined by the density $f(x) = 1/2$, for $0 < x < 2$. The expected value of a random variable X having this distribution is

$$EX = \lim_{n \to \infty} \sum_{k=1}^{n} 2 \frac{k-1}{n} \cdot \frac{1}{2} \cdot \frac{2}{n}$$

$$= \lim_{n \to \infty} \frac{2}{n^2} [0 + 1 + \cdots + n - 1]$$

$$= \lim_{n \to \infty} \frac{2}{n^2} \frac{n(n-1)}{2}$$

$$= \lim_{n \to \infty} \left(1 - \frac{1}{n}\right).$$

Even without experience in the rigorous handling of such limits it should be clear that as n grows without bound, the quantity $1/n$ vanishes, and the limit has the value 1. That is, $EX = 1$. Notice that this is the center of symmetry of the distribution: $f(1 - x) \equiv f(1 + x)$. The above calculation used the formula from algebra:

$$1 + 2 + \cdots + n - 1 = \frac{n(n-1)}{2}.$$

Using the formula

$$1^2 + 2^2 + \cdots + (n-1)^2 = \frac{n(2n^2 - 3n + 1)}{6}.$$

one can compute the expected square:

$$EX^2 = \lim_{n \to \infty} \sum_{k=1}^{n} \left[2 \frac{k-1}{n}\right]^2 \frac{1}{2} \cdot \frac{2}{n} = \lim_{n \to \infty} \frac{4n(2n^2 - 3n + 1)}{6n^3}.$$

This limit is 4/3, and the variance is then

$$\text{var } X = EX^2 - (EX)^2 = \frac{4}{3} - 1^2 = \frac{1}{3}.$$

The second moments again satisfy a "parallel axis theorem," exactly as in the discrete case:

$$E(X - b)^2 = \text{var } X + (b - EX)^2.$$

And from this it is evident that the variance is again the smallest of all second moments; for with $b = EX$, the right-hand side is small as it can be.

It will be necessary to know how the variance changes when a random variable X undergoes a linear change: $Y = aX + b$. It has already been observed that $EY = aEX + b$, so that

$$\text{var } Y = E[aX + b - aEX - b]^2 = E[a(X - EX)]^2$$
$$= a^2 E(X - EX)^2 = a^2 \text{ var } X.$$

That is, a translation does not affect the variance, but a change of scale by a factor a results in multiplication of the standard deviation by the magnitude of that factor:

$$\sigma_{aX+b} = |a|\sigma_X.$$

An important linear change or transformation is that referred to as *standardizing*:

$$Z = \frac{X - EX}{\sigma_X}.$$

The mean value of Z is

$$EZ = \frac{1}{\sigma_X} E(X - EX) = 0,$$

and the variance is

$$\text{var } Z = \frac{1}{\sigma_X^2} E(X - EX)^2 = 1.$$

This particular change moves the origin to the mean and changes the scale so that the standard deviation becomes the unit of measurement. The parameter values 0 and 1 for the mean and variance, respectively, are called *standard*, and hence the term "standardizing."

4.3 Percentiles

As discussed in Section 4.1, a distribution function $F(x)$, giving the probability assigned to the interval from $-\infty$ to x as a function of x, can be delineated by a table of values. Since the function $F(x)$ is increasing (as x

increases), there is just one value of $F(x)$ for each x and, conversely, just one x that produces a given value of $F(x)$. So a table for $F(x)$ can be constructed in either of two ways—by giving values of $F(x)$ corresponding to conveniently chosen values of x, or by giving values of x corresponding to conveniently chosen values of $F(x)$. Table I, for instance, is of the former type; but Table II is of the latter type. In using Table II, one specifies a probability and reads from the table a value of x such that the probability that $X \leq x$ is the amount specified. Figure 4-6 illustrates this idea; having specified a probability .6, a

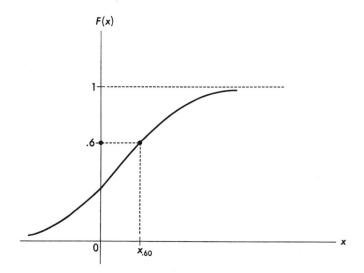

Figure 4-6 Determining a percentile.

value along the vertical axis, one locates a value x such that $F(x) = .6$ by moving horizontally to the graph and then down to the x-axis. The value of x so found, denoted by $x_{.60}$, is called a *percentile* of the distribution, specifically, the *sixtieth* percentile. In general the $100p$th percentile of a distribution is that value $x = x_p$ having the property that

$$F(x_p) = P(X \leq x_p) = p.$$

So Table II is a table of percentiles. (Actually, it is many tables in one, each horizontal line of the table giving percentiles for a distinct distribution.)

Certain percentiles have special names: the 25th, 50th, and 75th percentiles are referred to as the first, second, and third *quartiles*, respectively, although sometimes this numbering is reversed. The 50th percentile is also called the *median* of the distribution; 50 percent of the distribution (that is, of the probability) lies on either side of the median, so that the ordinate at the median divides the area under the density function's graph into two equal parts. The median is a measure of the centering of the distribution (as is the mean), but it need not coincide with the mean. In the case of a symmetrical distribution the median and the mean coincide and are equal to the x-coordinate of the center of symmetry. Figure 4-7 illustrates a case in which they do not coincide.

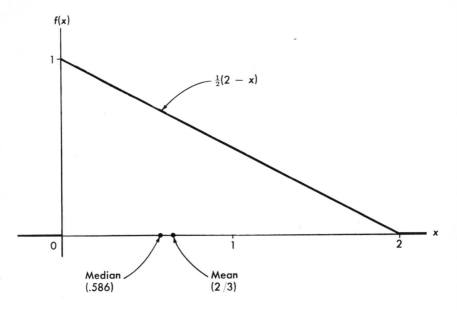

Figure 4-7 Mean and median distinct.

Problems

4-5. What is the expected value of a random variable whose density function is given in Problem 4-3?

4-6. The density of the distribution given in Table I is (except for a constant factor) $e^{-x^2/2}$. What is the mean? Determine the median and first and third quartiles from Table I.

4-7. Determine the quartiles of the distribution of Problem 4-3 geometrically.

4-8. Consider the random variable X with distribution defined by the density function

$$f(x) = \begin{cases} \dfrac{3}{4}(1 - x^2), & \text{if } -1 < x < 1 \\ 0, & \text{if } |x| > 1. \end{cases}$$

Sketch the graph of this density and determine the median. Determine EX.

4-9. Taking the region under the $f(x)$ of Problem 4-8 to the right of the median, show that the area is $1/2$ using the method of approximation by rectangles and passing to the limit (and using also the formula for a sum of squares given in Example 4-d).

4-10. Each horizontal line in Table II gives certain percentiles of a probability distribution; the quantity in the left column ("degrees of freedom") is actually the mean of the distribution in that row.

(a) Sketch the distribution function corresponding to five "degrees of freedom" and estimate from the·graph the first and third quartiles.

(b) Estimate from the graph in (a) the probability assigned to the interval from 3 to 7.

(c) Compare the medians with the means; which are larger?

4-11. Each horizontal line of Table III gives certain percentiles of a distribution. (Observe Note 1 at the bottom of the table.) Sketch the distribution function corresponding to five "degrees of freedom," that is, using the fifth row in the table. What is the first quartile?

4-12. Show that Property (b) for expected values is a special case of Property (a).

4-13. Show the equivalence of the two expressions for var X using property (a) of expected values.

4.4 In terms of calculus

The mathematical concepts introduced above are concepts that occur in continuous mathematical models generally and that have led to the calculus. In particular, to begin with, the notion of the area under a curve, used in specifying the probability that a random variable X falls in a certain set F, is precisely the notion of *definite integral*:

$$P(F) = P(X \text{ falls in } F) = \text{Area under } f(x) \text{ over } F$$
$$= \int_F f(x)\, dx,$$

where $f(x)$, the specified density function, is a nonnegative function such that

$$P(-\infty < X < \infty) = \int_{-\infty}^{\infty} f(x)\, dx = 1.$$

The probability assigned to the interval $a < x < b$ is then

$$P(a < X < b) = \int_a^b f(x)\, dx.$$

The distribution function associated with the given density function $f(x)$ is the probability assigned to the particular interval $(-\infty, x)$ considered as a function of the endpoint x:

$$F(x) = P(X \le x) = \int_{-\infty}^{x} f(u)\, du.$$

(Because x is used as the variable endpoint of the interval, the variable of integration has been changed to u. This is a "dummy variable," and the value of a definite integral does not depend on the letter used to denote the variable of integration.)

A fundamental theorem in calculus asserts that the derivative of a definite integral depending on a variable upper limit, with respect to that limit, is the integrand function evaluated at the upper limit:

$$\frac{d}{dx} \int_a^x f(u) \, du = f(x).$$

That is, the rate of change of area under a curve to the left of the ordinate at x with respect to x is just the height of the curve at that point; when the curve is high above the x-axis, area is added at a high rate as the ordinate is moved to the right, and when the curve is close to the x-axis, area is added at a low rate. Applied to the situation at hand the theorem implies that the density function is the derivative of the distribution function:

$$f(x) = F'(x) = \frac{d}{dx} \int_{-\infty}^x f(u) \, du.$$

EXAMPLE 4-e.   Consider the function

$$F(x) = \begin{cases} 1 - e^{-x}, & \text{for } x \text{ positive} \\ 0, & \text{for } x \text{ negative}. \end{cases}$$

This satisfies the conditions a distribution function must satisfy (increasing from 0 to 1 as x increases), and its derivative is the corresponding density function:

$$f(x) = F'(x) = \begin{cases} e^{-x}, & x \text{ positive}, \\ 0, & x \text{ negative}. \end{cases}$$

And then $F(x)$ can be obtained from $f(x)$ by integration:

$$F(x) = \int_{-\infty}^x f(u) \, du = \int_0^x e^{-u} \, du = 1 - e^{-x},$$

for positive x. Since $f(x) = 0$ for negative x, the integral from $-\infty$ up to a negative x is zero; thus, $F(x) = 0$ for x negative.

A limit of the type used in defining the expected value of a continuous distribution (from discrete approximations) is a definite integral, namely,

$$EX = \int_{-\infty}^{\infty} x f(x) \, dx.$$

(This is reminiscent of the formula for the expected value of a discrete distribution; the integration is the analogue of a sum, and the product $f(x) \, dx$ can be thought of as the probability in the tiny interval from x to

$x + dx$.) The expected value of a function of x turns out to be given by the following integral:

$$Eg(X) = \int_{-\infty}^{\infty} g(x)f(x)\, dx,$$

analogous to the formula for the discrete case. Of course, $g(X)$ is really another random variable, say Y, having a distribution of its own; and

$$Eg(X) = EY = \int_{-\infty}^{\infty} y f_Y(y)\, dy.$$

The equivalence of this and the first formula given for $Eg(X)$ will not be established here, but it will be seen in examples to relate to the idea of a change of variable of integration.

EXAMPLE 4-f. Consider again the distribution of Example 4-e, having the density e^{-x} for positive x. Let X be a random variable having this distribution. Then

$$EX = \int_0^\infty xe^{-x}\, dx = 1,$$

and

$$EX^2 = \int_0^\infty x^2 e^{-x}\, dx = 2.$$

The variance can be computed from these as follows:

$$\text{var } X = EX^2 - (EX)^2 = 2 - 1^2 = 1.$$

With t held fixed while averaging, the quantity $E(e^{tX})$ is a function of t, important in theoretical statistics, called the moment generating function. The significant values of t turn out to be those near zero, and for such values the moment generating function can be computed for the present example:

$$\psi(t) = E(e^{tX}) = \int_0^\infty e^{tx} e^{-x}\, dx = \int_0^\infty e^{-(1-t)x}\, dx$$

$$= \frac{e^{-(1-t)x}}{-(1-t)}\Bigg|_0^\infty = \frac{1}{1-t}.$$

Generation of moments of the distribution by this function will be considered in the problems.

In Section 4.2 it was asserted and seen intuitively from the mass analogue that the center of symmetry of a symmetrical distribution is the mean or center of gravity of the distribution. This can be shown as follows; it is given that $f(a - x) = f(a + x)$ for all x:

$$EX = \int_{-\infty}^{\infty} x f(x)\, dx = \int_{-\infty}^{\infty} (x - a + a)f(x)\, dx$$
$$= \int_{-\infty}^{\infty} (x - a)f(x)\, dx + a \int_{-\infty}^{\infty} f(x)\, dx$$
$$= \int_{-\infty}^{\infty} u f(a + u)\, du + a = a.$$

(The last integral is zero because the integrand is an "odd function"—symmetrical about the origin.)

Calculus can be used to obtain the density function of a random variable Y that is a linear function of a given X in terms of the density of X. Let $Y = aX + b$, where a is a positive number; then

$$F_Y(y) = P(Y \leq y) = P(aX + b \leq y)$$
$$= P\left(X \leq \frac{y - b}{a}\right) = F_X\left(\frac{y - b}{a}\right).$$

Differentiation of this relation between the distribution functions yields the desired relation between density functions:

$$f_Y(y) = \frac{1}{|a|} f_X\left(\frac{y - b}{a}\right).$$

Of course if a is positive, writing $|a|$ in place of a adds nothing, but the formula has been given as it is so as to be valid when a is negative, as a computation similar to the above will show. (Division of an inequality by a negative number reverses the sense of the inequality.)

Consider now the case of two random variables, (X, Y). Given a joint density function $f(x, y)$ for the distribution of probability in the plane of values (x, y), the probability of an event F in that plane is the volume under $f(x, y)$ above F:

$$P[(X, Y) \text{ falls in } F] = \iint_F f(x, y) \, dA.$$

The expected value of a function of X and Y is given by the formula

$$Eg(X, Y) = \int_{-\infty}^{\infty} \int_{-\infty}^{\infty} g(x, y) f(x, y) \, dx \, dy.$$

Similar formulas in terms of n-fold integrals apply in the case of the n random variables $X_1, \ldots, X_n$.

Problems

4-14. Determine the distribution function corresponding to each of the following densities:

  (a) $f(x) = 1 - |x|$ for $|x| < 1$, and equal to zero elsewhere.
  (b) $f(x) = 2e^{-2x}$ for x positive, and equal to zero for x negative.
  (c) $f(x) = \dfrac{1/\pi}{1 + x^2}$.

(d) $f(x) = 3(1 - x^2)/4$ for $|x| < 1$, and equal to zero elsewhere.

(e) $f(x) = \cos x$ for $0 < x < \pi/2$, and equal to zero elsewhere.

4-15. Determine the density function corresponding to each of the given distribution functions:

(a) $F(x) = 1 - e^{-3x}$ for positive x, equal to zero for negative x.

(b) $F(x) = \dfrac{1}{\pi} \left(\dfrac{\pi}{2} + \arctan x \right)$

(c) $F(x) = \displaystyle\int_{-\infty}^{x} \dfrac{e^{-u^2/2}}{\sqrt{2\pi}} \, du.$

4-16. Determine the mean of the distribution given by

(a) $f(x)$ in Problem 4-14(a).

(b) $f(x)$ in Problem 4-14(b).

(c) $f(x)$ in Problem 4-14(d).

4-17. Compute the variance of the distribution given by

(a) $f(x)$ in Problem 4-14(a).

(b) $f(x)$ in Problem 4-14(b).

(c) $f(x)$ in Problem 4-14(d).

4-18. Suppose that the random variable X has the density $f(x) = 1$ for $0 < x < 1$ and equal to zero outside that interval. (That is, X has a uniform distribution over the interval.) Let $Y = X^2$.

(a) Determine $F_Y(y) = P(Y \le y)$, for $0 < y < 1$.

(b) Determine the density function of Y from (a).

(c) Compute EX^2 from the distribution of X.

(d) Compute $EX^2 = EY$ from the distribution of Y in (b), and compare with the result in (c).

(e) In the integral defining EX^2 in (c) make the change of variable $x^2 = y$ and so obtain the integral for EY in (d).

4-19. From the fact that subject to very mild conditions

$$\frac{d}{dt} \int_a^b f(x, t) \, dx = \int_a^b \frac{\partial}{\partial t} f(x, t) \, dx,$$

it follows that (subject to those conditions)

$$\frac{d}{dt} E[g(X, t)] = E\left[\frac{\partial}{\partial t} g(X, t) \right].$$

Use this to show formally that if $\psi(t) = E(e^{tX})$, then $\psi'(0) = EX$, and more generally, that the kth derivative of $\psi(t)$ evaluated at $t = 0$ is the kth moment of X, EX^k.

4-20. Apply the result of Problem 4-19 to obtain the mean and variance of the random variable X in Example 4-f.

4-21. Suppose that Z is a random variable having the density function $f(u) = (e^{-u^2/2})/\sqrt{2\pi}$. Determine the density of $X = aZ + b$ where $a > 0$.

4.5 The normal distribution

The distribution defined by the density function

$$\phi(z) = \frac{1}{\sqrt{2\pi}} e^{-z^2/2}$$

is called the *standard normal* distribution. The constant $1/\sqrt{2\pi}$ is what is needed so that the area under the graph of $\phi(z)$ is equal to 1. (This is not obvious, but can be demonstrated using calculus.)

Because of the symmetry of the density function $\phi(z)$, the mean value of a random variable Z having this distribution is zero, the center of symmetry; indeed, for the same reason of symmetry, any moment of *odd* order (about $z = 0$) is zero:

$$EZ^{2k-1} = 0, \qquad k = 1, 2, \dots.$$

Moments of *even* order can be computed; the results are as follows:

$$EZ^{2k} = 1 \cdot 3 \cdot 5 \cdots (2k - 1), \qquad k = 1, 2, \dots.$$

The variance is then

$$\text{var } Z = EZ^2 - (EZ)^2 = 1 - 0^2 = 1.$$

Thus, Z has mean zero and variance 1. These are often referred to as *standard* parameter values, and hence the name "standard normal" for the distribution of Z.

Table I gives values of the *distribution function* for the standard normal distribution:

$$\Phi(z) = \int_{-\infty}^{z} \phi(u)\, du = P(Z \le z).$$

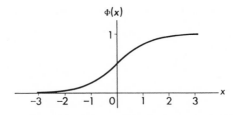

Figure 4-8 Standard normal distribution function.

From it one can compute the probability of an interval:

$$P(a < Z < b) = \Phi(b) - \Phi(a).$$

The term "normal"—referring only to the shape of the distribution, and in particular to the rate at which the density falls off for large values—is applied also to distributions obtained from the standard normal distribution by translation and/or change of scale:

$$X = aZ + b.$$

A random variable X related in this way to a standard normal Z is said to be a *normal random variable* (or sometimes, a normal *variate*), or to be *normally distributed*.

The distribution function of the normal X can be expressed in terms of the distribution function of the standard normal Z, as follows. First observe that

$$EX = E(aZ + b) = aEZ + b = b$$

and

$$\text{var } X = a^2 \text{ var } Z = a^2,$$

so that b and $|a|$ are respectively the mean μ and the standard deviation σ of X. Thus, for positive a:

$$Z = \frac{X - \mu}{\sigma}$$

is standard normal, and

$$F_X(x) = P(X \le x)$$
$$= P\left(\frac{X - \mu}{\sigma} \le \frac{x - \mu}{\sigma}\right) = \Phi\left(\frac{x - \mu}{\sigma}\right).$$

So, to find the value of the distribution function of X at the point x, one looks in Table I at the point

$$z = \frac{x - \mu}{\sigma}.$$

Subtracting the mean and dividing by the standard deviation in this way is is called *standardizing*, and amounts to measuring x in terms of how many standard deviations it is away from the mean.

EXAMPLE 4-g.   Let X be normally distributed with mean 16 and variance 7. One can use Table I to compute $P(|X - 16| > 3)$, as follows:

$$P(|X - 16| > 3) = 1 - P(|X - 16| < 3)$$
$$= 1 - P(-3 < X - 16 < 3)$$
$$= 1 - P(13 < X < 19)$$
$$= 1 - [F_X(19) - F_X(13)]$$
$$= 1 - \left[\Phi\left(\frac{19 - 16}{\sqrt{7}}\right) - \Phi\left(\frac{13 - 16}{\sqrt{7}}\right)\right]$$
$$= 1 - \Phi(1.13) + \Phi(-1.13)$$
$$= 1 - .8708 + .1292 = .2584.$$

Notice these features of the computation†: complementation was employed to express the given event in terms of an interval; the probability of the interval was then obtained as the rise in the distribution function over that interval; and then the endpoints of the interval were standardized (measured in terms of standard deviations from the mean) in order to use the standard normal table.

Problems

4-22. A random variable X has the standard normal distribution (mean zero and variance 1). Determine, using Table I, page 268,

(a) $P(X < 0)$,   (b) $P(1 < X < 3)$,

(c) $P(|X| < 3)$,   (d) $P(X = -1)$,

(e) $P(X > 2 \text{ or } X < -2)$.

4-23. Show that, when X is a standard normal variable,

(a) $P(|X| > k) = 2(1 - \Phi(k))$,

(b) $P(|X| < k) = 2\Phi(k) - 1$.

4-24. A random variable X is normally distributed with mean 50 and variance 25. Determine

(a) $P(X > 62)$,   (b) $P(|X - 50| < 8)$,

(c) $P(X = 60)$,   (d) $P(|X - 40| > 5)$.

4-25. A random variable X is normally distributed. If $E(X^2) = 68$ and $P(X < 10) = .8413$, determine μ and σ^2.

4-26. Suppose that a doorway being constructed is to be used by a class of people whose heights are (approximately) normally distributed with mean 5 feet 10 inches and standard deviation 3 inches. How low may the doorway be without causing more than 2 percent of the people to bump their heads?

4-27. It is found that following a certain crushing process, rock diameters are approximately normally distributed with mean diameter 1.5 inches and standard deviation .3 inch.

(a) What percentage of the rocks would have diameters exceeding 2 inches?

(b) What characteristic of rock diameters makes the normal distribution necessarily inexact in describing them?

(c) Assuming the weight of a rock to be kd^3, where d is the diameter, what is the expected weight (in terms of k)?

4-28. The acceptability of a capillary tube for a freezer is found by measuring the pressure drop in pounds per square inch between the two ends of the tube. The pressures obtained from a manufacturing process of capillary tubes shows an average of 130 pounds per square inch and a standard deviation of 4 pounds

---

† In such computations using decimals and tables it is to be understood that the computations are not exact, even though the equal sign (implying exact equality) is used.

per square inch. Assume that these pressures are random and normally distributed. Determine

(a) what percent of the pressures are below 121.5 pounds per square inch;
(b) what value is exceeded by 75 percent of the pressure readings;
(c) what limits include the middle 90 percent of the pressure readings;
(d) what percent of the pressure readings lie between 121.5 and 134.5 pounds per square inch.

4.6 Independence and correlation

The random variables X and Y are said to be *independent* if and only if for every event F on the x-axis and every event G on the y-axis F and G are independent events:

$$P(X \text{ in } F \text{ and } Y \text{ in } G) = P(X \text{ in } F)P(Y \text{ in } G).$$

Similarly, the n random variables $X_1, \ldots, X_n$ are independent if and only if the events X_1 in $E_1, \ldots, X_n$ in E_n are independent for all choices of intervals E_i. In particular, if the n random variables are independent, then any smaller number of them would be independent.

The notion of the density of a distribution can be extended to the case of several random variables; and a joint density function for *independent* random variables is the product of the individual densities. In the case of three variables, (X, Y, Z), this condition for independence is written as follows:

$$f_{X,Y,Z}(x, y, z) = f_X(x)f_Y(y)f_Z(z).$$

This is clearly the analogue of a similar relation for probabilities in the discrete case. (See Section 2.4.) And as in the discrete case, it follows that for given functions g, h, and k:

$$E[g(X)h(Y)k(Z)] = E[g(X)]E[h(Y)]E[k(Z)],$$

when X, Y, and Z are independent. (A similar relation holds for any finite number of independent random variables.) To establish such a relation requires a definition of expected value of a function of several variables; this can be given in terms of integral calculus, but this will be considered as beyond the scope of this discussion.

When X and Y are independent, it follows as a particular case of the last kind of relation above that

$$E(XY) = EX \, EY, \qquad (X, Y \text{ independent})$$

so that the covariance of X and Y is zero. The *covariance* is defined by the same formula in terms of expectations as in the discrete case:

$$\text{cov}\,(X,\,Y) = EXY - EX\,EY.$$

When this is zero, the variables X and Y are said to be *uncorrelated*, and this happens when they are independent—but *not* vice versa.

Given that X and Y are uncorrelated, the variance of their sum reduces to a particularly simple form:

$$\begin{aligned}
\text{var}\,(X + Y) &= E[X + Y - EX - EY]^2 \\
&= E(X - EX)^2 + E(Y - EY)^2 + 2E[(X - EX)(Y - EY)] \\
&= \text{var}\,X + \text{var}\,Y + 2\,\text{cov}\,(X,\,Y) \\
&= \text{var}\,X + \text{var}\,Y + 0.
\end{aligned}$$

More generally, if every two of the variables $X_1, X_2, \ldots, X_n$ are uncorrelated —which is certainly the case when the n variables are independent—then

$$\text{var}\,(X_1 + \cdots + X_n) = \text{var}\,X_1 + \cdots + \text{var}\,X_n.$$

The standard deviation of a sum of uncorrelated variables is then the square root of the sum of the squares of the standard deviations of the summands. This is true for discrete as well as for continuous variables.

4.7   Errors and tolerances

It is frequently appropriate to consider errors in computation or measurement as random variables. Indeed, it is usually the *random* nature of the quantity which requires treating it as an error, since a predictable miscalculation could be avoided by compensation. One often finds, too, that there are contributions to total error coming from several sources, which combine additively or approximately additively to make up the total error. The total error is then a sum of random variables.

EXAMPLE 4-h.   Consider a measurement A' of the concentration A of a certain chemical solution. The discrepancy may be attributable to random fluctuations in the measuring process and to small variations in concentration from one portion of the solution to another. That is, we may think of A' as

$$A' = A + \epsilon_1 + \epsilon_2.$$

where ϵ_1 and ϵ_2 are independent, random errors. If these errors have zero expectation, $E(A') = A$; or one might *define* the concentration A of the solution to be $E(A')$. The variance of the total error can be computed from the variances of the components using the additivity property:

$$\text{var } (A' - A) = \text{var } \epsilon_1 + \text{var } \epsilon_2.$$

The standard deviation is then the square root of this sum.

EXAMPLE 4-i. In analyzing the over-all error in a complex mechanical or electrical computing system caused by errors in various components (such as gyros, accelerometers, multipliers, summers, integrators, and so on), it is often the case that the total error can be expressed (at least to a first-order approximation) as a *linear* combination of component errors:

$$\epsilon = a_1\epsilon_1 + a_2\epsilon_2 + \cdots + a_k\epsilon_k.$$

The variance of this over-all error (assuming independence) is

$$\text{var } \epsilon = a_1{}^2 \text{ var } \epsilon_1 + a_2{}^2 \text{ var } \epsilon_2 + \cdots + a_k{}^2 \text{ var } \epsilon_k.$$

That standard deviations do not add, to yield the standard deviation of the sum, is an important observation, since the root-sum-square combination which is correct yields in general a *smaller* result than a straight addition. The root-sum-square takes into account the frequent cancellations provided by errors of opposite signs, whereas a straight sum would be overly pessimistic.

It is sometimes more important to consider *maximum* errors than their standard deviations. The relationship between these depends on the distributions of the errors and would usually be different in different situations. However, it has been found practical to assume that the errors are *normally* distributed and then to take $\pm 3\sigma$ as limits beyond which individual observations "never" occur. It can be seen from Table I that the probability of occurrence of a value of a normally distributed variable outside those limits is .0026, which is quite small—but not sacred. Thus, it is convenient to take $\pm 3\sigma$ as maximum departures from the mean, although one could (and perhaps in some cases should) take 2σ or 4.3σ or some other multiple of σ in place of 3σ.

The quantities $\mu \pm 3\sigma$ are thought of as "tolerance" limits. One thinks of them as "natural tolerances" if they describe actual errors. The "tolerance" terminology is especially common in fitting together manufactured parts. Let us introduce the notation $T = 3\sigma$ to signify such a tolerance. Observe that since σ's must be combined in root-sum-square fashion, so must tolerances. For example, if

$$\sigma = \sqrt{\sigma_1{}^2 + \sigma_1{}^2},$$

then for the corresponding tolerances:

$$T = \sqrt{T_1{}^2 + T_2{}^2} = \sqrt{9\sigma_1{}^2 + 9\sigma_2{}^2} = 3\sigma.$$

The $T = 3\sigma$ relation is still appropriate for the combination, since if the individual errors are normally distributed, so is a linear combination of them.

EXAMPLE 4-j. Suppose that bearings are manufactured with inside diameter $.5000 + \epsilon_1$ and that shafts on which the bearings are to fit have outside diameter $.4995 + \epsilon_2$, where ϵ_1 and ϵ_2 are assumed to be independent, normal random variables with tolerances .0006 and .0007, respectively. What percentage of misfits (due to interference) could be expected?

The "clearance" is the difference $.0005 + \epsilon_1 - \epsilon_2$. The combined tolerance is

$$T = \sqrt{(.0006)^2 + (.0007)^2} \doteq .00092,$$

and the corresponding standard deviation is .000307. The proportion of misfits expected is then the probability:

$$P(\text{clearance} < 0) = \Phi\left(\frac{0 - .0005}{.000307}\right) = \Phi(-1.63) = .052,$$

or 5.2 percent.

Problems

4-29.   What is the average weight of a box of 100 screws, if the weight of an individual screw is a random variable with expected value 1 ounce? What is the standard deviation of the weight of a box of screws, if the standard deviation of the weight of an individual screw is .01 ounce? (Assume independence.)

4-30.   Two dice are thrown. Let X be the number of points on one and Y the number of points on the other. Construct probability tables for X, Y, and $X + Y$ and compute the expected values and variances. Then verify the additivity properties of μ and σ^2, assuming independence of X and Y.

4-31.   Ten four-digit numbers presumed accurate are to be added. If the numbers are rounded off to three digits each and then added, what are the expected value and standard deviation of the error committed in this process? (Treat the error made in rounding off a number as a discrete random variable, assuming that the fourth digit is $0, 1, \ldots, 9$ with equal probabilities, and that the errors are independent.)

4-32.   A missile is fired at a point in a plane, and the amount of the miss is measured by X and Y, the components in two perpendicular directions. If each of these components has expectation zero and standard deviation 1000 feet, what is the expected value of $(X^2 + Y^2)$, the square of the radial miss?

4-33.   It is desired to make resistors of 200 ohms with a tolerance $\pm 3/4$ percent. These would cost 25 cents apiece. An employee suggests putting in series two 100-ohm resistors, with tolerances of ± 1 percent each; these 100-ohm resistors cost 2 cents apiece. Does he rate a bonus?

4-34. Referring to Example 4-j, determine the mean outside diameter of the shafts in order that the percentage of misfits be reduced to 1 percent.

4-35. Gear A has basic width .500 inch and a tolerance of $\pm.001$ inch. Gear B has basic width .300 inch and a tolerance of $\pm.004$ inch. Gear C has basic width .700 inch and a tolerance of $\pm.002$ inch. These are to be assembled side by side on a single shaft. What is the basic width and tolerance of the assembly?

4-36. The position error (in nautical miles) in a certain guidance system after a given time of operation is given by

$$\epsilon = 5\delta_a + 20\delta_g,$$

where δ_a is random accelerometer error (in feet per second per second) and δ_g is random gyro error (in degrees per hour). Determine the standard deviation of position error corresponding to standard deviations of .1 ft/sec^2 and .05 degree per hour of the accelerometer and gyro errors, respectively.

5

SAMPLING

The common notion that the subject of "statistics" deals with the gathering, presenting, and interpreting of data is basically correct. However, in attempting to make an interpretation or inference meaningful by putting them into a logical, mathematical framework, one finds that restrictions must be placed on the gathering process. One of the trickiest tasks encountered by a statistician is that of making sense out of a mass of data collected and presented to him by one who has little notion of the requirements for a tenable, theoretically sound inference.

A statistical inference is based on probability methods, and the data used consist of the results of performing a certain experiment of chance, perhaps repeatedly, that is, an experiment whose useful mathematical model is probabilistic (or *stochastic*, to use another word often encountered). This model would be unknown at least in some aspects, and statistical inference consists in the drawing of conclusions about the model, or possibly also in taking some action based on those conclusions.

EXAMPLE 5-a. Measurements of length tend to include a random error of measurement. In place of the actual length L, they give the incorrect quantity $X = L + \epsilon$, where ϵ is an unpredictable quantity subject to "statistical" fluctuation. Thus, it is useful to consider ϵ (the error), and hence X (the *measured* length) as random variables. It is often assumed that ϵ has mean zero, which essentially *defines* the "true" length of the object being measured as the expected value of the probability distribution of the measured length:

$$E(X) = E(L + \epsilon) = L + E(\epsilon) = L.$$

The "data" in a situation such as this would consist of several measurements of length, the results of performing the measuring operation several times; and the reason for gathering data might be to infer something about the actual or true length L, that is, about the mean of the distribution of X. One might also be interested in learning something about the variance of that distribution, which would give some idea as to the reliability of the measurement process.

5.1 Random sampling

The process of gathering data or of obtaining results from several performances of an experiment of chance is called *sampling*. The results themselves are called *observations*, and the collection of observations is called a *sample*,

Although the result of an experiment of chance may be more general, attention will be focused on the case in which the result of each performance of the experiment is a single random variable.

Some of the terminology of sampling stems from the following situations that are frequently encountered in statistics:

(1) Objects are drawn one at a time from an actual, finite collection of objects called a *population*, and a particular characteristic of interest is determined for each object drawn. After each observation, and before the next drawing, the object just drawn is replaced and the population of objects is thoroughly mixed.

(2) Objects are drawn from an actual, finite population as in (1) except that the objects are *not* replaced.

The population of objects is frequently a collection of people, and the observed characteristic may be such a thing as weight, eye color, political preference, etc., or a combination of these. The basic probability space—the experiment of chance—is this collection of people or objects, although probability would naturally be transferred to the space of "values" of the characteristic of interest; and this value space itself can be conceived of as the basic probability space.

When objects are drawn in such a way that at each drawing all remaining objects are equally likely to be chosen, the sampling is called *random*, a usage that conforms to the layman's notion of "selecting at random." It is to make each drawing random that the population should be mixed when objects drawn are replaced. With this understanding that each selection is random, the sampling in (1) is called *random sampling with replacement*; and in (2), *random sampling without replacement*.

In a sense, random sampling without replacement is better than random sampling with replacement, since in the former case objects that have been drawn are not put back into the pool of available objects to confound things. To take an extreme case, suppose that there are only two objects in the population; when one is drawn, selecting a second object would furnish complete information about the original population *if* the first were not replaced. Drawing without replacement is also sometimes more convenient in that the mixing required with the replacement of objects is not always easy to achieve. On the other hand, the mathematically simpler process is sampling with replacement. Of course, if a population is enormous with respect to the size of the sample to be drawn, it is practically immaterial whether the objects drawn are or are not replaced; sampling without replacement merges into sampling with replacement as the population size becomes infinite. The theory of one could then be used with the practice of the other.

Suppose that when an object is drawn, the characteristic measured or otherwise ascertained is X. This is a random quantity whose distribution is determined by the proportions of the various values of X among the objects in the population and the agreement that the objects are equally likely. It is this distribution of X that will be called the *population distribution*.

EXAMPLE 5-b.   In a group of 100 freshmen, 73 are 18, 22 are 17, 4 are 19, and 1 is 16 years old. Selecting one freshman from the group at random is represented by assigning probability .01 to each freshman. The population random variable X that is of interest is the age of a freshman drawn, and this variable has the following probability table:

Age	16	17	18	19
Probability	.01	.22	.73	.04

In a real statistical problem, this distribution would not be known completely, as it is here. More typical would be a situation in which one does not (or cannot, practically) know the population distribution, and draws a *sample* of, say, ten freshmen, the characteristics of which might be used to make an inference about the population distribution.

There is another type of data-gathering process, mechanically different from those labeled (1) and (2) above, but which is mathematically the same as (1), random sampling with replacement:

(3) Observations are obtained as the result of repeated, independent performances of an experiment, under conditions that are identical with respect to those factors that can be controlled.

This description actually includes situations of type (1) as special cases, but in general does not necessarily refer to a tangible "population" from which an object is to be selected. However, one may *imagine* a population of possible results, perhaps infinite, and consider that performing the experiment selects (in effect) one of those possible results. Repeating the experiment under identical conditions means that the first result is "replaced" and is again available in the population for the next drawing. Measurement processes are typically of this type, unless there is a possibility that the one making the measurements becomes more skilled at the job as the gathering of data proceeds. In such a case the later measurements would be more reliable, and would not be from the same "population" as the earlier measurements—the appropriate probability model would have changed.

EXAMPLE 5-c.   When a coin is tossed, the result is either Heads (H) or Tails (T). These two outcomes may be thought of as a "population," but one must imagine that the "object drawn" is replaced before another drawing, to represent the fact that in each successive toss of the coin both outcomes are possible. An equivalent experiment would be that of drawing a chip at random from a bowl containing as many chips marked H as chips marked T. In order for successive drawings to be like successive tosses of a coin, the chips drawn would have to be immediately replaced and mixed in with the rest. On the other hand, if one can conceive of a bowl with infinitely many chips, half marked H and half marked T, then drawing a finite number of chips from the bowl would not disturb the balance of Heads and Tails, and replacement would not be required.

The notation to be used is as follows: X_1 denotes the value of the first observation obtained, X_2 denotes the value of the second observation, and so on, so that a sample of n observations is $(X_1, X_2, \ldots, X_n)$. Capital letters are used because the result of any observation is a random variable, and one can speak of such things as $P(X_3 = 7)$, the probability that the third observation is 7. Of course, if 7 is actually obtained, this value itself is *not* a random variable; a specific realization of the sampling process is not a set of random variables, but a set of numbers. Saying that a sample is a set of n random variables $(X_1, \ldots, X_n)$ means simply that the outcomes cannot be predicted ahead of time, and that there is a certain probability distribution or model that describes the sampling process.

EXAMPLE 5-d.   Two chips are drawn, without replacement, from a bowl containing three chips numbered 1 and five chips numbered 2. There are four possible "values" of the sample (X_1, X_2): (1, 1), (1, 2), (2, 1), and (2, 2). Assuming that the available chips are equally likely to be drawn each time ("random sampling"), the probability distribution for this set of possible samples is as follows:

(X_1, X_2)	(1, 1)	(1, 2)	(2, 1)	(2,2)
Probability	6/56	15/56	15/56	20/56

These probabilities are easily computed; for instance,

$$\begin{aligned}
P\{(X_1, X_2) = (2, 1)\} &= P(\text{1st chip is 2, 2nd is 1}) \\
&= P(\text{2nd is 1} \mid \text{1st is 2}) \, P(\text{1st is 2}) \\
&= \frac{3}{7} \cdot \frac{5}{8} = 15/56.
\end{aligned}$$

It should be observed that one can calculate the distributions of the individual observations from the above table. For instance,

$$\begin{aligned}
P(X_1 = 1) &= P[(1, 2) \text{ or } (1, 1)] \\
&= 15/56 + 6/56 \\
&= 3/8.
\end{aligned}$$

The point is that not knowing which chip is selected on the first draw, one would bet on the second draw with odds of 3 to 5 against a 1, whether or not the first chip drawn is replaced. That is, the probability $P(X_2 = 1)$ is an *un*conditional probability (no information about X_1), as contrasted with, say,

$$P(X_2 = 1 \mid X_1 = 1) = 2/8.$$

This last example is intended to corroborate the assertion that in sampling without replacement from a finite population, the distribution of the ith observation is precisely the "population" distribution (that is, the distribution in the original population) even though $i - 1$ withdrawals were made previously. This is because it is the unconditional distribution that is referred to, with no information on the results of those $i - 1$ previous draws. So the observations in the sample $(X_1, X_2, \ldots, X_n)$ are *identically distributed*. They are not, on the other hand, independent random variables, inasmuch as the distribution of X_2 (for instance) surely depends on the result of the first draw, X_1.

If there is replacement and mixing between draws, or if the population is infinite so that replacement is immaterial, then not only are the observations in the sample identically distributed, they are also independent. And in the type of sampling typified in the making of physical measurements, in which the identical experiment is iterated with the result of no trial depending in any way on the outcomes of other trials—seen to correspond to sampling with replacement from an imagined population—the observations are again identically distributed and independent. Although the terminology is not uniform, a sample obtained in this way will be called here a *random* sample:

Definition A *random* sample is a sample whose n observations are independent and identically distributed. The common distribution is called the *population distribution.*

Actually, the term random sample will be applied not only to the mathematical model of a certain kind of distribution for $(X_1, \ldots, X_n)$, but also to a "real" sample obtained by a process that can be represented by the mathematical model of a random sample. Notice, however, that the question "is (3, 7, 16, 12) a random sample?" can only be answered by an examination of the process by which it was obtained. Random sampling refers to a *process* of gathering data and not to a particular set of numbers which might be obtained.

It is not always easy to obtain a sample from a specified population by a means that can be considered random. Even in the process of obtaining measurements it is necessary not only to make each measurement under the same conditions, but also to ensure that later readings are not influenced by a desire to make them come out to be near earlier readings, or otherwise to introduce dependence. In the case of sampling from actual populations, it is not always easy to put the population in a "bowl," and as a result one sometimes draws from a population that is somewhat different from the one that he assumes he is drawing from.

EXAMPLE 5-e.   Suppose that a sample of 100 is selected by taking the last name on every tenth page of a certain 1000-page telephone book, and that these 100 people are called on a certain evening. Not everyone who is called will be home, and it is tempting to use the responses of those who do answer as a sample (of size less than 100). But this sample will not be from the population of people who have telephones! Instead, it is a sample from the population of people who have telephones who, in addition, answer their phones on that evening; these populations may have different characteristics, depending on the response requested. For example, if one is trying to determine the distribution of the number of children in a family, there is perhaps less likelihood of the telephone's being answered in families with no children. Indeed, it may well be that in families not listed in the directory, the distribution of the number of children is quite different from that for the families having telephones. Using a sample of responses to telephone calls to infer something about the number of children per family in the given city is quite inappropriate, since the wrong population is being sampled.

EXAMPLE 5-f.   To determine the acceptability of an hour's production of a certain spot-welding process, five welds are to be selected and tested for tensile strength. In order that the five results constitute a random sample from the population of strengths of welds made during that hour, it is necessary to assume first that the welding process is not changing in its basic characteristics. If the welded materials are being collected, so that one can draw five welds "at random," this by definition leads to a random sample. But care must be taken that the five are not all taken off the top or all off the bottom; that is, not all at the end or all at the beginning of the hour's production, in case there should be a temporary or local phenomenon that could make the sample nonrepresentative. If the welds are passed on, as they are made, to another step in a manufacturing process, an inspector will then have to appear at the welding station at five randomly selected times during the hour period and make his test measurement.

Problems

5-1. A deck of cards is thoroughly shuffled and dealt into hands of 13 cards. Each hand can be thought of as a sample from the deck; what kind of sampling is involved?

5-2. Two dice are tossed 20 times in succession, and the total number of points showing at each toss is recorded. What kind of sampling is this, and what is the "population?"

5-3. In each of the following, what kind of sampling is involved, and what is the population:

(a) Standing by a roulette wheel one records the results of 20 consecutive spins.
(b) Five consecutive bottles are taken from a rotary filling device, and the quantity in each bottle is measured and recorded.

5-4. Which of the following would be likely to constitute a legitimate example of random sampling without replacement?

(a) Taking the top 13 cards from a shuffled deck of cards.
(b) Taking the top layer of apples from a crate (to obtain an estimate of overall quality).
(c) Querying 20 students lounging on a campus mall to determine dating habits of a college population.

5-5. Which would provide (and why) the better basis for estimating the variability in an inspector's measurement of a dimension of a certain part:

(a) Asking him to make ten such measurements for you while you wait, or
(b) Taking at random one of the measurements he has made in each of the preceding ten working days?

5-6. Discuss how you might go about obtaining a random sample (without replacement, if that is more convenient) from the population of students of voting age in a certain university.

5.2 Samples from discrete populations

In obtaining observations on a discrete random variable X with possible values $x_1, x_2, \ldots$, one naturally finds that only these values occur in the sample. Indeed, even if the list of possible values is considered to be infinite, only a finite number would occur in a finite sample, so that in any case the possible values can be taken to be $x_1, \ldots, x_k$ for some finite k. With the assumption (as in Chapter 3) that keeping track of the sequence in which the observations are obtained adds nothing to the process of inference, which can be shown to be true if the sample is a *random sample*, the data can be summarized in a table that shows the frequency in the sample of each possible value:

Possible value (x_i)	x_1	x_2	$\cdots$	x_k
Frequency (f_i)	f_1	f_2	$\cdots$	f_k

The *frequency* f_i is the number of times the value x_i appears in the sample— and it is a random variable! Notice that the frequencies must add up to the sample size: $f_1 + f_2 + \cdots + f_k = n$.

Thinking of $X = x_i$ as an event, with probability p_i, the number of times out of n trials in which X turns out to be x_i is a binomially distributed random variable, and as discussed in Chapter 3, the *relative frequency* f_i/n is a natural estimate of the probability p_i. One may think of the table of relative frequencies as the sample version or the sample estimate of the table of probabilities:

Possible value (x_i)	x_1	$\cdots$	x_k
Relative freq. (f_i/n)	f_1/n	$\cdots$	f_k/n

The *cumulative relative frequencies*

$$F_i = \frac{1}{n}(f_1 + \cdots + f_i)$$

would be natural estimates of the cumulative probabilities

$$F(x_i) = p_1 + \cdots + p_i.$$

The *sample distribution function* is the function formed from the relative frequencies defining the sample in the same way as the distribution function (c.d.f.) is formed from the probabilities:

$$F_n(x) = \sum_{\substack{\text{all } i \text{ for} \\ \text{which } x_i \leq x}} f_i/n.$$

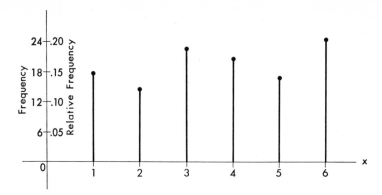

Figure 5-1   Sample frequencies for Example 5-g.

EXAMPLE 5-g.   To make an inference concerning the probabilities of the six faces of a die, it is tossed 120 times, with the following results:

Number of points	1	2	3	4	5	6
Frequency	18	16	23	21	18	24
Relative frequency	.150	.133	.192	.135	.150	.200

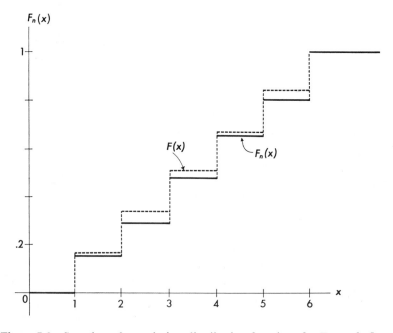

Figure 5-2   Sample and population distribution functions for Example 5-g.

The results may be exhibited graphically by erecting bars of height proportional frequency at each possible value, as shown in Figure 5-1. The cumulative frequencies corresponding to the above data are as follows:

Number of points	1	2	3	4	5	6
Cumulative frequency	18	34	57	78	96	120
Cum. rel. frequency	.150	.283	.475	.650	.800	1.0

The sample distribution function, a step function whose step heights are in fact the cumulative relative frequencies, is shown in Figure 5-2, along with the distribution function (c.d.f.) of the model in which the faces are equally likely.

5.3 Samples from continuous populations

Because the observed values of a continuous random variable can fall anywhere in an interval, it is not possible to prepare ahead of time a list of values that might be encountered (as it is in the case of a discrete population). One simply records the observed values, ending up with a list of numbers $(X_1, \ldots, X_n)$. A first step in the digestion of the information contained in the numbers is to put them in numerical order, and possibly to plot them on a scale of values. To aid in the visualization of what the sample contains, a plot can be made of the sample distribution function—the same function as defined in the case of data from a discrete population:

$$F_n(x) = k/n,$$

where k is the number of observations in the sample that do not exceed x. This is the distribution function corresponding to an imagined discrete probability distribution that places mass $1/n$ at each observation. The significance of this distribution is that the sample distribution function at x, $F_n(x)$, is a good estimate of the population distribution function, $F(x)$. For, the number of observations to the left of x is binomially distributed with p equal to the probability that an observation falls to the left of x, that is, $p = F(x)$.

EXAMPLE 5-h. Measurements of a certain dimension of each of twenty supposedly identical parts taken from a production line are recorded as follows:

3.364	3.384	3.414	3.381
3.433	3.445	3.470	3.376
3.405	3.380	3.442	3.426
3.417	3.401	3.434	3.396
3.407	3.450	3.453	3.409

The quickest way to order the observations is perhaps to make a mark on a scale of values for each observation, as done in Figure 5-3. Also shown in that figure is the sample distribution function, which rises an amount $1/20$ at each observation.

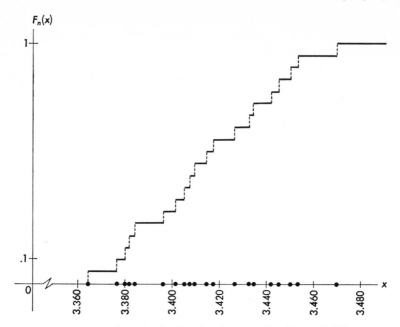

Figure 5-3   Sample distribution function for Example 5-h.

The observations in the above example happen to have been all distinct, but the more usual situation is that when they are rounded off to a specified degree of accuracy, there will be duplications, even though the probability of repeated values is zero for a continuous population. The point is that in the recording of data—and even prior to that, in the reading of scales on measuring devices—the observations from continuous populations are in fact rounded off. The result is that the recorded observations are actually observations from a *discrete* population that only approximates the true, continuous population. Because the population from which the recorded values are taken is discrete, there will generally be repeated values in a sample, and the presentation of the sample results in a frequency table (as in the preceding section) is in order. In this frequency table, the possible values are really rounded-off values; that is, an interval determined to be large enough to include all observations is divided into equal parts, each called a *class interval*, and all observations falling in a given class interval are rounded off to, say, the center of that interval. Indeed, any round-off procedure can be interpreted as defining such class intervals; the equality of the lengths of the class intervals is more a matter of convenience than of necessity.

For a graphical representation of data from a continuous population, as recorded in a frequency table, it is customary to construct a rectangle over each class interval whose area is proportional to the frequency of that interval. If the intervals are of equal width, the heights of the rectangles are then proportional to frequency—a good reason to use intervals of equal width. The resulting representation is called a *histogram*.

EXAMPLE 5-i. Table 5.1 below gives a tabulation of the observations in a sample of size ten from a continuous population, as described above. The corresponding histogram is shown in Figure 5-4.

Table 5.1   A frequency distribution

Class interval	Interval midpoint		Frequency
−.5 to .5	0	× ×	2
.5 to 1.5	1		0
1.5 to 2.5	2	× × ×	3
2.5 to 3.5	3	× × × ×	4
3.5 to 4.5	4	×	1
			$n = 10$

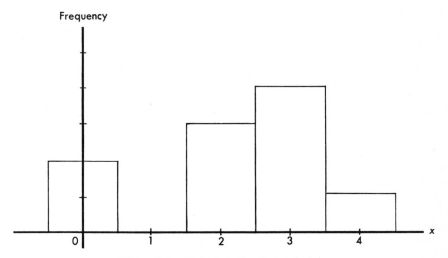

Figure 5-4   Histogram for Example 5-i.

The use of a rectangle to represent frequency, rather than a "rod" erected at the midpoint of the interval, is perhaps motivated by the fact that the observations falling in an interval do not necessarily fall at the midpoint, but can be any of the values in the interval. The rectangle suggests a smearing out of the observations over the interval, corresponding to the way probability is spread over intervals in a continuous distribution, rather than concentrated at points. On the other hand, in sampling from a discrete population there would be no point to using rectangles, even though the data are also recorded in the form of a frequency table.

The choice of class intervals is arbitrary—or at least as arbitrary as the round-off procedure, and different choices of class interval scheme result in different histograms for the same set of observations. This will be evident in the following example.

EXAMPLE 5-j.   Two hundred measurements of viscosity are given in Table 5.2, to the nearest tenth of a unit. Thus, for example, all readings of viscosity in the range 32.15 to 32.25 have been recorded as 32.2; this value is the midpoint of the class interval and is used to represent all observations that fall in the interval. The histogram corresponding to the data given in Table 5.2 is shown in Figure 5-5. This histogram shows considerable roughness. This reflects the fact that sampling fluctuations tend to be relatively large with a large number of class intervals. For instance, if a given interval has a probability .01, the expected number of the 200 observations falling in that interval is 2, and the standard deviation about 1.4. On the other hand, if fewer class intervals are used the sampling fluctuations are less effective; for instance, if a class interval has probability .1, the expected number of observations in it is 20 and the standard deviation is about 4.24. So a histogram like that in Figure 5-5 but for another sample of 200 observations may well have the positions of an adjacent high peak and low trough reversed. Regrouping the observations by a coarser rounding off of the original data eliminates some of this insignificant roughness. Table 5.3 gives a frequency distribution corresponding to a different choice of class intervals. The range 26.8 to 37.0 is divided into ten intervals of length 1.1. The first extends from 26.75 to 27.85 with midpoint 27.3, and so on. (Choice of boundaries so as not to coincide with observations avoids deciding which class is appropriate for an observation on the boundary; the width 1.1 avoids the misleading accuracy that might be inferred in using, say, 26.75 to 27.75 as a class interval with midpoint 27.25.) The histogram corresponding to Table 5.3 is shown in Figure 5-6.

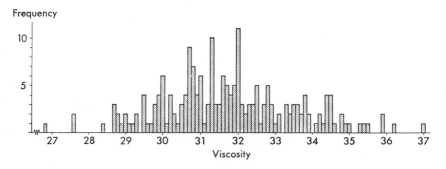

Figure 5-5   Histogram for data in Table 5.2.

Table 5.2 Characteristic measured—viscosity; method of measurement—Ostwald viscosimeter

Individual measurements in subgroups of 5

37.0	36.2	34.8	34.5	32.0
31.4	31.0	30.8	30.0	33.9
34.4	33.5	32.9	32.8	31.3
33.3	33.7	34.3	35.9	31.0
34.9	33.4	33.3	32.4	32.0
31.7	32.8	27.6	31.6	35.0
30.0	30.7	32.2	35.3	35.5
34.4	30.2	32.0	31.3	31.6
32.0	33.1	31.2	31.9	31.8
29.8	29.6	31.7	32.0	29.9
31.6	34.4	33.3	35.9	35.4
31.6	32.1	34.2	33.8	33.4
31.3	33.1	32.2	33.3	31.2
34.6	32.7	32.1	32.0	30.5
32.6	31.5	30.8	31.2	31.0
31.5	30.7	32.5	33.0	32.9
34.5	33.7	32.0	31.3	30.9
32.3	32.0	31.9	30.0	33.9
33.8	34.8	34.2	33.8	33.8
31.1	31.8	26.8	32.3	32.8
31.7	33.5	34.5	33.6	32.5
32.5	32.7	32.4	33.6	34.1
31.8	30.5	30.8	30.6	30.7
31.9	31.4	30.9	32.0	30.8
29.9	31.6	29.5	31.7	30.4
30.7	31.3	28.7	28.8	31.0
27.6	31.9	31.3	29.9	32.1
31.2	30.5	30.9	29.8	28.7
30.0	29.1	29.7	31.0	29.0
30.9	28.9	29.5	28.8	29.3
28.4	30.0	29.3	30.2	31.5
31.3	30.3	32.5	31.8	30.8
28.7	30.7	32.3	33.5	32.9
32.1	29.8	29.9	30.8	30.7
31.9	32.0	29.5	30.6	30.1
32.8	31.0	30.0	29.2	32.5
30.2	31.3	29.5	29.0	30.3
30.2	30.7	30.8	31.6	32.7
32.4	32.8	31.3	31.4	30.7
30.7	30.6	31.3	30.6	31.7

Table 5.3   Frequency table for grouping the 200
viscosity measurements

(1) Interval number i	(2) Interval boundaries	(3) Interval midpoint x_i	(4) Frequency f_i	(5) Relative frequency f_i/n
1	26.75–27.85	27.3	3	.015
2	27.85–28.95	28.4	7	.035
3	28.95–30.05	29.5	25	.125
4	30.05–31.15	30.6	42	.210
5	31.15–32.25	31.7	56	.280
6	32.25–33.35	32.8	30	.150
7	33.35–34.45	33.9	22	.110
8	34.45–35.55	35.0	11	.055
9	35.55–36.65	36.1	3	.015
10	36.65–37.75	37.2	1	.005
		Totals:	$n = 200$	1.000

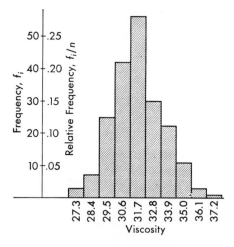

Figure 5-6   Histogram for grouped data, Table 5.3.

In regrouping to obtain a smoother histogram it should be remembered
that taking too few class intervals will smooth the significant features of the
underlying population distribution as well as the roughness. Indeed, going
to the extreme of taking a single class interval produces a singularly smooth
histogram; but it tells little about the population distribution. A population
can, of course, have a very jagged distribution, but the sharper the jags the

more sampling is required to learn about them, as might be expected. There is no precise rule, then, for setting up class intervals, but a reasonable rule of thumb suggests that from eight to twenty class intervals would be appropriate for more than fifty observations.

Problems

5-7. Regroup the data of Table 5.2 using a class interval width of .7. Construct the histogram for the resulting frequency distribution.

5-8. The following are coating weights as measured by reflectance density:

40	44	37	70	63	45	48	51
53	66	58	62	62	60	47	50
53	67	75	64	48	66	52	55
62	28	51	59	45	67	48	72
50	60	46	60	47	61	28	50
49	42	33	48	51	56	44	45
50	43	41	49	50	28	67	48
34	45	38	37	59	53	70	49
57	63	47	40	74	52	64	55
57	83	48	28	52	45	66	
83	53	48	62	53	61	72	
63	52	46	67	55	66	55	
43	52	59	66	45	56	55	

Make a frequency distribution using a class interval length of 5 units, and construct a histogram.

5-9. Each of a sample of 200 instruments is tested for dial tension, with results as follows:

Dial tension (grams)	Frequency
6.5	3
7.0	2
7.5	30
8.0	42
8.5	36
9.0	28
9.5	28
10.0	15
10.5	8
11.0	3
11.5	1
12.0	1
12.5	1
13.0	0
13.5	1
14.0	1

Construct a histogram and a sample distribution function for these data.

5-10. The following data giving power consumption (kilowatts per 24 hours), represent the results of twenty-five freezer performance checks after operational tests have been made on the production line.

4.72	4.32	4.61	4.89	4.61
4.57	4.95	4.55	4.70	4.54
4.47	4.90	4.74	4.59	4.35
4.34	4.75	4.83	4.43	4.55
4.46	4.66	4.66	4.54	4.91

(a) Construct the sample distribution function.

(b) Construct histograms corresponding to at least two distinct round-off schemes. Observe the relative instability of the pattern of variation evident in the histogram as the class intervals are changed—resulting from the fact that the number of observations is not very large.

5-11. The following set of data represents weights (in ounces) of sixty "one-pound" packages of bacon. Construct a histogram.

$16\frac{1}{4}$	16	$15\frac{7}{8}$	$16\frac{1}{4}$	$15\frac{7}{8}$
$15\frac{3}{4}$	16	16	17	$16\frac{1}{8}$
$16\frac{1}{8}$	$16\frac{1}{8}$	$15\frac{7}{8}$	$16\frac{1}{4}$	$16\frac{1}{4}$
$15\frac{7}{8}$	16	16	$16\frac{1}{8}$	$16\frac{1}{8}$
$15\frac{7}{8}$	16	$15\frac{7}{8}$	$16\frac{1}{2}$	16
16	$15\frac{7}{8}$	$16\frac{1}{4}$	$16\frac{1}{8}$	$16\frac{1}{8}$
$16\frac{1}{8}$	$16\frac{1}{4}$	$16\frac{1}{4}$	$16\frac{1}{4}$	$16\frac{1}{4}$
$15\frac{7}{8}$	$16\frac{1}{4}$	16	$15\frac{7}{8}$	16
$16\frac{1}{8}$	$16\frac{7}{8}$	$15\frac{7}{8}$	$15\frac{3}{4}$	$15\frac{7}{8}$
$16\frac{1}{4}$	16	$16\frac{1}{2}$	$16\frac{1}{8}$	16
$16\frac{1}{8}$	$16\frac{1}{8}$	$15\frac{7}{8}$	$16\frac{1}{8}$	$16\frac{1}{4}$
$16\frac{1}{4}$	$16\frac{1}{8}$	16	$16\frac{1}{8}$	16

5.4 Some useful statistics

It is often sufficient in a problem of statistical inference to use some quantity computed from the data (a "reduction" of the data) rather than the original observations, which are ponderous to use as well as to digest. Any quantity computed from a set of data is called a *statistic*. Certain statistics will be presented here which find frequent application in problems of inference for continuous populations, namely, the sample mean, sample variance, sample range, and sample median.

With the observations arranged in numerical order (a natural first step in organizing a mass of data) the middle value—if there is one—is called the *sample median*. If the number of observations is odd, there *is* a middle value;

if it is even, the median is usually taken to be the ordinary arithmetic average of the *two* middle values. Thus, the median of the numbers 23, 26, 30, 31 is the average of 26 and 30, or 28. The *sample range* is defined to be the width of the interval over which the observations extend, that is, the largest observation minus the smallest. The range of the set of four numbers 23, 26, 30, 31 is $31 - 23 = 8$. The range and median of a sample are statistics—quantities computed from the observations in a sample, and so are random variables; they vary from sample to sample.

The operation of taking the arithmetic average of a set of numbers defines, for a sample $X_1, X_2, \ldots, X_n$, the *sample mean*:

$$\bar{X} = \frac{X_1 + \cdots + X_n}{n} = \frac{1}{n} \sum_{i=1}^{n} X_i.$$

For the particular sample values 23, 26, 30, 31, this is as follows:

$$\bar{X} = \frac{1}{4}(23 + 26 + 30 + 31) = 27.5.$$

Notice that the mean of this sample differs from the median, as will generally be the case, even though they attempt to measure the same characteristic of the data, namely, the location or centering. This characteristic is not precisely defined, and so there is not a unique way of measuring it.

When there are repeated values in a sample, as in the case of the frequency distributions such as found in Tables 5.1 and 5.3, the mean (though defined in the same way as above) can be computed from a formula that appears to be slightly different. Suppose that in the list of sample values the distinct numbers, usually listed in numerical order, are $x_1, x_2, \ldots, x_k$, and that the number x_i appears in the sample f_i times, for $i = 1, \ldots, k$. These frequencies of course add up to n:

$$\sum_{i=1}^{k} f_i = n.$$

The sample mean is then

$$\frac{1}{n}(x_1 + \cdots + x_1 + x_2 + \cdots + x_2 + \cdots + x_k + \cdots + x_k)$$

$$= \frac{1}{n}(f_1 x_1 + f_2 x_2 + \cdots + f_k x_k)$$

$$= \frac{1}{n} \sum_{i=1}^{k} f_i x_i = \sum_{i=1}^{k} \left(\frac{f_i}{n}\right) x_i.$$

The last form show the mean to be a weighed sum of the distinct values, the weights being the relative frequencies of the respective values.

When the observations in a sample undergo a linear transformation (translation and change of scale), the sample mean experiences the same transformation. For, if $Y_i = aX_i + b$, for each i, then

$$\bar{Y} = \frac{1}{n} \sum_{i=1}^{n} (aX_i + b) = a\bar{X} + b.$$

In particular, for $a = 1$ and $b = -\bar{X}$, so that $Y_i = X_i - \bar{X}$,

$$\bar{Y} = \frac{1}{n} \sum_{i=1}^{n} (X_i - \bar{X}) = \bar{X} - \bar{X} = 0.$$

That is, the average of the deviations about the mean of a sample is zero—as is then also the sum of those deviations.

The *sample variance* is a measure of spread or dispersion in the set of observations based on the squared deviations about the mean; it is defined as follows:

$$s_x^2 = \frac{1}{n} \sum_{i=1}^{n} (X_i - \bar{X})^2.$$

(The squaring of the deviations eliminates the kind of cancellation that makes the sum of the deviations about the mean equal to zero. Taking the absolute values of the deviations would accomplish this also, but squaring is a more convenient operation to analyze.) It should be mentioned that the sample variance is often defined with a division by $n - 1$ instead of n; the result differs only slightly from the above, unless n is quite small. Since at this point there is no guide to the quality of a statistic, the n will be used here for simplicity. (Even when criteria for "good" statistics are developed, in texts on mathematical statistics, there is no justification for the $n - 1$ except that certain tables are more natural to use with that form.) In reading statistics books or statistical analyses, it is a good idea to check on which definition of sample variance is being used.

As in the case of discrete distributions, the average squared deviation about some other value than the mean, say about $x = b$, can be expressed in terms of the variance as follows:

$$\sum_{i=1}^{n} (X_i - b)^2 = \sum_{i=1}^{n} [(X_i - \bar{X}) + (\bar{X} - b)]^2$$
$$= ns_x^2 + n(b - \bar{X})^2 + 0.$$

(The cross product sum vanishes because the sum of the deviations $X_i - \bar{X}$ is zero.) The resulting formula, referred to as the "parall-axis theorem,"

$$s_x^2 = \frac{1}{n} \sum_{i=1}^{n} (X_i - b)^2 - (b - \bar{X})^2$$

is useful in computations of variance.

It is useful to know how the variance changes when the observations under-go the linear change $Y_i = aX_i + b$. Since $\bar{Y} = a\bar{X} + b$,

$$s_y^2 = \frac{1}{n} \sum_{i=1}^{n} (Y_i - \bar{Y})^2$$

$$= \frac{1}{n} \sum_{i=1}^{n} (aX_i + b - a\bar{X} - b)^2 = a^2 s_x^2,$$

or in terms of the *standard deviation*—defined to be the positive square root of the variance,

$$s_y = |a| s_x.$$

Notice in particular that the translation constant b does not enter; that is, a shift in location does not alter the dispersion of the observations.

In the case of data given in a frequency table, the formula for sample variance is modified in a manner analogous to that in the case of the mean:

$$s_x^2 = \frac{1}{n} \sum_{i=1}^{n} (x_i - \bar{X})^2 f_i,$$

where again $x_1, \ldots, x_k$ are the distinct values and $f_1, \ldots, f_k$ the corresponding frequencies.

EXAMPLE 5-k.   The frequency distribution of Table 5.3 is repeated below, together with computations of the mean and variance. A transformation to Y's

x_i	f_i	$y_i = \dfrac{x_i - 31.7}{1.1}$	$f_i y_i$	$f_i y_i^2$
27.3	3	-4	-12	48
28.4	7	-3	-21	63
29.5	25	-2	-50	100
30.6	42	-1	-42	42
31.7	56	0	0	0
32.8	30	1	30	30
33.9	22	2	44	88
35.0	11	3	33	99
36.1	3	4	12	48
37.2	1	5	5	25
	200		-1	543

as shown simplifies the arithmetic, and is referred to as a "coding." A value 31.7 is selected arbitrarily, except that it appears to be near the "center" of the distribution; this is called 0 in the code, and the other values are numbered in steps of one unit on either side of 0. Since the class intervals are of equal size, this is a linear transformation—as shown in the column heading. In that transformation, the denominator is the class interval width. The equation giving y_i can be solved for x_i to yield $x_i = 1.1 y_i + 31.7$, which implies $\bar{X} = 1.1 \bar{Y} + 31.7$. The computations are as follows:

$$\bar{Y} = \frac{1}{200}(-1) = -.005, \qquad \bar{X} = 1.1\bar{Y} + 31.7 = 31.6945 \doteq 31.7,$$

$$s_y{}^2 = \frac{1}{200} 543 - \bar{Y}^2 = 2.715 - (-.005)^2 \doteq 2.715,$$

$$s_x{}^2 = (1.1)^2 s_y{}^2 \doteq 3.285, \qquad s_x = \sqrt{3.285} \doteq 1.81.$$

What has been computed is a set of statistics relating to the sample given in Table 5.3, obtained by rounding off the sample values as recorded in Table 5.2. The mean and variance of the original sample are then only approximated by the mean and variance computed above.

It is perhaps of interest to observe that the sample mean and variance as defined above are precisely the expectation and variance, respectively, of the distribution defined by the sample distribution function. That is, if one *imagines* a distribution of "probability" in which mass $1/n$ is placed at each observation, the sample distribution function is just the c.d.f. of this imagined distribution, and the expected value is of course

$$x_1 \cdot \frac{1}{n} + \cdots + x_n \cdot \frac{1}{n} = \bar{X}.$$

Similarly, the variance of the imagined distribution is the sample variance.

Problems

5-12. Compute the mean and variance of the data in Table 5.2 as regrouped in Problem 5-7. Compare the results with those in Example 5-k.

5-13. Compute the mean and variance of the data in Problem 5-8 from the frequency distribution obtained there.

5-14. Determine the median and range of the original sample in Problem 5-8.

5-15. Using a one-foot ruler, measure the length, to the nearest sixteenth of an inch, of some article of furniture such as a bed or a large table. Obtain ten such measurements and compute their mean and variance.

5-16. Compute the mean and variance of the data in Problem 5-9.

5-17. Given the data in Problem 5-10,

(a) Compute the mean of the entire set of 25 observations.
(b) Compute the mean of each set of five observations, and compute their mean. How does this compare with the mean you computed in (a)?

(c) Compute the variance of the sample of 25 observations.

(d) Determine the median and range of the sample.

5-18. Compute the median, range, mean, and variance of the observations in Problem 5-11.

5.5 Sampling distribution of statistics

It has been emphasized that a sampling process yields a sequence of random variables $(X_1, \ldots, X_n)$. That is, although the results in a particular sample are specific (nonrandom) numbers, these results would vary from sample to sample. As a result, the value of a statistic $T = t(X_1, \ldots, X_n)$ is a random variable; although for a particular sample it has a specific value, the quantity T would vary from sample to sample. Thus, one can think of the process of obtaining a sample and calculating from it a value of T as an experiment of chance. In a particular problem of inference, one conducts only a single "trial" of this experiment and obtains a single value of T. However, in terms of what might be encountered, considered prior to actually obtaining a specific value of T, there is a set or space of possible values of T and a distribution of probability over the space. This distribution is called the *sampling distribution* of T.

The sampling distribution of a statistic does not appear explicitly—not even empirically in an actual problem of inference. Yet this distribution and, in particular, certain of its characteristics such as its mean and variance do play a role in evaluating the performance of a statistical procedure, as this performance would be observed over a long sequence of trials (of the experiment of obtaining a sample and calculating a corresponding value of T). For example, in Chapter 3 the notion of judging the performance of an estimator on the basis of its mean squared error of estimate was introduced. One would never know in a single sample how close the estimated value lies to the actual parameter value; he can say only such things as "on the average, the squared error has such and such a value." So the performance of the estimator (and of statistical procedures generally) is judged on the basis of average success over many uses of the method.

EXAMPLE 5-1. From a box containing 32 black and 32 white beads, 50 random selections of six beads were obtained. Each selection of six is a sample, without replacement, from a Bernoulli population with $p = 1/2$. (The fact that p is known, at least a priori, stems from the fact that this experiment is artificial.) If p were unknown, the proportion of black beads in a sample of size six could be used as an estimate of p, having one of the values $0/6, 1/6, \ldots, 6/6$. With Y denoting the number of black beads among the sample of six, the probability distribution of the estimator is as follows:

$$P(\text{proportion} = k/6) = P(Y = k) = \frac{\binom{32}{k}\binom{32}{6-k}}{\binom{64}{6}}, \qquad k = 0, 1, \ldots, 6.$$

This defines the sampling distribution of $T = Y/6$. An equivalent display of this distribution is given in the following table, whose entries were calculated from the above formula:

$Y/6$	0	1/6	2/6	3/6	4/6	5/6	1
Probability	.012	.086	.238	.328	.238	.086	.012

The mean value of the estimator is then easily obtained from this table, or from the mean of Y:

$$E(Y/6) = \frac{1}{6}E(Y) = \frac{1}{2},$$

as is the variance:

$$\text{var}(Y/6) = \frac{1}{36}6pq\frac{64-6}{64-1} = \frac{29}{189}\cdot\frac{1}{4}.$$

The results of the 50 samples drawn were tabulated according to the proportion of black beads among the six, as follows:

Proportion of blacks	Number of samples	Proportion of samples
0/6	1	.02
1/6	5	.10
2/6	9	.18
3/6	18	.36
4/6	11	.22
5/6	5	.10
6/6	1	.02
Totals:	50	1.00

The proportion of samples in which, say, two of the six beads were black, is an estimate of the probability (another Bernoulli estimation!) that when six beads are drawn, two are black. If the proportions in the last column are interpreted as probabilities for the values in the first column, the mean and variance of that distribution (called an "empirical" distribution of $Y/6$) are found to be $3.04/6$ and $1.5584/36$, as compared with the theoretical values of $3/6$ and $1.38/36$, using $p = 1/2$.

It is not always a simple matter to determine the sampling distribution of a statistic, or even its moments, for that matter. In the case of sampling (fixed size) from a Bernoulli population, the sampling distribution of the number of successes was evidently either binomial or hypergeometric, but this is an unusually straightforward case.

The sampling distribution of the statistic $\bar{X}$ is not usually simple to determine, but its first two moments are readily obtained—if the sample is a random sample (independent, identically distributed observations). Thus

$$E(\bar{X}) = E\left(\frac{1}{n}\sum X_i\right) = \frac{1}{n}\sum EX_i = \mu,$$

where μ is the "population" mean—the common mean of all the observations: $\mu \equiv E(X_i)$. Similarly,

$$\text{var } \bar{X} = \text{var }\left(\frac{1}{n}\sum X_i\right) = \frac{1}{n^2}\text{var }\left(\sum X_i\right)$$

$$= \frac{1}{n^2}\sum \text{var } X_i = \frac{n\sigma^2}{n^2} = \frac{\sigma^2}{n},$$

where σ^2 is the population variance: $\sigma^2 \equiv \text{var } X_i$.

The sample variance, being a more complicated function of the observations, is harder to analyze. From the identity (a special case of the "parallel axis theorem"),

$$s_x{}^2 = \frac{1}{n}\sum (X_i - \mu)^2 - (\bar{X} - \mu)^2.$$

There follows

$$Es_x{}^2 = \frac{1}{n}\sum E(X_i - \mu)^2 - E(\bar{X} - \mu)^2$$

$$= \frac{n\sigma^2}{n} - \text{var } \bar{X} = \sigma^2(1 - 1/n).$$

The higher moments are more complicated. (Cf. the result on page 169 for the case of a normal population.)

As a final illustration of a sampling distribution, consider the statistic Y defined as the largest among the n observations in a random sample from a population with c.d.f. $F(x)$. The c.d.f. of Y can be obtained in terms of $F(x)$ as follows:

$$P(Y \le y) = P(\text{all observations are} \le y)$$
$$= P(X_1 \le y, \ldots, \text{and } X_n \le y)$$
$$= P(X_1 \le y)\ldots P(X_n \le y) = [F(y)]^n.$$

EXAMPLE 5-m.†   If a population has a constant density on $0 \le x \le \theta$, where θ is an unknown parameter, one sometimes uses the largest observation Y in a sample to estimate θ. Here

$$F(x; \theta) = \begin{cases} 0, & x < 0 \\ x/\theta, & 0 \le x \le 1 \\ 1, & x > 1 \end{cases}$$

The c.d.f. of Y is then

$$F_Y(y) = [F(y; \theta)]^n = \begin{cases} 0, & x < 0 \\ y^n/\theta^n, & 0 \le x \le \theta \\ 1, & x > \theta \end{cases}$$

and the density is the derivative:

$$f_Y(y) = \frac{d}{dy}(y^n/\theta^n) = ny^{n-1}/\theta^n, \quad 0 \le x \le \theta.$$

From this one could compute

$$E(Y) = \int_0^\theta y F_Y(y)\, dy = \frac{1}{\theta^n} \int_0^\theta ny^n\, dy = \frac{n\theta}{n+1}.$$

Problems

5-19.   Five chips in a bag are numbered from 1 to 5. Two chips are drawn at random, without replacement. Let S be the sum of the numbers on the chips drawn. Obtain the sampling distribution of S and determine ES and var S. [Hint: list all possible samples with corresponding probability for each, and calculate S for each such sample.]

5-20.   If $(X_1, \ldots, X_n)$ is a random sample from a population with $EX = 0$ and var $X = \sigma^2$, calculate the expected value of the statistic $T = (1/n) \sum X_i^2$.

5-21.†   Calculate var Y in Example 5-m.

5-22.   Toss four coins 25 times and construct an empirical sampling distribution of the number of Heads in four coin tosses. Compare the mean of this empirical distribution with the expected value of the number of Heads in four tosses.

† Requires calculus.

6

SOME LARGE SAMPLE STATISTICS

Statistical inference using "large" samples is often much simpler than with small samples owing to the fact that the distribution of the particular population from which the sample is drawn becomes increasingly less significant as the sample size increases. Some of the aspects of this phenomenon will be explained in the first two sections and applied to problems of inference in the later sections of this chapter. It will be seen that just how big a sample has to be in order to be considered "large" is not well defined and depends on the desired accuracy as well as on the population distribution.

6.1 Laws of large numbers

The terminology "law of large numbers" has long been employed in referring to the fact that in the mathematical model for probability theory the relative frequency of occurrence of an event, in a sequence of independent trials of a given experiment, "tends toward" the probability of the event. That is, the model does represent what is observed to happen in practice—relative frequencies in actual experiments do tend toward limits.

Two forms of what is meant by "tend toward," that is, by the notion of limit as applied to relative frequencies, are as follows:

$$\lim_{n \to \infty} P\left(\left|\frac{f}{n} - p\right| > \epsilon\right) = 0, \qquad \text{for any } \epsilon > 0, \tag{W}$$

$$P\left(\lim_{n \to \infty} \frac{f}{n} = p\right) = 1. \tag{S}$$

These are referred to, respectively, as the *weak* and *strong* laws of large numbers. Here, f denotes the frequency (number of occurrences) of the given event among n trials and p is the probability of the event in any one trial; and to say that $\lim A_n = B$ means that A_n can be made arbitrarily close to B by taking n large enough. Thus, the weak law says that the probability that the relative frequency differs from p by more than any fixed small amount can be made as small as desired by taking n large enough. And the strong law says that the probability is zero that a sequence of trials arises in which one cannot find a point beyond which relative frequencies are arbitrarily close to p by going far enough out in the sequence.

A more general form of the law of large numbers deals with a sequence of independent, identically distributed random variables $Y_1, Y_2, \ldots$ each having mean EY, and states that the averages

$$\overline{Y}_n = \frac{1}{n} \sum_{i=1}^{n} Y_i$$

tend towards the common mean EY. Again there is a strong and a weak form of what is meant by "tend toward," and the law is true in both senses. This form of the law of large numbers includes that given first; for, if $Y_i = 1$ or 0 according as the event A occurs or does not occur in a given trial, then $Y_1 + \cdots + Y_n$ is precisely the number of A's in n trials, and $\overline{Y}_n$ is the relative frequency f/n. Moreover, $EY = P(Y = 1) = P(A) = p$.

As suggested by the names, the strong convergence of the "strong" law implies the weak convergence of the "weak" law. Neither this nor the laws themselves will be proved here. (Reference is made for these proofs to any good text in probability theory.) It can be shown that the weak law follows from the fact that

$$E(\overline{Y}_n) \to EY \qquad \text{and} \qquad \text{var } \overline{Y}_n \to 0.$$

These conditions are readily established:

$$E(\overline{Y}_n) = E\left(\frac{1}{n}[Y_1 + \cdots + Y_n]\right)$$

$$= \frac{1}{n}[EY + \cdots + EY] = EY,$$

and $$\text{var } \bar{Y}_n = \frac{1}{n^2} \text{var } [Y_1 + \cdots + Y_n]$$

$$= \frac{1}{n^2} [\text{var } Y_1 + \cdots + \text{var } Y_n] = \frac{1}{n} \text{var } Y,$$

which tends to zero as n becomes infinite provided var $Y < \infty$. (Nevertheless, it happens that the weak law *is* true even when var $Y = \infty$.)

Application of the above result to the case in which the Y's are sample observations shows that the mean of a random sample tends to the population mean. The center of gravity of the distribution of the sample mean is the population mean, and the dispersion or "width" of the distribution (as measured by the variance) tends to zero as the sample size becomes infinite—it is very small for large sample sizes. The probability of finding $\bar{X}$ outside the interval from $\mu - \epsilon$ to $\mu + \epsilon$ (where $\mu = EX$) is arbitrarily small for large enough n, no matter how small an ϵ be given.

Application of the law of large numbers to the case in which the Y's are the kth powers of the sample observations:

$$Y_n = X_n^k,$$

shows that the kth sample moment about zero tends to the population kth sample moment about zero:

$$\frac{1}{n} \sum_{i=1}^{n} X_k^n \to E(X^k).$$

From this it can be shown also that any sample moment (that is, about any point) tends to the corresponding population moment in the sense of weak convergence. It is for this reason that the former are taken as natural estimates of the latter, in large samples.

6.2   The central limit theorem

Because so many statistics that arise naturally in inference problems involve sums of random variables, the following result of probability theory is central to the theory of large sample statistics—hence, its name:

Central limit theorem. *Let X_1, X_2,... be a sequence of identically distributed random variables, each with mean μ and variance σ^2, having the property that any finite number of them are independent. Then for each z*

$$\lim_{n \to \infty} P\left\{ \frac{X_1 + \cdots + X_n - n\mu}{\sigma \sqrt{n}} \le z \right\} = \Phi(z),$$

where $\Phi(z)$ is the standard normal distribution function.

The mean and variance of the sum $X_1 + \cdots + X_n$ are, respectively, $n\mu$ and $n\sigma^2$, so the probability on the left is the distribution function of the "standardized" sum. Again, stating that the limit of this distribution function is $\Phi(z)$ for a given z means that the distribution function of the standardized sum, at that z, can be made arbitrarily close to the value $\Phi(z)$ by taking a large enough n.

The remarkable feature of this result is the single limiting distribution that results, no matter what the distribution of the summands (as long as the variance σ^2 exists). In particular, the summands can be discrete variables; and one important application will be to the case of Bernoulli summands, given in the next section.

The central limit theorem is used to assert that for a large sample, the distribution of a sum of the type considered can be approximated by a normal distribution:

$$P\left\{\frac{X_1 + \cdots + X_n - n\mu}{\sigma\sqrt{n}} \leq z\right\} \doteq \Phi(z),$$

or with $z = (y - n\mu)/\sigma\sqrt{n}$,

$$P(X_1 + \cdots + X_n \leq y) \doteq \Phi\left(\frac{y - n\mu}{\sigma\sqrt{n}}\right).$$

The range of validity of this approximation is not easy to assess. As pointed out earlier, its usefulness depends in part on the desired accuracy in a given computation. It depends also on how nearly the population distribution resembles the normal distribution—in having a single hump and being rather symmetrical, for example. Indeed, it can be shown that if the population itself is normal, the sample sum is normal for any finite sample size! When little is known about the population distribution, the normal approximation for the distribution of the sample sum is only used for samples of, say, twenty-five or more.

EXAMPLE 6-a.   Boxes of cereal are filled by machine, and the net weight of a filled box is considered as a random variable with mean 10 ounces (oz) and variance 0.5 oz^2. A carton of forty-eight boxes of this cereal would have a combined average weight (not counting the carton itself) of 48 × 10 or 480 oz, and the variance of the total weight is .5 × 48 oz^2 (assuming independence of the weights of the individual boxes). And the total weight is approximately *normally* distributed, with mean 480 oz and variance 24 oz^2. From this one can compute approximately, for instance, the probability that a carton weighs more than 31 pounds (lb):

$$P(\text{total weight} > 31 \text{ lb}) = 1 - P(\text{total weight} < 31 \text{ lb})$$
$$\doteq 1 - \Phi\left(\frac{496 - 480}{\sqrt{24}}\right) = .0006.$$

EXAMPLE 6-b. A die is cast sixty times. At a given throw the expected number of points is 7/2 and the variance is 35/12. Hence, the sum of the points thrown in the sixty trials is approximately normally distributed with mean $60 \times 7/2 = 210$ and variance $60 \times 35/12 = 175$. And, for example,

$$P(\text{total number of points} \leq 200) \doteq \Phi\left(\frac{200 - 210}{\sqrt{175}}\right) = .225.$$

EXAMPLE 6-c. A lot contains 100 articles, a fraction p of which are defective. One article drawn from the lot is then defective with probability p, and with the coding $1 = $ defective and $0 = $ good, the code number of the article drawn is a Bernoulli variable. If ten articles are drawn from the lot, the sum of the Bernoulli variables assigned to the articles is precisely the number of defectives among the ten drawn; if the drawing is with replacement and mixing the distribution of the sum is binomial, but if the drawing is without replacement the distribution is hypergeometric. In the former case the "observations" are independent and the distribution of the sum might be approximated by the normal distribution. However, ten is not very large in view of the usually small probability of a defective article in such situations, and the approximation would tend to be rather poor. On the other hand, for small values of p the Poisson approximation can be used successfully for $n = 10$. In the case of sampling without replacement the observations are not independent, and the central limit theorem as given does not apply.

Since the mean of a random sample is a sum of independent, identically distributed random variable the central limit theorem can be used to assert that the distribution of the mean of a large sample is approximately normally distributed, with expected value EX and variance $(\text{var } X)/n$, where X is the population variable. This is true for any population or random variable which has second moments. More generally, the sample kth moment about zero,

$$\overline{X^k} = \frac{1}{n} \sum_{i=1}^{n} X^k,$$

is a sum of independent, identically distributed variables, and so has an approximately normal distribution for large n (assuming the existence of EX^{2k}). From this it can also be shown that *any* sample moment (whether about zero, about the mean, or about any other point) is asymptotically normally distributed. Thus, in statistical inference on the basis of large samples the use of sample moments is simplified by this knowledge of an approximating distribution.

Problems

6-1. Let $\bar{X}$ denote the mean of a random sample from a population with mean 100 and variance 25. Determine the probability that $|\bar{X} - 100| > 1$

(a) if the sample size is 25;

(b) if the sample size is 100.

6-2. Referring to the $\bar{X}$ of Problem 6-1, determine a sample size n such that

(a) $P(|\bar{X} - 100| > .5) \leq .01$;

(b) $P(|\bar{X} - 100| > .5) \leq .001$.

6-3. Estimate the probability that a total of 190 or fewer points result from sixty throws of a die. (Cf. Example 6-b.)

6-4. Referring to Example 6-a, determine an approximation to the probability that a carton of forty-eight boxes weighs in excess of 30.5 lb.

6-5. Packages of "100" screws are filled until the weight is at least 10 oz. Assuming that individual screws weigh a random amount, with mean .1 oz and standard deviation .008 oz, determine the probability that a box actually containing 98 screws is counted as containing 100.

6.3   Normal approximation to the binomial distribution

As seen in Chapter 3, a binomial random variable Y can be expressed as a sum: $Y = X_1 + \cdots + X_n$, where the X's are independent and each is a Bernoulli variable with parameter p. Moreover, $EY = np$ and var $Y = npq$. According to the central limit theorem, then,

$$\lim_{n \to \infty} P\left\{ \frac{Y - np}{\sqrt{npq}} \leq z \right\} = \Phi(z),$$

or for large n,

$$P(Y \leq y) \doteq \Phi\left(\frac{y - np}{\sqrt{npq}} \right),$$

where again $\Phi(z)$ is the standard normal distribution function.

The distribution function $P(Y \leq y)$ is a "step function," being constant between integer values of y, and increasing from left to right. The normal distribution function used to approximate it is a continuous function that more or less passes through the middle of the steps of the step function. This will be seen in the following example.

EXAMPLE 6-d.   Let X denote the number of "successes" among eight independent trials with $p = .5$ as the probability of success in a single trial. The binomial distribution function for X is

$$P(X \leq x) = \sum_{k \leq x} \binom{8}{k} \left(\frac{1}{2}\right)^k \left(\frac{1}{2}\right)^{n-k}.$$

The normal approximation to this is as follows:

$$P(X \leq x) \doteq \Phi\left(\frac{x-4}{\sqrt{2}}\right).$$

where the 4 is the mean np and the $\sqrt{2}$ is the standard deviation $\sqrt{npq}$. The graphs of the actual distribution function and the approximation are shown in Figure 6-1. Observe that the approximation is quite good about halfway between

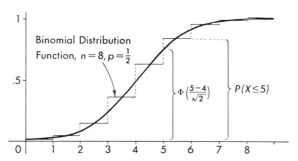

Figure 6-1 Normal approximation to the binomial, Example 6-d.

integer values of x. But it is usually at the integers that the value of $P(X \leq x)$ is needed, and from the graph it is clear that a much better approximation (though still an approximation) is obtained by taking the ordinate on the continuous curve one-half unit to the right of the integer of interest:

$$P(X \leq k) \doteq \Phi\left(\frac{k + 1/2 - np}{\sqrt{npq}}\right).$$

Using the correction of Example 6-d for the distribution function values at integer values of x the normal approximation can be quite good even for rather small values of n, as in the following example.

EXAMPLE 6-e. Consider the binomial distribution with $n = 4$ and $p = 1/2$. Using the correction given in Example 6-d one has

$$P(X \leq k) \doteq \Phi\left(\frac{k + 1/2 - 2}{\sqrt{1}}\right).$$

The following table gives both the approximate values obtained in this way and the actual values of the binomial distribution function, each to four decimal places:

k	0	1	2	3	4
$F_X(k)$	.0625	.3125	.6875	.9375	1.0000
Normal approx	.0668	.3085	.6915	.9332	.9938

Probabilities of individual values of a binomial variate can of course be computed also with the aid of the normal approximation, since they can be expressed as differences between adjacent values of the distribution function —as the heights of the steps. Making the continuity correction is not so essential when such differences are computed, since the approximation errors will tend to cancel, if n is not too small.

EXAMPLE 6-f.   Suppose it is desired to compute $P(X = 5)$, where X is binomial with $n = 8$ and $p = 3/8$. The binomial formula gives

$$P(X = 5) = \binom{8}{3}\left(\frac{3}{8}\right)^5\left(\frac{5}{8}\right)^3 \doteq .1014.$$

Since $EX = 3$ and var $X = 15/8$, the normal approximation gives

$$P(X = 5) = P(X \leq 5) - P(X \leq 4)$$
$$\doteq \Phi\left(\frac{5 - 3}{\sqrt{15/8}}\right) - \Phi\left(\frac{4 - 3}{\sqrt{15/8}}\right) = .1606,$$

and with the continuity correction:

$$P(X = 5) \doteq \Phi\left(\frac{5 + 1/2 - 3}{\sqrt{15/8}}\right) - \Phi\left(\frac{4 + 1/2 - 3}{\sqrt{15/8}}\right) = .1030.$$

For $X = 4$, the probability is .2112 and the normal approximation is .267 without and .221 with the continuity correction.

The normal approximation is not so successful when p is near 0 or 1; for such values of p the binomial distribution is quite skewed, and it takes a fairly large n to make the normal approximation work well. Sometimes a rule of thumb is given stating that the normal approximation can be used if np and nq are greater than 5. Of course, for small p or small q, the Poisson approximation works well.

EXAMPLE 6-g.   Consider a binomial variate with $n = 20$ and $p = .8$. The exact probability that $X \geq 16$, say, is

$$P(X \geq 16) = \sum_{16}^{20} \binom{20}{k}(.8)^k(.2)^{20-k} \doteq .6296.$$

The normal approximation is as follows:

$$P(X \geq 16) = 1 - P(X \leq 15)$$
$$\doteq 1 - \Phi\left(\frac{15 + 1/2 - 16}{\sqrt{3.2}}\right) = .6103.$$

The Poisson approximation is obtained from

$$Y = \text{number of "failures" in } n \text{ trials} = 20 - X,$$

which is binomial with $p = .2$. Thus, using $20 \times .2$ as the Poisson parameter,

$$P(X \geq 16) = P(Y \leq 4) = \sum_{0}^{4} e^{-4} \frac{4^k}{k!} = .629,$$

which value was found in Table XII. It is considerably closer than the normal approximation.

EXAMPLE 6-h.   The following table gives a comparison between the normal and Poisson approximations to the binomial distribution function, in the case $n = 8$ and $p = 1/8$. One should perhaps be interested in $k = 5, \ldots, 8$, in addition to the entries $k = 0, \ldots, 4$ shown, but the binomial distribution function has already reached 1 (to four decimal places) at $k = 4$. The Poisson approximation is not quite 1 at $k = 4$, and in fact is still not quite 1 at $k = 8$, since it assigns probability to the values beyond $k = 8$. The same is true of the normal approximation, which also assigns probability to values less than $k = 0$.

Table 6.1   Binomial distribution function $P(X \leq k)$ and approximations

k	Binomial ($n = 8, p = 1/8$)	Normal approx	Poisson ($\mu = 1$)
0	.3516	.300	.368
1	.7443	.704	.736
2	.9407	.946	.920
3	.9961	.996	.981
4	1.0000	1.000	.996

The normal approximation facilitates the computation of power functions in the testing of hypotheses about a Bernoulli population based on the binomially distributed number of successes. This is illustrated in the following example and in some of the problems that follow it.

EXAMPLE 6-i.   Consider the test $Y \leq 50$ (that is, this is the critical region—set of values calling for "rejecting H_0"), where Y is the number of successes in 100 independent Bernoulli trials. This kind of test is appropriate for one-sided hypotheses of the form $H_0: p \geq p_0$ versus $H_1: p < p_0$. Whatever the particular hypotheses being tested, the power function is

$$\pi(p) = P(\text{reject } H_0 \mid p) = P(Y \leq 50 \mid p)$$

$$= \sum_{k=0}^{50} \binom{100}{k} p^k (1 - p)^{100-k}$$

$$\doteq \Phi\left(\frac{50 - 100p}{\sqrt{100pq}}\right).$$

The graph of this function is shown in Figure 6-2. The approximation was used

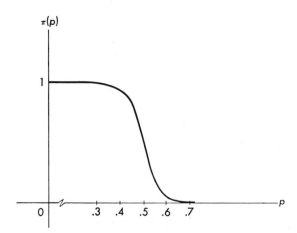

Figure 6-2   Power function for Example 6-i.

in constructing the power function even when p is small or close to 1; since the power function is practically zero for p close to 1, what might be a large relative error is unimportant in sketching the curve.

Problems

6-6.   Suppose that a process yields 20 percent defective units. If 100 units are to be taken from the production line for inspection, what is the probability that 15 or less will be defective?

6-7.   Determine an approximation to the probability that in 180 throws of a die
  (a) more than 40 result in 6's;
  (b) the number of 6's is between 25 and 35 (inclusive);
  (c) the number of 5's and 6's is less than 50.

6-8.   If 55 percent of the voters of a (large) city are in favor of a given proposal, what is the probability that a random sample of 100 voters would not show a majority in favor?

6-9. Observations are drawn from two identical populations in pairs. Mark down a plus sign ($+$) if the observation from population A exceeds that from B, otherwise a minus sign ($-$). Assuming that the probability is 1/2 that the A observation exceeds the B at a given drawing, determine the probability that in 144 independent drawings one gets 85 or more $+$'s (with the rest $-$'s).

6-10. Two dice are cast seventy-two times. What is the probability of two or less 12's? (Compare the answers obtained using the normal approximation and the Poisson approximation. Which is more accurate?)

6-11. Sketch power functions (on the same set of axes) for tests with critical regions $Y > 40$, $Y > 50$, $Y > 60$, where Y is the number of "successes" in 100 independent trials of a Bernoulli experiment.

6-12. Sketch power functions (on the same axes) for the tests that reject H_0 when there are more than 4 successes in 10 trials, when there are more than 40 successes in 100 trials, and when there are more than 400 successes in 1000 trials—again referring to independent trials of a Bernoulli experiment.

6.4 Testing hypotheses about *EX*

One can make use of the asymptotic distribution of $\bar{X}$ and the large sample stability of the sample variance to construct large sample tests for hypotheses about the expected value, $\mu = EX$. Use of the particular statistic $\bar{X}$ is on an intuitive basis, although it can be shown that for many populations this statistic is quite appropriate.

The critical regions to be used will also be set forth intuitively; the guiding notion is that large values of $\bar{X}$ will tend to suggest that the population mean is large, and small values of $\bar{X}$ that the population mean is small. Whether or not tests constructed on this basis are the best possible, they can be analyzed in terms of the power function and their performance judged on that basis.

Consider first a one-sided critical region of the form $\bar{X} > K$. The power function of the test defined by this region is

$$\pi(\mu) = P(\bar{X} > K \mid \mu).$$

Because $\bar{X}$ is asymptotically normal with mean μ and variance σ^2/n (σ^2 is the population variance), the power function can be given approximately in terms of the standard normal distribution function:

$$\pi(\mu) = 1 - P(\bar{X} < K \mid \mu)$$
$$\doteq 1 - \Phi\left(\frac{K - \mu}{\sigma/\sqrt{n}}\right) = \Phi\left(\frac{\mu - K}{\sigma/\sqrt{n}}\right).$$

(The approximation is, in fact, exact when the population is normal, since $\bar{X}$ is exactly normal in that case.) With the assumption that the population variance is known the graph of the power function $\pi(\mu)$ can be plotted, and the result will be something like that of Figure 6-3; it is a normal distribution function graph centered at K.

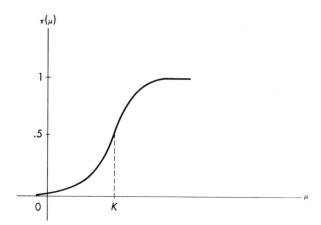

Figure 6-3 Power function for the test $\bar{X} > K$.

Since ideally one would want a test to reject H_0 with probability 1 when H_0 is false and with probability 0 when H_0 is true, the above test would be good for testing between hypotheses such that the H_1 has in it large values of μ and H_0 small values of μ, that is, for a "one-sided" null hypothesis, $\mu \le \mu^*$. The choice of K determines the horizontal centering of the power function; increasing K moves the curve to the right and decreases the power on H_1 but in return makes it less likely that H_0 will be rejected when it is true. The size of the sample used determines the steepness of the curve, and large samples generally provide better discrimination than small ones. Given the size of the sample and the value of K (that is, the critical region) the power function of the test is determined; conversely, if one wishes to specify two points through which the power function is to pass, these will determine the K and the sample size. Thus, one can test a particular value μ_0 against another particular value μ_1 according to specified α and β with a one-sided critical region $\bar{X} > K$; the two points on the power function corresponding to the given error sizes determine the test.

EXAMPLE 6-j.   In testing $\mu = 0$ against $\mu = 2$ based on a sample of size 100 from a population with unit variance, it is decided that the probability of rejecting $\mu = 0$ when $\mu = 0$ should be only .01. This fixes the critical region as follows:

$$.01 = P(\bar{X} > K) \mid \mu = 0)$$
$$\doteq 1 - \Phi\left(\frac{K - 0}{1/\sqrt{100}}\right) = \Phi(-10K).$$

Thus, $-10K$ is the 1st percentile of the standard normal distribution, found in Table I:

$$-10K = z_{.01} = -2.33.$$

Hence, $K = .233$, and from this the other error size can be computed:

$$\beta = P(\bar{X} < K \mid \mu = 2) = \Phi\left(\frac{K - 2}{1/\sqrt{100}}\right) = \Phi(-17.67) \doteq 0.$$

EXAMPLE 6-k. A certain type of light bulb is reputed to have a life of 1000 hours, whereas the life is, in fact, random, having an approximately normal distribution with $\sigma = 200$ hours. Suppose that it is desired to test H_0: $\mu = 1000$ against H_1: $\mu < 1000$ using a sample of n bulbs and a critical region of the form $\bar{X} < K$, where $\bar{X}$ is the mean life of the n bulbs. It is decided that the probability should only be .05 that H_0 is rejected when the mean life is actually 1050 hours, and .05 that H_0 is accepted if the mean life is only 800 hours. That is,

$$\begin{aligned} .05 &= P(\text{reject } H_0 \mid \mu = 1050) \\ &= P(\bar{X} < K \mid \mu = 1050) \\ &= \Phi\left(\frac{K - 1050}{200/\sqrt{n}}\right) \end{aligned}$$

and

$$\begin{aligned} .05 &= P(\text{accept } H_0 \mid \mu = 800) \\ &= P(\bar{X} > K \mid \mu = 800) \\ &= 1 - \Phi\left(\frac{K - 800}{200/\sqrt{n}}\right). \end{aligned}$$

From Table I it is found that the 95th percentile of the standard normal distribution is 1.65, and so

$$1.65 = \frac{K - 800}{200/\sqrt{n}} = \frac{1050 - K}{200/\sqrt{n}}.$$

From this it is easily deduced that $K = 925$ hours and $n = 7$. That is, the test calls for rejection of $\mu = 1000$ in favor of $\mu < 1000$ if the mean life in a sample of seven bulbs is less than 925 hours. This sample size is not large, but use of the central limit theorem is not out of order since it was assumed that the individual bulb lives were already approximately normal.

In testing $\mu = \mu_0$ against the alternative $\mu \neq \mu_0$ it is natural to reject μ_0 in favor of a different value if the mean of a sample is excessively far from μ_0 on either side. A critical region of this type is given by the inequality

$$|\bar{X} - \mu_0| > K.$$

The power function of the test defined by this critical region can be computed (if the population variance is again assumed to be known) if the sample size is large, or if the population is normal:

$$\pi(\mu) = P(\text{reject } H_0 \mid \mu)$$
$$= 1 - P(-K < \bar{X} - \mu_0 < K)$$
$$= 1 - \Phi\left(\frac{\mu_0 + K - \mu}{\sigma/\sqrt{n}}\right) + \Phi\left(\frac{\mu_0 - K - \mu}{\sigma/\sqrt{n}}\right).$$

Since H_0 is not really a simple hypothesis (specifying the mean value to be μ_0 does not define the population except in certain cases), the size of the type I error (probability of rejecting H_0 when it is true) is not uniquely defined. However, given the population variance this size is approximately unique:

$$\alpha = P(\text{reject } H_0 \mid \mu = \mu_0) = \pi(\mu_0) \doteq 2\Phi\left(\frac{-K}{\sigma/\sqrt{n}}\right).$$

If, then, α is given (the "significance level"), the value of K is thereby determined—for a given sample size:

$$K = -(\sigma z_{\alpha/2})/\sqrt{n},$$

where z_α is the 100α percentile of the standard normal distribution. If, on the other hand, the sample size is not given, it and the critical limit K are determined by specification of two points on the power function graph—in particular, by α and one point for $\mu \neq \mu_0$.

EXAMPLE 6-1.   A manufactured part is to fit other parts, and a certain critical dimension is designed to be 2 inches. Owing to variations in the manufacturing process, however, the actual dimension is random with a variance of .0025 in². It is desired to determine a sample size and critical region for the mean of a random sample to test $\mu = 2$ subject to the conditions that the probability is .05 of rejecting $\mu = 2$ when the mean *is* 2, and that the probability is at most .1 of accepting $\mu = 2$ when the mean actually differs from 2 inches by more than .02 inches either way. Assuming that the sample will turn out to be large enough to warrant a normal approximation, the desired two-sided test is subject to these conditions:

$$.05 = P(|\bar{X} - 2| > K \mid \mu = 2) \doteq 2\Phi\left(\frac{-K}{.05/\sqrt{n}}\right)$$

and

$$.1 = P(|\bar{X} - 2| < K \mid \mu = 2.02)$$
$$\doteq \Phi\left(\frac{K + 2 - 2.02}{.05/\sqrt{n}}\right) - \Phi\left(\frac{-K + 2 - 2.02}{.05/\sqrt{n}}\right).$$

(Identifying $\mu = 2.02$ with the "type II" probability .1 is in anticipation of the fact that the probability of accepting H_0 when μ is in the range $|\mu - 2| > .02$ is highest for $\mu = 2.02$ or 1.98. This will be seen in the graph of the power function, Figure 6-4 below.) The first condition implies

$$\frac{K\sqrt{n}}{.05} = -z_{.025} = 1.96,$$

and substitution of this into the second condition yields

$$.1 = \Phi\left(1.96 - \frac{.02\sqrt{n}}{.05}\right) + \Phi\left(1.96 + \frac{.02\sqrt{n}}{.05}\right) - 1.$$

This in turn can be solved for n when it is realized that the second Φ on the right will be practically 1, so that

$$1.96 - \frac{2}{5}\sqrt{n} = z_{.1} = -1.28,$$

and

$$n \doteq 66, \qquad K = .0121.$$

The power function for this test, shown in Figure 6-4, is given by

$$\pi(\mu) = P(|\bar{X} - 2| > .0121)$$
$$= 1 - \Phi\left(\frac{2 + .0121 - \mu}{.00617}\right) + \Phi\left(\frac{2 - .0121 - \mu}{.00617}\right).$$

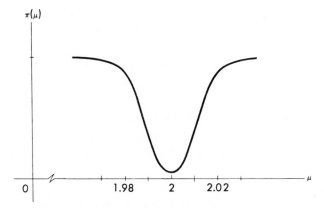

Figure 6-4 Power function for Example 6-1.

It should be observed that the critical limit K is proportional to the population standard deviation. Thus, the amount by which $\bar{X}$ differs from μ_0 is measured as so many standard deviations, and for a given significance level α, the critical region is

$$\left|\frac{\bar{X} - \mu_0}{\sigma/\sqrt{n}}\right| > z_{1-\alpha/2}.$$

The statistic on the left is often thought of as the test statistic; and if the population variance is not known, the σ is replaced by the standard deviation of the sample, assuming (as is the case) that the error in so doing is not appreciable for large samples.

Problems

6-13. Determine the critical region and the size of the type II error for a test (based on $\bar{X}$) of $\mu = 0$ against $\mu = 2$, given $n = 100$, $\alpha = .05$, and $\sigma^2 = 9$.

6-14. Sketch the power function of the test in Problem 6-13.

6-15. Determine the sample size and critical region for testing $\mu = 0$ against $\mu = 2$ given $\alpha = \beta = .01$ and $\sigma^2 = 4$.

6-16. Determine the power function of a test for $\mu = 2$ inches against the alternative $\mu \neq 2$ inches (as in Example 6-l) using a sample of size 100 and a significance level of .02. Determine in particular the probability of accepting $\mu = 2$ when $\mu = 2.01$.

6-17. Given $\sigma^2 = 1$, construct a test of $\mu = 0$ against $\mu \neq 0$ with $\alpha = .01$ and the probability of accepting $\mu = 0$ when $\mu = .1$ equal to at most .05.

6.5 Confidence limits for the mean

Because the sample mean tends in probability (cf. Section 6.1) to the population mean, it is used commonly as an estimate of the population mean. The reliability or repeatability of this estimate is indicated by its variance, inversely proportional to the sample size; and this is often included in the estimation procedure by giving what is called an *interval estimate* of μ, as opposed to the point estimate $\hat{\mu} = \bar{X}$.

For large samples with known population mean one can write such approximate equalities as, for instance,

$$P(|\bar{X} - \mu| < 1.96\,\sigma/\sqrt{n}) \doteq .95.$$

(This is exact for a normal population and otherwise an approximation based on the central limit theorem.) That is, $\bar{X}$ is approximately normal with standard deviation $\sigma/\sqrt{n}$, and the area outside ± 1.96 standard deviations under a normal curve is about .05. The inequality whose probability is given above as about .95 can also be written as

$$|\mu - \bar{X}| < 1.96\,\sigma/\sqrt{n},$$

or in the form

$$-1.96\,\sigma/\sqrt{n} < \mu - \bar{X} < 1.96\,\sigma/\sqrt{n}.$$

Adding $\bar{X}$ to each member of this extended inequality, one obtains

$$\bar{X} - 1.96\,\sigma/\sqrt{n} < \mu < \bar{X} + 1.96\,{-}/\sqrt{n}.$$

This is equivalent to the inequality given at the outset and, therefore, it has the same probability:

$$P(\bar{X} - 1.96\,\sigma/\sqrt{n} < \mu < \bar{X} + 1.96\,\sigma/\sqrt{n}) \doteq .95.$$

It should be kept in mind that the P refers to what is random inside the parentheses, namely, $\bar{X}$. The mean μ is a constant, and it is *not* the intention here to impute randomness to μ, saying that the "probability that μ falls in the range such and such is .95." Rather, the interval

$$\bar{X} - 1.96\,\sigma/\sqrt{n} \qquad \text{to} \qquad \bar{X} + 1.96\,\sigma/\sqrt{n}$$

has random endpoints and is thus a *random interval*. And the probability that this random interval (which would vary from sample to sample) includes within it the actual population mean μ is about 95 percent. The endpoints of this random interval are called 95 percent *confidence limits*, and the interval between them is called a 95 percent *confidence interval* for μ. A given confidence interval either includes μ within it or it does not, and one would never know (unless he knew μ); if he were in the business of computing confidence intervals for μ from samples he would be successful about 95 percent of the time in trapping the mean inside his intervals.

Confidence coefficients other than .95 are used, of course, and the multiplier 1.96 must be modified accordingly. Some commonly used confidence coefficients γ and the corresponding multipliers k_γ are given in the following table:

γ	k_γ
.99	2.57
.9545	2.00
.95	1.96
.90	1.64

The relationship used to determine these is

$$1 - \gamma = 2[1 - \Phi(k_\gamma)].$$

An unknown population variance is usually estimated, in the case of large samples, by the sample variance, giving the approximate limits

$$\bar{X} \pm k_\gamma s_x/\sqrt{n}.$$

Two approximations are involved here; first, the determination of k_γ from a given confidence coefficient γ using the normal table is an approximation based on the central limit theorem, and second, the approximation of σ by s_x is based on the convergence in probability of s_x to σ as n becomes infinite. A modification of the above limits in the case of a "small" sample from a normal population will be given in the next chapter.

EXAMPLE 6-m. The mean and variance of the 200 measurements of viscosity in Table 5.2 were computed in Example 5-m with the results $\bar{X} = 31.7$, $s_x^2 = 3.285$, $s_x = 1.81$. A 90 percent confidence interval for μ would then have the endpoints

$$31.7 \pm 1.645 \times 1.81/\sqrt{200},$$

or 31.49 to 31.91.

The confidence intervals constructed above are centered at $\bar{X}$, a consequence of starting with a probability statement involving two equal tails of a normal distribution. Thus, they are (arbitrarily) two-sided; and a two-sided test of hypotheses about μ can be phrased in terms of confidence intervals, namely, reject $\mu = \mu_0$ if the confidence interval constructed from the sample does not contain μ_0. For, the statement that the confidence interval does not contain μ_0 is equivalent to the inequality

$$|\bar{X} - \mu_0| > k_\gamma \sigma/\sqrt{n}.$$

If $\mu = \mu_0$, the probability of this rejection region is $1 - \gamma$, so the α or significance level of the test is 1 minus the confidence coefficient.

6.6 Confidence limits for p

When a random variable X has a Bernoulli distribution, its mean value is the parameter p giving the probability of "success": $EX = p$. The sample mean $\bar{X}$ is the relative frequency of successes in the n trials in the sample, and the asymptotic normal distribution of $\bar{X}$ can be used to construct a confidence interval for p. Since $E\bar{X} = p$ and var $\bar{X} = p(1 - p)/n$, it follows that for large n,

$$P(|\bar{X} - p| < k_\gamma\sqrt{p(1 - p)/n}) \doteq \gamma,$$

where k_γ and γ are related as in the preceding section. The inequality here is equivalent to what is obtained by squaring both sides:

$$(\bar{X} - p)^2 < k^2(p - p^2)/n,$$

where the subscript on k has been suppressed for convenience. Transposition of the right member to the left produces a quadratic in p that is to be negative, and the quadratic is negative between the points where it vanishes. These roots of the equation

$$\left(1 + \frac{k^2}{n}\right)p^2 - 2p\left(\bar{X} + \frac{k^2}{2n}\right) + \bar{X}^2 = 0$$

are then the confidence limits for p:

$$\frac{1}{1 + k^2/n}\left(\bar{X} + \frac{k^2}{2n} \pm k\sqrt{\frac{\bar{X}(1 - \bar{X})}{n} + \frac{k^2}{4n^2}}\right),$$

since the probability that the interval between these limits covers the actual p is γ.

These confidence limits are approximate, since the normal distribution is assumed in relating γ to k; but a further approximation is possible if n is sufficiently large, obtained by neglecting the terms involving k^2/n and k^2/n^2:

$$\bar{X} \pm k\sqrt{\frac{\bar{X}(1 - \bar{X})}{n}}.$$

Observe that these limits are precisely $\bar{X} \pm ks_x/\sqrt{n}$, since the sample variance and sample mean are related (for the Bernoulli population) as follows: $s_x^2 = \bar{X}(1 - \bar{X})$. For this second approximation to be successful, it is necessary that k^2/n be small compared with 1, with $\bar{X}$, and with $\bar{X}(1 - \bar{X})$.

EXAMPLE 6-n. Given that a certain treatment is effective in sixteen out of twenty-five cases in which it is tried, a 99 percent confidence interval for the probability of effectiveness in a single case can be constructed as follows. The sample size is 25 and the sample mean is the relative frequency, $\bar{X} = 16/25 = .64$; the k for a confidence coefficient of 99 percent is 2.57. The simpler of the formulas derived above yields the following confidence limits:

$$.64 \pm 2.57\sqrt{\frac{.64 \times .36}{25}} = .64 \pm .25,$$

and the corresponding confidence interval is $.39 < p < .89$. This sample size is not particularly large, and $k^2/n = .264$, which is not really small compared to 1 or to $\bar{X}$. Using the more exact formula for confidence limits, one obtains the interval $.28 < p < .95$. Thus, the sample size 25, while reasonably good for the normal approximation, is not large enough for the simple formula in which σ is replaced by s_x.

Problems

6-18. A group of 30 out of 500 freshman men have an average height of 5 feet 10 inches, with standard deviation 2 inches. Determine an approximate 95 percent confidence interval for the average height of the 500 freshmen.

6-19. A series of measurements of a certain dimension of twenty-five parts has a mean of 2.3 and a standard deviation of .1. Assuming that the "actual" dimension is the mean, μ, of the population of possible dimensions, construct a confidence interval for μ

(a) using a 99 percent confidence coefficient;

(b) using a 95 percent confidence coefficient.

6-20. If it is known from long experience that the variability in a certain method of determining the concentration of a chemical in solution is indicated by a standard deviation of .005 gram per cubic centimeter, determine the number of measurements necessary to obtain a 99 percent confidence interval for concentration which is only .001 gram per cubic centimeter wide.

6-21. Verify the entries in the table of values of k_y.

6-22. Out of 200 identical thumbtacks tossed on a table, 140 are found to have landed with points up. Determine a 90 percent confidence interval and a 99 percent confidence interval for the probability that a single tack lands with point up.

6-23. Out of 40 identical thumbtacks tossed on a table, 28 are found to have landed with points up. Determine a 90 percent confidence interval for the probability that a single tack lands with point up.

6-24. 10 out of a certain sample of 100 articles produced in a certain process are found to have defects. Construct a 95 percent confidence interval for the probability that a single article produced in the process is defective.

6-25. Referring to Example 6-n, compare the results using the simple and the more complicated formulas for confidence limits, if the experiment had included 100 cases, with effectiveness found in 64.

6-26. A geiger counter records 120 counts in a certain one-minute period. Construct a 95 percent confidence interval for λ, the average number of counts in a one-second period. [Hint: Let X denote the total number of counts in a one-minute period. This is assumed to have the Poisson distribution, with $\mu = \sigma^2 = 60\lambda$. For this large value of λt the Poisson distribution is nearly normal, and therefore

$$P(|X - 60\lambda| < 1.96 \sqrt{60\lambda}) \doteq .95.$$

Solve the inequality here for λ, and thereby obtain the desired (approximate) confidence limits.]

7

INFERENCE FOR NORMAL POPULATIONS

Among the most thoroughly studied and completely developed statistical procedures are those designed for the case of a *normal* model. This is in part because the normal model seems to be appropriate in a great many applications, and in part because it is particularly tractable mathematically. Statistical procedures can be derived and results concerning them can be established which constitute a rather complete structure for a wide variety of problems of inference, and which provide points of reference for models in which the derivations do not come so easily. And it is sometimes argued that random phenomena are frequently of the form of a sum of independent random contributions that, according to the central limit theorem, tend to yield a normal distribution.

The normal model is not the simplest one, involving as it does two parameters that sometimes seem to get in the way of each other. These two parameters, μ and σ^2, however, do describe—more or less independently—notions that are close to the intuition, namely, location (or centering) and spread (or variability). In the case of a single parameter, on the other hand, both notions are linked to that parameter.

Normal models are applied most often in the case of measurements that can be repeated so that the model of a random sample, consisting of independent, identically distributed observations, is applicable. It will be

167

assumed, then, that for inference in normal populations one has on hand a random sample $(X_1, X_2, \ldots, X_n)$, where each X_i has the distribution of the population X; that is, the X_i's are each normally distributed with mean μ and variance σ^2. They are assumed also to be independent. It can be shown that an application of the principle of maximum likelihood introduced in Chapter 4 (with the likelihood function defined for this continuous case as the product of the densities of the observations) yields $\bar{X}$ and s_x^2, that is, the sample mean and variance, as estimates of μ and σ^2, respectively. It can also be shown that nothing is really lost by basing statistical procedures on these first two sample moments, rather than on some more complicated features of the sample. As might be expected, the sample mean turns out to be particularly relevant in problems concerning location (that is, concerning μ), and the sample variance in problems concerning variability (σ^2). The latter are basically simpler and will be considered first.

7.1 Inference about σ^2

The sample variance,

$$s_x^2 = \frac{1}{n} \sum_{i=1}^{n} (X_i - \bar{X})^2,$$

is often used as an estimate of the population variance σ^2. The sample variance is a random variable (varying from sample to sample) with moments computed as follows.

According to the "parallel axis theorem" the sample variance can be expressed in terms of the second moment about μ, in the form:

$$s_x^2 = \frac{1}{n} \sum_{i=1}^{n} (X_i - \mu)^2 - (\bar{X} - \mu)^2.$$

Equating the expected values of the two sides of this relation one obtains:

$$E(s_x^2) = \frac{1}{n} \sum_{i=1}^{n} E(X_i - \mu)^2 - E(\bar{X} - \mu)^2.$$

Each X_i has the population distribution, so that $E(X_i - \mu)^2$ is just the population variance σ^2. And because $E\bar{X} = \mu$, the second term on the right is the variance of $\bar{X}$, namely, σ^2/n. Hence,

$$E(s_x^2) = \frac{1}{n} (\sigma^2 + \cdots + \sigma^2) - \frac{\sigma^2}{n}$$
$$= \sigma^2 - \sigma^2/n = (1 - 1/n)\sigma^2.$$

This, incidentally, is true whether or not the population is normal.

The variance of the random variable s_x^2 (designed to measure variability in the sample variances from sample to sample) is more complicated to derive; the result is given here without proof for the case of a normal population:

$$\text{var } (s_x^2) = 2\sigma^4 \frac{n-1}{n^2}.$$

Notice that this tends to zero as n becomes infinite—in very large samples, there is not much variation in the value of the sample variance. This and the fact that the expected value of s_x^2 tends to σ^2 imply (see Section 6.1) that s_x^2 converges in probability to σ^2.

The distribution of the sample variance is asymptotically normal for any population that has second moments; but when the population itself is normal, the variance of a sample from that population has a distribution that has been well studied and tabulated for samples of finite size. To be precise, the distribution of

$$ns_x^2/\sigma^2 = \sum_{i=1}^{n} \left(\frac{X_i - \bar{X}}{\sigma}\right)^2$$

has what is called a *chi-square* distribution with $n - 1$ "degrees of freedom." These distributions are tabulated by percentiles in Table II for sample sizes up to $n = 30$; for sizes greater than this, the asymptotic normal distribution can be used, as discussed towards the end of this section. The term "degrees of freedom" can be taken here to be simply a name attached to a parameter indexing a family of distributions. If the $\bar{X}$ in the definition of s_x^2 were replaced by μ—as it would be were μ known—then the distribution would have n degrees of freedom, and one thinks of a degree of freedom as being "lost" in the estimation of μ by $\bar{X}$.

The knowledge of the distribution of s_x^2 permits the construction of *confidence intervals* for σ^2, as follows. Considering first the case in which the sample size is quite large, the asymptotic normal distribution of s_x^2 implies such statements as

$$P(|s_x^2 - (n - 1)\sigma^2/n| < k_\gamma \sqrt{2\sigma^4(n - 1)/n^2}) = \gamma,$$

where k_γ and γ are related as in Section 6.5. The inequality here is linear in σ^2 and easily rearranged so as to put σ^2 in the middle; the extremes are then the confidence limits:

$$\frac{s_x^2}{(n - 1)/n \pm k_\gamma \sqrt{2(n - 1)}/n}.$$

EXAMPLE 7-a.   The 200 observations in Table 5-2 were found in Example 5-m to have a variance of 3.285. The above formula then gives the following 99 percent confidence limits ($k\gamma = 2.57$):

$$\frac{3.285}{199/200 \pm 2.57\sqrt{398/200}},$$

or $2.62 < \sigma^2 < 4.45$.

When the sample size is not large, the chi-square distribution can be used to obtain a confidence interval. For a 90 percent confidence coefficient, say, one begins with the following statement:

$$P({\chi_{.05}}^2 < ns_x^2/\sigma^2 < {\chi_{.95}}^2) = .90,$$

where the two extremes in the inequality are the fifth and 95th percentiles of the chi-square distribution with $n - 1$ degrees of freedom. (The probability between these two percentiles is .90.) The inequality is easily juggled to obtain:

$$\frac{ns_x^2}{\chi_{.95}^2} < \sigma^2 < \frac{ns_x^2}{\chi_{.05}^2}.$$

which is the desired confidence interval.

If χ^2 denotes a random variable having a chi-square distribution with ν degrees of freedom it is true that the variable,

$$\frac{\chi^2 - \nu}{\sqrt{2\nu}}$$

is approximately standard normal; but it happens that a better approximation for chi-square percentiles is obtained using the random variable

$$\sqrt{2\chi^2} - \sqrt{2\nu - 1},$$

which is also approximately standard normal. (This will not be shown here.) It follows then that for any given p,

$$p = P(\chi^2 < \chi_p^2) = P(\sqrt{2\chi^2} < \sqrt{2\chi_p^2})$$
$$= P(Z < \sqrt{2\chi_p^2} - \sqrt{2\nu - 1}),$$

where Z is standard normal. Denoting by z_p the $100p$th percentile of the standard normal distribution one obtains

$$z_p \doteq \sqrt{2\chi_p^2} - \sqrt{2\nu - 1},$$

and therefore

$$\chi_p^2 = \frac{1}{2}(z_p + \sqrt{2\nu - 1})^2.$$

EXAMPLE 7-b. The 95th percentile of the chi-square distribution with 30 degrees of freedom is computed from the corresponding standard normal percentile $z_{.95} = 1.645$:

$$\chi_{.95}^2 \doteq \frac{1}{2} (1.645 + \sqrt{59})^2 \doteq 43.5.$$

Use of the first approximation discussed results in 41.5, and the actual value (as given in Table II) is 43.8.

EXAMPLE 7-c. Consider again the data of Table 5-2. With $v = n - 1 = 199$, the percentiles $\chi^2_{.005}$ and $\chi^2_{.995}$ are found (as in the preceding example) to be 150 and 253. The confidence interval for σ^2 based on $s_x^2 = 3.285$ and an assumption of a normal population is then

$$\frac{200 \times 3.285}{253} < \sigma^2 < \frac{200 \times 3.285}{150},$$

or from 2.60 to 4.38, or very nearly that found in Example 7-a.

A one-sided hypothesis-testing problem is that in which the hypotheses are as follows:

$$H_0: \quad X \text{ is normal with } \sigma^2 \leq \sigma_0^2,$$
$$H_1: \quad X \text{ is normal with } \sigma^2 > \sigma_0^2.$$

Assuming that a large sample variance is reason to infer a large population variance, intuition suggests a one-sided critical region $s_x^2 > K$. Whether or not this is a reasonable inference can be analyzed from the power function of this test:

$$\pi(\sigma^2) = P(s_x^2 > K \mid \sigma^2) = P(ns_x^2/\sigma^2 > nK/\sigma^2 \mid \sigma^2)$$
$$= 1 - F_{\chi^2}(nK/\sigma^2),$$

where F_{χ^2} denotes the distribution function of a chi-square distribution with $n - 1$ degrees of freedom.

It is worth noting that the power function is really a function of just σ^2, and not as might be expected a function of both μ and σ^2. This is because the sample variance has a distribution that does not depend on the population mean. A further implication of this lack of dependence on μ is that in testing σ_0^2 against σ_1^2 there would be uniquely defined error sizes α and β even though these are not simple hypotheses (since there are many normal populations having a given variance).

EXAMPLE 7-d. Consider a sample of size twenty and a test defined by the rejection region $s_x^2 < 5$. The power function of this test is

$$P(s_x^2 < 5) = F_{\chi^2}(100/\sigma^2),$$

where $100 = nK$. The graph of this function is shown in Figure 7-1.

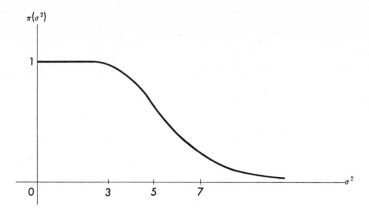

Figure 7-1   Power function for Example 7-d.

The power is seen to be high for small values of σ^2 and low for large values of σ^2, making the test appropriate for testing $H_0: \sigma^2 \geq \sigma_0^2$ against $H_1: \sigma^2 < \sigma_0^2$.

To test a hypothesis of the form $\sigma^2 = \sigma_0^2$ against the alternative $\sigma^2 \neq \sigma_0^2$ a test with both large and small values of s_x^2 in the critical region suggests itself. Such a test is provided by the confidence interval for σ^2 based on s_x^2, namely, reject H_0 if the confidence interval does not cover the value σ_0^2 that defines H_0.

EXAMPLE 7-e.   Suppose that it is desired to test $\sigma^2 = 4$ against $\sigma^2 \neq 4$ using a sample of size twenty-five, and that α is to be .10. The 90 percent confidence interval for σ^2 is given by the inequality

$$\frac{25s_x^2}{36.4} < \sigma^2 < \frac{25s_x^2}{13.8}.$$

This has the probability .90 when $\sigma^2 = 4$. The power function of the test that rejects $\sigma^2 = 4$ unless the value 4 is included in the above interval is computed as follows:

$$\pi(\sigma^2) = 1 - P\left(\frac{25s_x^2}{36.4} < 4 < \frac{25s_x^2}{13.8}\right)$$

$$= 1 - P\left(13.8\,\frac{4}{\sigma^2} < \frac{25s_x^2}{\sigma^2} < 36.4\,\frac{4}{\sigma^2}\right)$$

$$= 1 - F_{\chi^2}(146/\sigma^2) + F_{\chi^2}(55.2/\sigma^2).$$

This is 1 at $\sigma^2 = 0$ and $\sigma^2 = \infty$ and dips down to .1 at $\sigma^2 = 4$.

Problems

7-1.   Outside diameters of seventy supposedly identical parts are given in the frequency table as follows:

Diameter (inches)	Frequency
1.0950	2
1.0945	2
1.0940	9
1.0935	15
1.0930	26
1.0925	10
1.0920	6

Assuming a normal population, construct a 90 percent confidence interval for the population variance, using the chi-square distribution and also using normal approximation.

7-2.   Use the data of the preceding problem to test $\sigma^2 = 25 \times 10^{-8}$ in^2 against the alternative that $\sigma^2 = 36 \times 10^{-8}$ in^2, given $\alpha = .20$.

7-3.   Determine and sketch the power function of the test used in Problem 7-2. Compute the size of the type II error, β.

7-4.   Sketch the power function in Example 7-e above.

7-5.   Construct a test of the hypothesis of a variance of 2 against the hypothesis of a variance of 4 in a certain normal population, using a sample of size 5 and an α of .05. Determine β and sketch the power function. Apply the test to the data obtained as follows: 56, 58, 54, 57, 54.

7-6.   Construct a two-sided confidence interval for σ^2 on the basis of the sample given in Problem 7-5 using a confidence coefficient of (a) 95 percent, and (b) 80 percent.

7-7.   Show that if the sample variance had been defined as follows:

$$\tilde{s}_x^2 = \frac{1}{n-1} \sum_{i=1}^{n} (X_i - \bar{X})^2,$$

the relations encountered in the preceding section would be

(a) $E(\tilde{s}_x^2) = \sigma^2$;

(b) var $\tilde{s}_x^2 = 2\sigma^4/(n-1)$;

(c) $(n-1)\tilde{s}_x^2/\sigma^2$ has the chi-square distribution, $n-1$ degrees of freedom.

7.2   The sample range

The *range* of a sample is the width of the interval over which the observations extend, namely, the largest observation minus the smallest. It is an indicator of variability that might be considered as useful in problems of inference about the variance of a normal population.

The sample range is, of course, a statistic, being computed from the sample, and so it has a probability distribution. This distribution is not usually simple, nor is it especially pleasant in the normal case; however, for normal populations the distribution has been extensively studied and tabulated. The distribution of R/σ (where R denotes the sample range) turns out to be independent of the parameters of the normal population from which the sample is drawn, and it is this distribution that is given in Table V, by its percentiles. Also given in that table are the constants a_n and b_n, defined as follows:

$$a_n = E(R/\sigma), \qquad b_n^2 = \text{var}(R/\sigma).$$

The subscripts call attention to the fact that the distribution of R/σ does depend on the sample size. Notice then that

$$ER = E\left(\sigma\frac{R}{\sigma}\right) = a_n\sigma,$$

and

$$\text{var } R = \text{var}\left(\sigma\frac{R}{\sigma}\right) = b_n^2\sigma^2.$$

And again,

$$E(R/a_n) = \sigma, \qquad \text{var}(R/a_n) = \left(\frac{b_n}{a_n}\right)^2\sigma^2.$$

The statistic R/a_n is often used as an estimate of the standard deviation σ.

An interval estimate for σ can be constructed from the distribution of R/σ as follows. Let $w_{.025}$ and $w_{.975}$ denote the indicated percentiles of the distribution of R/σ. Then

$$P(\sigma w_{.025} < R < \sigma w_{.975}) = .95.$$

Solving the inequality for σ yields the 95 percent confidence interval for σ:

$$\frac{R}{w_{.975}} < \sigma < \frac{R}{w_{.025}}.$$

Squaring each member of this inequality would give a confidence interval for the population variance.

EXAMPLE 7-f.   The range of the sample consisting of the first twenty observations of Table 5.2 is found to be 7. Assuming that the population involved is normal, the corresponding confidence interval for σ is

$$\frac{7}{5.30} < \sigma < \frac{7}{2.45}.$$

or $1.32 < \sigma < 2.86$. The "point estimate" of σ given by R/a_n is here $7/3.74 = 1.87$.

Squaring the endpoints of the above interval gives $1.74 < \sigma^2 < 8.18$ as a confidence interval for the variance, as compared with the 95 percent confidence interval based on $s_x^2 = 3.63$ (for the same data) and a chi-square distribution for ns_x^2/σ^2: $2.21 < \sigma^2 < 8.15$. The narrower interval obtained using s_x^2, for the same confidence coefficient, reflects the fact that the sample variance makes better use of the data (in problems dealing with σ^2) than does the sample range.

The sample range can be used to test hypotheses concerning the variance of a normal population. If the values of σ^2 in H_0 are to the left of those in H_1, the kind of critical region that suggests itself intuitively is $R > K$. The power function of this test can be obtained from the distribution of the "standardized" range R/σ:

$$\pi(\sigma) = P(R > K \mid \sigma) = 1 - P(R/\sigma < K/\sigma)$$
$$= 1 - F_{R/\sigma}(K/\sigma).$$

This function does have a tendency to be high on H_1 and low on H_0.

EXAMPLE 7-g.   The operating characteristic ($1 -$ power) for the test $R > 6$ is plotted as a function of σ^2 in Figure 7-2 for a sample of size twenty. Also shown

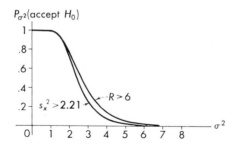

Figure 7-2   Power functions sample range and sample variance, Example 7-g.

is the operating characteristic for the test with critical region $s_x^2 > 2.21$. These tests have the same probability (.90) of accepting H_0 when $\sigma^2 = 1.63$, but clearly the test based on sample variance is more powerful for larger values of σ^2.

The sample range is not usually used for inference from samples of more than, say, fifteen to twenty, owing to the low efficiency relative to procedures using the sample variance for large samples. However, there is another procedure involving ranges that can be used fairly successfully in large samples; this will be taken up in Section 7.4.

Problems

7-8.   In determining the flow characteristics of oil through a valve the inlet oil temperature is measured, in degrees Fahrenheit. Estimate the population standard deviation (assuming normality of the population) using the following sample of nine readings: 93, 99, 97, 99, 90, 96, 93, 88, 89. Compare this value with the sample standard deviation. Construct 90 percent confidence limits for σ based on (a) the sample range, and (b) the sample standard deviation.

7-9. Repeat Problem 7-5 but using, instead of the sample variance, the sample range. Determine also 95 and 80 percent confidence intervals for the variance, using the sample range, and compare with the results in Problem 7-6.

7-10. Sketch the power function of the test that accepts $\sigma = \sigma_0$ if σ_0 lies in the 90 percent confidence interval for σ based on R in Problem 7-8.

7.3   Small sample inference about μ

The statistic used to test a given value $\mu = \mu_0$ as the mean of a normal population using a large sample, in Section 6.4, was essentially

$$\frac{\bar{X} - \mu_0}{\sigma/\sqrt{n}},$$

with the understanding that this is approximately normal—even if the standard deviation σ is unknown and replaced by s_x. If the sample is not large, the approximation is not good. On the other hand, it seems reasonable that the size of a deviation about μ_0 should be measured with respect to something related to standard deviation, and thus that a statistic of the form

$$T' = \frac{\bar{X} - \mu_0}{s_x/\sqrt{n}}$$

should be used. The distribution of this random variable is not simple, owing to the fact that the denominator cannot be considered constant in the case of a small sample—indeed, it is random. The distribution of T' is known and tabulated, both under the assumption that $EX = \mu_0$ and when EX is different from μ_0. Available tables are devised so that a constant times T' is more convenient:

$$T = \sqrt{\frac{n-1}{n}}\, T' = \sqrt{n-1}\, \frac{\bar{X} - \mu_0}{s_x}.$$

(Had s_x^2 been defined with division by $n - 1$, this conversion would not have been needed.) The statistic T has the "*t-distribution* with $n - 1$ degrees of freedom," as given in Table III, when $EX = \mu_0$. Otherwise, the distribution is of a type called the *noncentral t*-distribution; tables of this are not included here, but can be found in more extensive collections, for example, *Handbook of Industrial Statistics*, by Bowker and Lieberman (Prentice-Hall, 1955).

As might be expected, for $EX = \mu_0$, the distribution of T (or T') becomes asymptotically normal as the sample size becomes infinite, since the denominator s_x tends to the constant value σ. This is evident in Table III, which gives normal percentiles in a row corresponding to $n = \infty$.

To test the hypothesis $H_0: \mu = \mu_0$ one employs the statistic T with a critical region depending on the alternative he has in mind:

One-sided: $T > K$,   for H_1: $\mu > \mu_0$ or $\mu = \mu_1 > \mu_0$.

Two-sided: $|T| > K$,   for H_1: $\mu \neq \mu_0$.

The value of K to be used, for a given sample size, is determined by a specified α, or size of the type I error. Notice that since the distribution of the static T does not depend on σ^2, the probability assigned to the critical region under H_0 is uniquely determined, even though H_0 is not a simple hypothesis:

$$\alpha = P(\text{critical region} \mid H_0)$$
$$= \begin{cases} 1 - F_T(K), & \text{for the critical region } T > K, \\ 2F_T(-K), & \text{for the critical region } |T| > K. \end{cases}$$

The last formula results from the fact that the distribution of T (under H_0) is symmetrical about 0, and that therefore $P(T > K) = P(T < -K)$. Power functions for these tests require knowledge of the distribution of T for μ different from μ_0, that is, the noncentral t-distribution. Since this is not included in the tables, power functions will not be called for here.

EXAMPLE 7-h. A manufacturing process is adjusted so that the mean of a certain dimension of the manufactured part is 20 cm. A sample of ten parts is checked as to this dimension, with the following results

19.66	19.66
20.04	19.88
19.96	19.82
19.92	20.10
20.04	19.72

The question is whether it can be assumed that the mean dimension is 20 cm, or has departed significantly from this value. The mean and variance of the sample are respectively $\bar{X} = 19.88$ and $s_x^2 = .02336$. With $\mu_0 = 20$, the value of the test statistic is

$$T = \sqrt{9} \frac{19.88 - 20.00}{\sqrt{.02336}} = -2.35.$$

The critical limit for a two-sided test at the 5 percent level is $t_{.975} = 2.26$, and the above value of T would call for rejection of $\mu = 20$ with this test. On the other hand, at the 1 percent level the critical limit is 3.25, and $\mu = 20$ would be accepted. The latter test is less powerful to detect $\mu \neq 20$ but has a smaller α.

A confidence interval for μ can be constructed using the fact that if $EX = \mu$, the random variable

$$T = \sqrt{n - 1} \, \frac{\bar{X} - \mu}{s_x}$$

has a t-distribution with $n - 1$ degrees of freedom. If the confidence coefficient is .90, for example, one begins with the fact that the probability between the 5th and 95th percentiles of T is .90:

$$P(t_{.05} < T < t_{.95}) = .90.$$

With T replaced by its expression in terms of $\bar{X}$ the inequality can be "solved" so that μ is in the middle:

$$P(\bar{X} + t_{.05}s_x/\sqrt{n - 1} < \mu < \bar{X} + t_{.95}s_x/\sqrt{n - 1}) = .90.$$

The extremes of this extended inequality are the 90 percent confidence limits for μ. Observe that as n becomes infinite these confidence limits approach those given in Section 6.5 for large samples.

EXAMPLE 7-i.   A confidence interval for μ based on the sample of the preceding example (7-h), with $\gamma = .95$, is given as follows:

$$19.88 - 2.26\sqrt{.02336}/\sqrt{9} < \mu < 19.88 + 2.26\sqrt{.02336}/\sqrt{9},$$

or from 19.765 to 19.995. Notice that this interval does not (quite) cover the value 20; the test that rejects μ_0 when it is not included in a confidence interval with confidence coefficient γ is equivalent to the t-test with $\alpha = 1 - \gamma$.

The density function of the t-distribution will not be derived here; it is (for ν degrees of freedom)

$$f(t; \nu) = (\text{const})(1 + t^2/\nu)^{-(\nu + 1)/2}.$$

(The constant is chosen so that the total area under the curve is 1.) The symmetry about $t = 0$ can be seen from this formula, as can the convergence to the standard normal density as ν becomes infinite.

Problems

7-11.   In testing $\mu = 2$ in a normal population, a sample yields $\bar{X} = 2.19$ and $s_x = .36$. Should $\mu = 2$ be accepted at the 5 percent level if $n = 15$ and

(a) the alternative is $\mu \neq 2$?
(b) the alternative is $\mu > 2$?

7-12.   Construct a 90 percent confidence interval for μ on the basis of the follow-ing data, assuming a normal population and random sampling:

3.79	3.53	3.59	3.83	3.75
3.53	3.71	3.35	3.84	3.90
3.85	3.89	3.69	3.59	3.67
3.57	3.85	3.77	3.49	3.63

7-13.   Use the data in Problem 7-12 to test the hypothesis that $\mu = 3.5$ against the alternative $\mu > 3.5$ at the 10 percent level.

7-14.   Use the observations of oil temperature given in Problem 7-8 to construct 90 and 99 percent confidence intervals for μ.

7-15.   Use the observations of Problem 7-8, would the hypothesis that $\mu = 97$ be accepted rather than $\mu < 97$, at the 10 percent level?

7.4   A variance common to several populations

In studying the variance of a certain kind of measurement it may be that one has on hand several small samples of such measurements corresponding to measuring different objects for the different samples. That is, the means of the populations from which the respective samples are drawn may differ though the variances be the same; the mean relates to the object measured but the variance to the measurement process. It is possible to estimate and to test hypotheses concerning the common variance using the several samples even though they are drawn from different populations.

Suppose then that k samples are obtained, one each from populations $X_1, X_2, \ldots, X_k$:

$$X_{11}, \quad X_{12}, \quad \ldots, \quad X_{1n_1} \quad \text{from} \quad X_1,$$
$$X_{21}, \quad X_{22}, \quad \ldots, \quad X_{2n_2} \quad \text{from} \quad X_2,$$
$$\cdot \quad \cdot \quad \cdot \quad \cdot \quad \cdot \quad \cdot \quad \cdot \quad \cdot \quad \cdot$$
$$X_{k1}, \quad X_{k2}, \quad \ldots, \quad X_{kn_k} \quad \text{from} \quad X_k,$$

where n_i is clearly the size of the ith sample. Let $EX_i = \mu_i$ and var $X_i = \sigma^2$, the latter being the same for all i. A "variance" computed from all $n = n_1 + \cdots + n_k$ of the observations as though they made up a single sample would not necessarily be related to σ^2, since it would include a contribution due to the variation among the population means. (This is actually exploited, as will be seen in Chapter 10, to construct a test for equality of population means.) What is required is some means of combining or pooling the sample variances, but an ordinary average of these would give equal weight to all samples even though their degrees of precision in estimating σ^2 are different (corresponding to the different sample sizes). Thus, a weighted average is used, where the weights are the relative sample sizes, n_i/n:

$$s^2 = \frac{n_1}{n} s_1^2 + \cdots + \frac{n_k}{n} s_k^2 = \frac{1}{n} \sum_{i=1}^{k} \sum_{j=1}^{n_i} (X_{ij} - \bar{X}_i)^2,$$

where $\bar{X}_i$ denotes the mean of the ith sample and s_i^2 the variance of the ith sample.

The above pooled variance is composed of the squared deviations of the sample observations about the corresponding sample means. Its distribution, required if it is to be used in inference, is obtained as follows. According to Section 7.1, the distribution of

$$\sum_{j=1}^{n_i} (X_{ij} - \bar{X}_i)^2/\sigma^2$$

is of the chi-square type, with $n_i - 1$ degrees of freedom, since $X_{i1}, X_{i2}, \ldots,$ X_{in_i} is a random sample from a normal population. It can be shown that when independent chi-square variates are added, the sum has a chi-square distribution with a number of degrees of freedom equal to the sum of the numbers of degrees of freedom of the summands. Thus, adding together the k sample sums of squared deviations, divided by σ^2, the result

$$\sum_{i=1}^{k} \sum_{j=1}^{n_i} (X_{ij} - \bar{X}_i)^2/\sigma^2$$

has a chi-square distribution with $(n_1 - 1) + \cdots + (n_k - 1) = n - k$ degrees of freedom. Because the mean of this sum is the number of degrees of freedom (as can be shown to be the case for any chi-square variate), the quantity

$$\bar{s}^2 = \frac{1}{n - k} \sum_{i=1}^{k} \sum_{j=1}^{n_i} (X_{ij} - \bar{X}_i)^2$$

has mean σ^2. This is commonly used as the pooled variance, rather than s^2, although the only plausible reason seems to be a matter of convenience in using existing tables.

It can be seen by inspection of the chi-square table that an estimate based on $n - 1$ degrees of freedom is more precise (yields narrower confidence intervals, for instance) than one based on $n - k$ degrees of freedom, if $k > 1$. This would mean that it would be better to use a single sample of n obtained by measuring a single object ($n - 1$ degrees of freedom) than to use k samples with a total of n measurements ($n - k$ degrees of freedom). However, this might mean a new series of measurements as opposed to a set of k samples already on hand; moreover, when the n measurements are taken for the express purpose of studying variability, the person making them is apt to exercise more care than would be represented by the variance parameter being studied—namely, the one associated with the usual measurements of the type found in the smaller samples on hand.

The testing of hypotheses and construction of confidence intervals, for the common variance σ^2, are carried out (using $\tilde{s}^2$) along the lines of such procedures for the case of a single population.

EXAMPLE 7-j. Suppose that the following three sets of observations are obtained from three normal populations whose variances are known to be equal.

Sample	Mean	$\sum_j (X_{ij} - \bar{X}_i)^2$
11, 9, 13, 11	11	8
25, 28, 31, 27, 30, 33	29	42
19, 23, 19, 21, 20	20.4	11.2

Total sum of squared deviations: 61.2

The point estimate of σ^2 is then

$$\tilde{s}^2 = \frac{61.2}{15 - 3} = 5.1.$$

An interval estimate is given by the following 90 percent confidence interval for σ^2:

$$\frac{61.2}{\chi^2_{.95}} < \sigma^2 < \frac{61.2}{\chi^2_{.05}}$$

or

$$2.91 < \sigma^2 < 11.7.$$

Inference concerning a variance common to several normal populations is also possible using the ranges $R_1, R_2, \ldots, R_k$ of samples from the populations, but it is best now to have samples of the same size: $n_1 = \cdots = n_k = m$. The statistic used is the average of the sample ranges:

$$\bar{R} = \frac{1}{k}(R_1 + \cdots + R_k).$$

Since the sample ranges are independent and identically distributed with $ER_i = a_m \sigma$ and var $R_i = b_m^2 \sigma^2$, it follows that

$$E\bar{R} = \frac{1}{k}\sum_{i=1}^{k} ER_i = a_m \sigma,$$

and

$$\operatorname{var} \bar{R} = \frac{1}{k^2} \sum_{i=1}^{k} \operatorname{var} R_i = b_n^2 \sigma^2 / k.$$

Moreover, according to the central limit theorem $\bar{R}$ is asymptotically *normal* with these parameters. The approximation of the distribution of $\bar{R}$ by a normal distribution, valid for "large" k (that is, for many samples—but not necessarily many observations per sample), should be fairly successful even for moderate values of k, since the distribution of R_i is reasonably smooth with a single hump.

Even when observations are available in a single sample, dividing that sample into k subsamples of m each and using $\bar{R}$ as the basis of inference is a more satisfactory procedure than using the range of the original sample, because of the deterioration of the efficiency of the range as the sample size increases.

Once an approximate distribution for $\bar{R}$ is on hand, inference proceeds in the usual ways. For instance, if z_1 and z_2 are percentiles of the standard normal distribution including between them 95 percent of the distribution, then

$$P\left(z_1 < \frac{\bar{R} - a_m \sigma}{b_m \sigma / \sqrt{k}} < z_2\right) = .95,$$

and rearrangement of the inequality so that σ is in the middle yields the 95 percent confidence interval for σ:

$$\frac{\bar{R}}{a_m + z_2 b_m / \sqrt{k}} < \sigma < \frac{\bar{R}}{a_m + z_1 b_m / \sqrt{k}}.$$

EXAMPLE 7-k. Dividing the data in Table 5.2 into forty subgroups of five each (that is, $k = 40$, $m = 5$) one finds the average range to be $\bar{R} = 3.64$. With $a_5 = 2.326$, a point estimate of σ would be given by $3.64/2.326 = 1.57$. A 95 percent confidence interval (using $b_5 = .864$) is given by

$$\frac{3.64}{2.326 + 1.96 \times .864/\sqrt{40}} < \sigma < \frac{3.64}{2.326 - 1.96 \times .864/\sqrt{40}}$$

or (1.40, 1.77). Division of the same data into twenty-five subgroups of eight each results in $\bar{R} = 4.14$, a point estimate of 1.45 for σ, and a 95 percent confidence interval (1.31, 1.64).

Problems

7-16. Express the power function of the test with critical region $s^2 > K$ in terms of the chi-square distribution function.

7-17. Express the power function of the test with critical region $\bar{R} > K$ in terms of the standard normal distribution function (assuming k to be large enough for a normal approximation).

7-18. Ten physics lab students each construct a simple pendulum and make three measurements of the period of the pendulum with results as shown in the following table. Give point and interval estimates of the variance of the time measurement process (assumed to be the same for all students) based on s^2 and based on $\bar{R}$. (Use $\gamma = .95$.)

				Periods in seconds					
1	2	3	4	5	6	7	8	9	10
3.93	4.02	4.12	3.78	4.04	4.15	4.13	4.13	4.04	4.12
3.90	4.07	4.08	3.83	4.00	4.15	4.13	4.13	3.94	4.09
3.91	4.07	4.11	3.80	4.03	4.09	4.13	4.16	4.04	4.09

7-19. Determine a test using $\bar{R}$ from twenty samples of size seven for $H_0: \sigma^2 = 6$ against $H_1: \sigma^2 = 10$ having the property $\alpha = .10$. Determine β for this test.

7.5 Control charts

In many applications it is helpful to record the results of a series of significance tests on a *control chart*, which in its rudimentary form is simply a graphical device for allowing relatively unskilled personnel to conduct such tests systematically and thereby keep a watchful eye on the quality of some process. The "quality" is measured according to the value of some parameter of a probability distribution, as, for example, the mean diameter of a part to be used in such a way that this dimension is critical. A certain amount of variability in this dimension from piece to piece is unavoidable, but to avoid too many misfits it is desired that the expected diameter remain constant throughout the manufacturing of these parts. When the probability distribution for the diameter remains constant as the process proceeds, the process is said to be *in control*. If there is an appreciable change in either the mean of the distribution or in its variability, it is essential to stop the process and root out the causes of the deterioration—called *assignable* causes, as opposed to the causes producing the tolerated randomness.

To keep an eye on the process, one periodically samples its output and makes some measurements, and in this way he can see to some extent how things are going. Each sample can be used to estimate the mean and variance of the critical variable or to conduct a test of the hypothesis that there has been no change (hence, the term "null" hypothesis) against the alternative that there has been a change. Accepting the null hypothesis when actually there has been a change results in continued production of too many unusable items, whereas rejecting the hypothesis of no change when there is in fact no change results in shutting down production and spending time looking in vain for assignable causes that are not present. The specification of a test would depend ordinarily on the tolerable sizes of these type I and type II errors—and so would be expected to vary from one application to another, but certain convenient "standard" practices have developed that are taken at least as a starting point, with modification if the particular situation warrants it. Specifically, one sets up *control limits* as values of the test statistic lying three standard deviations (of that statistic) on either side of its mean value, corresponding to $\alpha = .0027$ for a normally distributed statistic. (In Great Britain, the standard practice involves warning limits at $\alpha = .05$ and outer rejection limits at $\alpha = .002$, corresponding to 1.96 and 3.09 standard deviations, respectively.) Then if a value of the test statistic falls outside the control limits, action is taken to eliminate the causes that are assumed to have intruded.

A plot of the results of repeated sampling is made on a vertical scale against the time of sampling plotted horizontally, and on this chart, lines are drawn at the heights of the control limits. Points falling above the upper control limit (UCL) or below the lower control limit (LCL) call for action. Ordinarily such control charts are kept for both a measure of centering or level and a measure of variability; sample means are used to keep track of centering, and either sample ranges or sample standard deviations are used to watch variability—although sample ranges are often preferred over standard deviations because of the greater simplicity in computation and their respectable relative efficiency for small samples.

The size of samples used in practice is usually on the order of five to ten. Although greater precision in testing is possible with larger samples, the very nature of the application suggests that the size of the sample should not be so great that the population is apt to change during the time a single sample is being obtained.

In controlling quality to predetermined standards it is assumed that past experience has resulted in rather precise knowledge of the parameters of the distribution when the process it describes is operating acceptably. Since it is ordinarily assumed that the distribution is *normal*, the mean μ and variance σ^2 serve to describe the distribution. (If the distribution is not normal, charts based on the assumption of normality are used anyway, at least as a start, on the grounds of practicability.) To monitor centering one computes for each sample, as it is obtained, the value of $\bar{X}_i$ (the sample mean of sample number i) and plots it on a control chart on which control lines have been drawn at the levels $\mu \pm 3\sigma/\sqrt{n}$, the quantity $\sigma/\sqrt{n}$ being, of course, the standard deviation of $\bar{X}_i$ and n the sample size.

In conjunction with the $\bar{X}$ chart it is customary to keep an R chart (although a standard deviation chart could be used for variability). The sample ranges R_i are plotted on a control chart with control lines at the levels

$$ER_i \pm 3\sqrt{\text{var } R_i} = (a_n \pm 3b_n)\sigma,$$

where $a_n = E(R_i/\sigma)$ and $b_n^2 = \text{var }(R_i/\sigma)$ as in Section 7.2, computed on the assumption of a normal population (see Table V). Thus, the center line (CL) of the chart is at the level $a_n\sigma$ and the control lines at $D_1\sigma$ (LCL) and $D_2\sigma$ (UCL), where D_1 and D_2 are standard notation in quality control practice for the multipliers $(a_n - 3b_n)$ and $(a_n + 3b_n)$, tabled on page 199. (When $a_n < 3b_n$, the constant D_1 is defined to be zero, since the range is never negative.) Notice that 3 is used as a multiplier of the standard deviation of the range R_i, even though R_i is certainly not normally distributed.

EXAMPLE 7-1.   A process is known to have been in control with $\mu = 0$ and $\sigma = 1.715$. For samples of size five the $\bar{X}$ control chart constants are as follows:

Center line: $\mu = 0$
Upper control limit: $0 + 3 \times 1.715/\sqrt{5} = 2.30$
Lower control limit: $0 - 3 \times 1.715/\sqrt{5} = -2.30.$

Twenty samples of size five were obtained and the results plotted on the control chart shown in Figure 7-3; observe that the process remains in control—none of

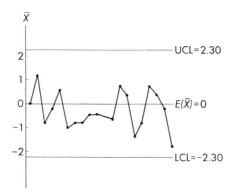

Figure 7-3 $\bar{X}$ control chart for Example 7-1.

the twenty sample means fall outside the control limits. The constants for the range control chart are as follows:

Center line:　　　　　　　$a_5\sigma = 2.326 \times 1.715 = 3.99$
Upper control limit:　$D_2 = 4.918 \times 1.715 = 8.43$
Lower control limit:　$D_1 = 0 \times 1.715 = 0.$

The ranges of the twenty samples are plotted on the control chart shown in Figure 7-4. The process variability remains in control.

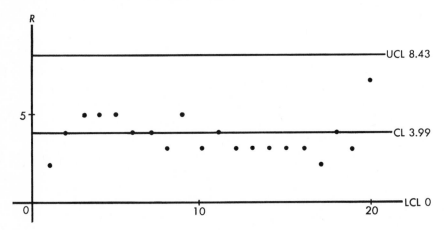

Figure 7-4　Range control chart for Example 7-1.

A control chart is also used to check control of a process based on current data, and based on the assumption that there is control within each of the several samples used. Control lines are computed from the data and therefore put on the chart after the data are obtained. In this situation the term "in control" means that the population being sampled remains constant—but not necessarily controlled to specified characteristics.

The center line of the control chart for centering should be the population mean (which exists when the process is in control), but since this is unknown the estimate $\bar{X}$, the mean of the sample means, is used instead. The control limits should be $3\sigma/\sqrt{n}$, but an estimate of σ must be used; an estimate of variability based on the within samples variation is used—either the pooled variance or $\bar{R}/a_n$ as discussed in Section 7.3. In terms of the simpler $\bar{R}/a_n$, the control limits are

$$\bar{X} \pm 3\,\frac{\bar{R}}{a_n\sqrt{n}} = \bar{X} \pm A_2\bar{R},$$

where again A_2 is customary quality control notation.

To keep track of the sample ranges, one would want a chart with center line at $a_n\sigma = E(R_i)$ and control limits determined by var $R_i = b_n^2\sigma^2$. If there is control, σ can be approximated by $\bar{R}/a_n$, yielding $\bar{R}$ as the center line and

$$\bar{R} \pm 3b_n\bar{R}/a_n = (1 \pm 3b_n/a_n)\bar{R}$$

as the control limits. The multipliers, under the standard names D_3 and D_4, are tabulated below (with $D_3 = 0$ when $3b_na_n > 1$).

Table 7.1. Control chart constants

	Sample size						
	2	3	4	5	6	8	10
a_n	1.128	1.693	2.059	2.326	2.534	2.847	3.078
A_2	1.880	1.023	.729	.577	.483	.373	.308
D_1	0	0	0	0	0	.387	.687
D_2	3.686	4.358	4.698	4.918	5.078	5.307	5.469
D_3	0	0	0	0	0	.136	.233
D_4	3.268	2.574	2.282	2.114	2.004	1.864	1.777

EXAMPLE 7-m. Suppose that the first twenty-five samples of five in Table 5.2 (page 142) are to be checked for control. The mean of all 125 observations is $\bar{X} = 32.36$ and the mean range of the twenty-five samples is $\bar{R} = 4.136$. The

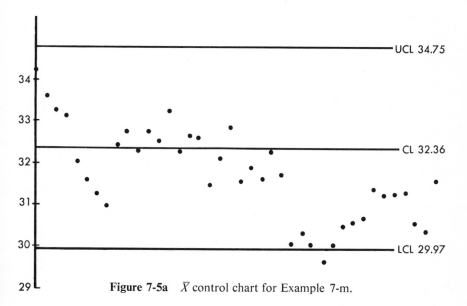

Figure 7-5a $\bar{X}$ control chart for Example 7-m.

control lines for $\bar{X}_i$ are then $32.36 \pm .577 \times 4.136$ or 29.97 and 34.75. For the ranges R_i the control limits are $D_3\bar{R} = 0$ and $D_4\bar{R} = 8.74$. The plots in Figure 7-5 shows none of the $\bar{X}_i$ and none of the R_i outside the control lines. Assuming control, then, these lines become the control lines for future observations, and the remaining fifteen samples of five in Table 5.2 are shown (as to $\bar{X}_i$ and R_i) also in Figure 7-5; there is an evident shift in level—which is really obvious once the results are plotted, even without the sophistication of control lines.

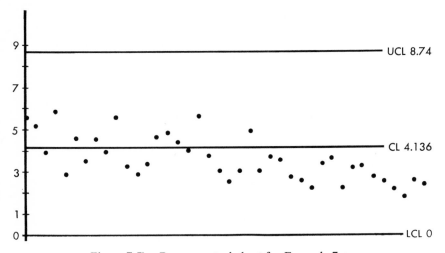

Figure 7-5b   Range control chart for Example 7-m.

Problems

7-20.   A process is known to have been in statistical control with expectation 15 and standard deviation 3.5. Samples of size eight are obtained in order to test for continued control.

(a) Determine the center line and control limits for $\bar{X}$ and R charts.

(b) Suppose that the mean shifts to 16 with no change in standard deviation. Compute the probability that this shift will be detected on the first sample after the change in level. (Assume a normal population.) Determine also the probability that the shift is detected in either the first or second sample after the change.

7-21.   Mark 201 slips of paper with the numbers -8 through 12, according to the frequencies in the following table:

x_i	-8	-7	-6	-5	-4	-3	-2	-1	0	1	2	3	4	5	6	7	8	9	10	11	12
f_i	1	1	1	3	5	8	12	16	20	22	23	22	20	16	12	8	5	3	1	1	1

The number on a slip drawn at random will then be approximately normal with mean 2 and standard deviation 3.5. Obtain twenty (or more) samples of size five (replace and mix between observations), compute the means and ranges, and plot these on a control chart with lines set according to the control specifications $\mu = 0$ and $\sigma = 1.715$.

7-22. Using the entries in Table V, compute (and so verify) several of the entries in Table 7.1.

7-23. Consider the following six subgroups of four observations each taken in sequence. The data were obtained by measuring the power consumption of a unit and are given in kilowatt hours per 24 hours. No standards have been determined for the process.

3.79	3.53	3.59	3.83	3.75	3.73
3.53	3.71	3.35	3.84	3.90	3.82
3.85	3.89	3.69	3.59	3.67	3.75
3.57	3.85	3.77	3.49	3.63	3.65

(a) Estimate the expected value of the power consumption.
(b) Determine the control limits for the $\bar{X}$ control chart.
(c) Determine the control limits for the R control chart.
(d) Remark about the statistical control from the above data.

7.6   Comparisons

A common null hypothesis concerning normal distributions is that there is or has been no change from one population to another. Different statistical tests of this hypothesis are appropriate according to the alternative to this null hypothesis.

For the general alternative simply stating that the populations are not identical, a test similar to the Kolmogorov-Smirnov test given in Chapter 6 can be used—and can, indeed, be used in problems in which the distributions in question are not necessarily normal. The test is based again on the notion of sample distribution function. If the random variables being compared are X and Y with distribution functions $F(x)$ and $G(x)$, respectively, and if random samples $X_1, \ldots, X_m$ and $Y_1, \ldots, Y_n$ are drawn defining corresponding sample distribution functions $F_m(x)$ and $G_n(x)$, the statistic used is

$$D = \max_{-\infty < x < \infty} |F_m(x) - G_n(x)|.$$

The *Smirnov test* calls for rejection of the hypothesis that $F(x) \equiv G(x)$ whenever D exceeds a specified constant, determined by a specified size of type I error. This constant depends only on the sample sizes and the desired α, and in particular is independent of the common null distribution. Rejection limits have been computed and are given in Table VII.

EXAMPLE 7-n.   Consider the two sets of data given in the frequency tabulations below. The maximum absolute difference in cumulative relative frequencies is

X_i	Frequencies		Cumulative frequencies	
	Sample 1	Sample 2	Sample 1	Sample 2
0	5	6	5	6
1	9	2	14	8
2	4	5	18	13
3	5	7	23	20
4	7	8	30	28
5	2	4	32	32
6	8	4	40	36
7	4	9	44	45
8	9	6	53	51
9	7	9	60	60
	$n_1 = 60$	$n_2 = 60$		

.1, and the 5 percent critical value of D from Table VII is about .25. Thus, the hypothesis of identical distributions is accepted at the 5 percent level.

For the alternative that one normal population is shifted from the other tests based on the difference in sample means are generally best. Given population means $EX = \mu$ and $EY = \nu$ and variances var $X = \sigma^2$ and var $Y = \tau^2$, the parameters of the normal distribution of the difference $\bar{X} - \bar{Y}$ are

$$E(\bar{X} - \bar{Y}) = \mu - \nu \quad \text{and} \quad \text{var } (\bar{X} - \bar{Y}) = \text{var } \bar{X} + \text{var } \bar{Y}$$
$$= \sigma^2/m + \tau^2/n.$$

When the population variances are *known*, the variable Z defined as

$$Z = \frac{\bar{X} - \bar{Y}}{\sqrt{\sigma^2/m + \tau^2/n}}$$

is a statistic, and moreover is a random variable with a standard normal distribution if the population means are equal—that is, under the null hypothesis. Tests of hypotheses expressed in terms of $\mu - \nu$ are constructed using this Z just as tests relating to μ are constructed using $\bar{X}/\sqrt{\sigma^2/m}$.

EXAMPLE 7-o. A shearing pin has a hexagonal head. A metallurgist wishes to compare the Rockwell hardness readings taken on the shank of the pin with those taken on the hexagonal head. He finds that the mean and standard deviation of fifty readings on the shank are 41.63 and 1.8, respectively, and that the mean and standard deviation of fifty readings taken on the head are 40.67 and 2.0, respectively. Assuming that hardness readings are normally distributed, the quantity Z defined above is normal, and is standard normal if the population means are equal. Here the population variances are not known, but making the assumption that the samples are large enough that approximation of population by sample variances is good enough, the value of Z is approximately:

$$Z = \frac{41.63 - 40.67}{\sqrt{3.24/50 + 4.0/50}} = 2.51.$$

Against the alternative $\mu \neq \nu$ a two-sided critical region $|Z| > 1.96$ would be used for $\alpha = .05$. Since the observed value of Z is in this critical region, the null hypothesis is rejected—a difference in hardness is accepted.

When the population variances are not known, they can be successfully approximated by sample variances in computing Z, as done in the above example, provided the sample is quite large (the 50 above is probably marginal—a size of 100 or more would be safer). For smaller samples this substitution is not so good, but if it is assumed that the population variances are equal: $\sigma^2 = \tau^2$, a t-test can be constructed using a pooled variance $(m + n - 2$ degrees of freedom):

$$s^2 = \frac{\sum (X_i - \bar{X})^2 + \sum (Y_j - \bar{Y})^2}{m + n - 2}.$$

The statistic used is

$$T = \frac{\bar{X} - \bar{Y}}{s\sqrt{1/m + 1/n}},$$

which has a t-distribution under the null hypothesis ($\mu = \nu$).

EXAMPLE 7-p. Independent samples from two populations X and Y yield results according to the following table:

	Sample size	Sample mean	Sample variance	Sum of squares
X:	10	23.5	4.3	43.0
Y:	15	19.2	5.1	76.5

The pooled variance estimate is

$$s^2 = \frac{43.0 + 76.5}{10 + 15 - 2} = 5.2,$$

and the test statistic is

$$T = \frac{23.5 - 19.2}{\sqrt{5.2(1/10 + 1/15)}} = 4.62.$$

This is well outside the acceptance region $|T| > 2.07$ defined by $\alpha = .05$ (obtained from the t-table using 23 degrees of freedom), so the hypothesis of equal means is rejected at that level of significance. The power function for this test requires the distribution of T under the alternative hypothesis, which can be obtained using tables of the noncentral t-distribution.

When the population variances cannot be considered equal, the situation is quite complicated; this problem (called the Behrens-Fisher problem) has a long history of controversy without yet a solution satisfactory to all. It will not be discussed here.

To test the hypothesis that the variances of two normal populations are equal: $\sigma^2 = \tau^2$, it is natural to use the sample variances s^2 and t^2 in some combination. If the same unit of measurement is used for the two population variables, the *ratio* of the sample variances does not depend on that common unit and is used as the basis of a test. Sample variances are (except for constant factors) of the chi-square type in distribution, and so it is pertinent that the ratio of two independent chi-square variables, each divided by its number of degrees of freedom, can be shown to have what is called an F-distribution (F after R. A. Fisher) with density

$$f(x; j, k) = (\text{const}) \frac{x^{j/2 - 1}}{(1 + jx/k)^{(j+k)/2}}.$$

where j and k are respectively the number of degrees of freedom in the numerator and denominator. Thus, if $\sigma^2 = \tau^2$, the ratio of (unbiased) variance estimates:

$$Z = \frac{\tilde{s}^2}{\tilde{t}^2} = \frac{\sum(X_i - \bar{X})^2/(m - 1)}{\sum(Y_j - \bar{Y})^2/(n - 1)} = \frac{ms^2}{(m - 1)\sigma^2} \bigg/ \frac{nt^2}{(n - 1)\sigma^2}$$

has the F-distribution with parameters $(m - 1, n - 1)$, which are respectively the numerator and denominator degrees of freedom. The 95th and 99th percentiles of this distribution, for several combinations of numerator and denominator degrees of freedom, are given in Tables IVa and IVb, respectively. Observe that the 1st and 5th percentiles can be obtained from these; for example, since

$$.05 = P(Z < F_{.05}) = 1 - P(Z > F_{.05}) = 1 - P(1/Z < 1/F_{.05}),$$

it follows that $1/F_{.05}$ is the 95th percentile of $1/Z$. This means (because $1/Z$ is a random variable of the same type as Z but with numerator and denominator degrees of freedom reversed) that the 5th percentile of an F-distribution is read from the table of 95th percentiles by taking the reciprocal of the entry corresponding to interchanged degrees of freedom.

The obvious kind of test, at least on an intuitive basis—and intuition turns out here to work quite well—is that in which the ratio σ^2/τ^2 is assumed to be large when and only when Z is large. Thus, for instance, if the alternative to equal variances is $\sigma^2/\tau^2 > 1$, the type of test used has a critical region of the form $Z > K$. The power function of this test is

$$P(Z > K) = P\left(\frac{\tilde{s}^2/\sigma^2}{\tilde{t}^2/\tau^2} > K\frac{\tau^2}{\sigma^2}\right) = 1 - F_F(K\tau^2/\sigma^2),$$

where F_F is the (admittedly awkward) notation for the distribution function of the F-distribution (with the appropriate numbers of degrees of freedom). The four percentiles available in Table IV do not really give an adequate profile of this distribution function; operating characteristics of the test and of two-sided tests are given in Bowker and Lieberman, *Handbook of Industrial Statistics* (Prentice-Hall, 1955).

EXAMPLE 7-q. Two methods of performing a certain task are to be compared; the results are assumed to be normal random variables, with possibly different variances for the two methods. Samples of sizes $m = 13$ and $n = 7$ are obtained, with the following results:

$$\bar{X} = 73.6, \qquad \tilde{s}^2 = 6.2,$$
$$\bar{Y} = 61.0, \qquad \tilde{t}^2 = 8.8.$$

A two-sided test of equal variances at $\alpha = .10$ (that is, against the alternative that the variances are unequal) calls for accepting equality if the sample variance ratio lies between the 5th and 95th percentiles of the F-distribution with parameters $(12, 6)$, if the numerator variance is that of the sample of size 13. These percentiles are $1/3$ and 4, respectively. Since the variance ratio is $6.2/8.8 = .704$, which does lie in the acceptance interval, the hypothesis of equal variances is accepted at the 10 percent level.

Problems

7-24. Construct frequency distributions for each of the two sets of 100 observations obtained by dividing the data of Table 5.2 horizontally at the middle of the table. Apply the Smirnov test discussed in the above section to test the hypothesis that the two samples of 100 are from the same population.

7-25. Measurements of viscosity for a certain substance were made with the following results.

First day:	37.0,	31.4,	34.4,	33.3,	34.9,
	36.2,	31.0,	33.5,	33.7,	33.4,
	34.8,	30.8,	32.9,	34.3,	33.3,
Second day:	28.4,	31.3,	28.7,	32.1,	31.9,
	32.8,	30.2,	30.2,	32.4,	30.7.

Has the population changed from one day to the next?

7-26. Two analysts each make fifty independent determinations of the melting point of a certain chemical. The sample mean and variance of the readings found by analyst I are, respectively, 73.6, and 10 while the sample mean and variance found by analyst II are, respectively, 72.4 and 8. It is argued that there is a tendency for analyst I to get higher results. What is your conclusion? If you conclude that the analysts differ, determine the 90 percent confidence limits for the difference.

7-27. Wire of type *B* will be replaced by wire of type *A* if the resistance per unit length is not significantly decreased. The data shown below were presented as the results of twenty tests on each wire.

(a) If we know that the standard deviations of the two testing procedures are both .0017 ohms, what is your recommendation?

Wire *A*	Wire *B*
.051 (ohms)	.054
.047	.051
.049	.052
.048	.051
.048	.051
.049	.055
.049	.049
.049	.049
.049	.051
.051	.052
.049	.057
.051	.051
.053	.054
.050	.051
.053	.052
.047	.052
.049	.050
.050	.052
.051	.052
.049	.048

(b) Construct the OC curve for your test.

(c) If we assume that the two standard deviations are unknown (but equal) would you change your recommendation?

(d) Construct the 95 percent confidence limits for the difference. (Does the value 0 lie between these limits?)

7-28. To determine whether a fertilizer is effective, 100 plants out of 1000 are left unfertilized. Of the 100, 53 are found to have satisfactory growth, and out of the fertilized plants, 783 are found satisfactory. Is the fertilizer effective?

7-29. Suppose that two samples of ten and sixteen observations, respectively, have variances $s_1^2 = .3888$ and $s_2^2 = 2.25$. At a 5 percent significance level would you accept the hypothesis $H_0 : \sigma_1^2 \leq \sigma_2^2$?

7-30. Would you conclude that the methods of testing the resistance of wire A and wire B given in Problem 7-27 have equal variances? State your conclusion on the basis of a 10 percent level of significance.

7-31. A control laboratory is interested in whether two methods of analysis are equally reliable. Do the following data substantiate the assumption of equal variances for the two methods?

Determinations in Percent Nickel

Aqueous: 4.27, 4.32, 4.29, 4.30, 4.31, 4.30, 4.30, 4,32, 4.28, 4.32.

Alcoholic: 4.28, 4.32, 4.32, 4.29, 4.31, 4.35, 4.29, 4.32, 4.33, 4.28, 4.37,
 4.38, 4.28, 4.32.

8

SELECTION

OF PROCEDURES

The statistical procedures discussed thus far have been introduced on an intuitive basis; indeed, in many cases more than one procedure is available for a given problem. How to derive a "best" procedure was not discussed. Unfortunately, there is no universally acceptable definition of "best," and consequently no single best procedure in a given case. Several intuitively reasonable principles have been proposed and used, each leading to definite procedures, but not necessarily to the same ones, although it can happen that they do. Some of these principles will be taken up in this chapter.

A basic ingredient in a statistical problem is a collection or family of possible distributions of the data on which inference is to be based. Sometimes this family is indexed by a real *parameter*, as in the case of a family of densities of the form $f(x; \theta)$; but in any case the various possible distributions are thought of as possible "explanations" of the data, and frequently referred to as states of "nature." The inference consists of deciding which is the "best" explanation in some well-defined sense, and then making the estimate or taking the action that would be appropriate if that best state of nature were actually correct.

8.1 The maximum likelihood principle

Consider first a problem in which the data X has a discrete distribution with probability function

$$f(x; \theta) = P(X = x|\theta),$$

where θ is a real valued parameter indexing the various possible distributions of X. The quantity $f(x; \theta)$ is really a function of two variables, x and θ, and the term "probability function" refers to the dependence of $f(x; \theta)$ on x for a given state of nature θ. The dependence of $f(x; \theta)$ on θ for a given x is referred to by the name *likelihood function*:

$$L_x(\theta) = f(x; \theta) = P(X = x|\theta).$$

For a given observed value $X = x$ this gives the probability of that observation under the various possible states or explanations. The *principle of maximum likelihood* asserts that the state θ which maximizes the likelihood function is "best," and that inference should be carried out as though that best state were the *actual* state of nature.

If the statistical problem is one of estimating a parameter θ, the estimate to be announced, according to the principle of maximum likelihood, is just the θ that maximizes $L_x(\theta)$ for the given data. This is called the *maximum likelihood estimate* of θ, and is often denoted by $\hat{\theta}$. When thus defined for each outcome x, $\hat{\theta}$ defines a function of X—an *estimator* of θ.

EXAMPLE 8-a. A bag contains eight beads, some white and the rest black. If M denotes the number of white beads in the bag, and two beads are drawn at random (without replacement) from the bag, the distribution of the number of white beads in the sample is a hypergeometric distribution indexed by M, which is then the state of nature:

$$L_k(M) = P(k \text{ white among } 2 | M \text{ white in bag})$$

$$= f(k \mid M) = \binom{M}{k}\binom{8 - M}{2 - k} \Big/ \binom{8}{2}, \qquad k = 0, 1, 2.$$

The parameter M in this context is discrete, having one of the values $M = 0, 1, 2, \ldots, 8$. If the sample contains, say, two white beads, the probability of this would depend on M, and (as computed from the formula above) is as shown in the following table:

M	0	1	2	3	4	5	6	7	8
$L_2(M)$	0	0	1/28	3/28	6/28	10/28	15/28	21/28	28/28

The value of M that yields the largest probability of two white beads in a random selection of two beads from the bag is $M = 8$. That is, observing that both beads in the sample are white, one takes as the best explanation (according to the principle of maximum likelihood) the statement that all of the beads in the bag were white to begin with. Similar computations will show that if one observes one white bead in the sample of two, the best explanation is that there are four white and four black beads in the bag; that is, that $M = 4$. And finally if both beads in the sample are black, the best explanation is that $M = 0$, or that all of the beads in the bag were black at the outset. Summarizing, the maximum likelihood principle would say:

> If $X = 0$, one should announce $M = 0$,
> if $X = 1$, one should announce $M = 4$, and
> if $X = 2$, one should announce $M = 8$.

This rule, which assigns a value to announce to each possible value of the observation X, is a function $T(X)$, called an *estimator*, and in particular the above rule is the *maximum likelihood estimator* of M.

EXAMPLE 8-b. The random variable X defined to be the number of Heads in five independent tosses of a "coin" (that is, performances of a Bernoulli experiment with probability p of success at each trial) has a distribution that depends on p as follows:

$$P(X = k|p) = \binom{5}{k} p^k (1 - p)^{5-k}, \qquad \text{for } k = 0, 1, \ldots, 5.$$

As a function of p for a given outcome $X = k$, this is the likelihood function. Thus, for example, if $X = 0$, the likelihood function is $L_0(p) = (1 - p)^5$. As p ranges over the interval $0 \le p \le 1$, the maximum of $L_0(p)$ is clearly assumed at $p = 0$, which is then the maximum likelihood estimate of p corresponding to $X = 0$. Similarly, if $X = 5$, the likelihood function is p^5 with a maximum at $p = 1$. For $X = 1, 2, 3,$ and 4 the maximum of $L(p)$ is found by a method of calculus; that is, by setting the derivative $L'(p)$ equal to zero and solving. The result is the maximum likelihood estimator $p = X/5$, which includes the results for $X = 0$ and $X = 5$ as special cases. More generally, for n independent trials, the maximum likelihood estimator of p is simply the relative frequency of success among the trials—an estimator that was introduced on an intuitive basis in Chapter 3.

For continuous models it is necessary to alter the notion of "likelihood" somewhat, since the probability of obtaining a given observed result is zero. Because the probability of a tiny interval about a given value of a continuous random variable is proportional to the density function of its distribution, the *likelihood function*, given data Z with a continuous distribution, is defined to be the density of the distribution at the given Z-value, considered as a function of the state of nature. If the data are in the form of a random sample— independent, identically distributed observations $X_1, X_2, \ldots, X_n$—this density is just the product of the population density values at those observed values:

$$L(\theta) = f(X_1|\theta)f(X_2|\theta)\cdots f(X_n|\theta).$$

Because this is a product, and because the larger the number the larger its logarithm, it is both convenient and customary to maximize the logarithm of the likelihood function:

$$\log L(\theta) = \sum_{i=1}^{n} \log f(X_i|\theta).$$

Determining a state of nature (that is, value of θ) that maximizes $L(\theta)$ or $\log L(\theta)$ is usually an exercise in calculus, and this technique will not be developed here in detail. It is seen, however, that no matter how the maximizing θ is obtained, this quantity $\theta = \hat{\theta}$ depends on the observations used in constructing the likelihood function; it is, therefore, a statistic, and a random variable.

EXAMPLE 8-c.   Consider a random sample of size n from a normal population with mean unknown and unit variance. The population density function is

$$f(x|\mu) = \frac{1}{\sqrt{2\pi}}\, e^{-(x-\mu)^2/2},$$

and so the likelihood function, given the sample $(X_1, \ldots, X_n)$, is

$$L(\mu) = \frac{1}{(2\pi)^{n/2}} \exp\left[-\tfrac{1}{2}\Sigma(X_i - \mu)^2\right]$$

Taking logarithms to the base e on both sides, one obtains

$$\log L(\mu) = -\frac{n}{2}\log(2\pi) - \frac{1}{2}\sum_{i=1}^{n}(X_i - \mu)^2$$

$$= (\text{const}) - \frac{n}{2}(\mu^2 - 2\mu\bar{X}),$$

where the constant indicated involves no μ. This log-likelihood, and hence the likelihood, will be a maximum when the quadratic function $\mu^2 - 2\mu\bar{X}$ is a minimum; this will be the case for $\mu = \bar{X}$, which is then the state of nature that "best explains" the given sample:

$$\hat{\mu} = \bar{X}.$$

This is then the *maximum likelihood estimator.*

It should be realized that a maximum likelihood estimator is derived from a principle, the maximum likelihood principle, whose basis is purely intuitive.

There is no really convincing reason why the principle should lead to good procedures of statistical inference. On the other hand, in many instances the maximum likelihood estimator turns out to be a good estimator, when assessed on the basis of mean squared error, for instance. (But there are examples, somewhat pathological perhaps, in which the maximum likelihood estimate is worse than a guess.) It is also true that maximum likelihood estimators can be shown to have asymptotic properties—for large samples— that are quite appealing. For example, subject to very mild conditions satisfied in most practical situations, a maximum likelihood estimator approaches (as $n \to \infty$) the parameter being estimated in the sense of limit in probability, or weak limit, as defined at the beginning of Chapter 6. This characteristic is described as *consistency*. It is also true that, under these same conditions, the asymptotic distribution of a maximum likelihood estimator is normal. And, further, a maximum likelihood estimator (subject to the same general conditions) has asymptotically as small a variance as any estimator can have, although this condition should be examined in its precise statement to be understood (cf. Cramer, H., *Mathematical Methods of Statistics*).

Whether these "large sample" properties of maximum likelihood estimates should really give the statistician comfort in the case of finite samples is a moot question. Perhaps the safest approach in using the maximum likelihood method is, having determined such an estimator, to study its characteristics, such as mean squared error of estimation.

Problems

8-1. Write out the likelihood function for a random sample of size n from each of the following populations:
  (a) normal with mean 0 and variance v;
  (b) Poisson with unknown mean m;
  (c) geometric with unknown p: $f(x;p) = p(1 - p)^x$, $x = 0, 1, 2, \ldots$;
  (d) exponential with density $f(x; \theta) = (1/\theta) \exp(-x/\theta)$, $x > 0$.

8-2. For the bag with eight beads of Example 8-a, determine the maximum likelihood estimator of M, the number of white beads in the bag, based on the color of a single bead drawn at random from the bag.

8-3. Sketch the likelihood functions for the various numbers of possible successes in *three* independent trials of a Bernoulli experiment with probability p of success in a given trial. Determine the maximum either graphically or using methods of calculus, in each case. What is the maximum likelihood estimator of p in terms of Y, the number of successes in the three trials?

8-4. (a)† Show that $A \log_e x + B/x$ is a minimum for $x = B/A$.

  † Requires calculus.

(b) Use the result of (a) to determine the maximum likelihood estimate of θ in the family of distributions with density $(1/\theta) \exp(-x/\theta)$ for $x > 0$, based on a random sample of size n. [Hint: Maximizing $\log L(\theta)$ is equivalent to maximizing $L(\theta)$.]

8-5. Use the result of Problem 8-4(a) to determine the maximum likelihood estimate of the variance v in the normal family with density function $f(x; v) = (2\pi v)^{-\frac{1}{2}} \exp[-x^2/(2v)]$, based on a random sample of size n.

8.2 Likelihood ratios in testing

When, as in testing a simple hypothesis against a simple alternative, there are just two states of nature or possible distributions that can be used as explanations of certain data X, the maximum likelihood principle would assert that one should act as though that state were true which gives the larger probability of the observed value of X. That is,

$$\text{Accept } \theta_0 \text{ if } L(\theta_0) > L(\theta_1);$$
$$\text{Reject } \theta_0 \text{ if } L(\theta_0) < L(\theta_1).$$

(If $L(\theta_0) = L(\theta_1)$, one is indifferent and could take either action.) The maximum likelihood rule just given could also be stated in terms of the *ratio* $\Lambda = L(\theta_0)/L(\theta_1)$: Accept θ_0 if $\Lambda > 1$ and reject if $\Lambda < 1$.

This test is frequently not particularly useful in that it insists on treating the two types of error somewhat symmetrically—or at least inflexibly. Thus, a *family* of tests is introduced by generalizing the notion so that small values of Λ call for rejection, but not necessarily those smaller than 1. A *likelihood ratio test* for θ_0 against θ_1 is a test that calls for rejecting θ_0 for $\Lambda < K$, where K is a suitably chosen constant:

$$\text{Reject } \theta_0 \text{ if } \frac{L(\theta_0)}{L(\theta_1)} < K;$$

$$\text{Accept } \theta_0 \text{ if } \frac{L(\theta_0)}{L(\theta_1)} > K.$$

The value of K is often chosen so that the critical region has size α, a specified significance level or size of type I error:

$$\alpha = P(\Lambda < K | \theta_0).$$

EXAMPLE 8-d. Suppose that it is desired to test the hypothesis that a Bernoulli parameter p has the value $1/2$ against the alternative that it is $1/4$; that is, $p_0 = 1/2$ versus $p_1 = 1/4$. Denoting by X the number of "successes" in eight independent trials of the experiment, the likelihood function for an observed result $X = k$ is as follows:

$$L(p) = \binom{8}{k} p^k (1 - p)^{8-k}.$$

The likelihood ratio for the given testing problem is

$$\Lambda = \frac{L(p_0)}{L(p_1)} = \frac{L(1/2)}{L(1/4)} = \frac{(1/2)^8}{(1/4)^k (3/4)^{8-k}} = 3^k (2/3)^8.$$

This is clearly an increasing function of k—the larger the k the larger the value of Λ. Hence, small values of Λ correspond to small values of k, and so the critical region of the form $\Lambda < K$ is equivalent to a critical region of X-values of the form $X < C$, where again C is a constant that may be chosen to satisfy a specification of the type I error size. Since the values of X are finite in number, there are actually only a finite number of different tests of the form $X < C$. These are listed in the following table which defines the tests by their critical regions and gives the values of α and β, the type I and type II error sizes, respectively.

Test no.	Critical set (X-values)	α	β
1	empty	0	1
2	0	.00391	.90
3	0, 1	.0351	.633
4	0, 1, 2	.1446	.322
⋮	...	...	...
10	0, 1, 2, ..., 8	1	0

The values of α and β shown in the table are computed as follows:

$$\alpha = P(\text{reject } H_0 | p_0) = P(\text{critical set} | p = 1/2)$$

$$= \sum_{\substack{\text{critical} \\ \text{set}}} \binom{8}{k} \left(\frac{1}{2}\right)^k \left(\frac{1}{2}\right)^{8-k}$$

$$\beta = P(\text{accept } H_0 | p_1) = 1 - P(\text{critical set} | p = 1/4)$$

$$= 1 - \sum_{\substack{\text{critical} \\ \text{set}}} \binom{8}{k} \left(\frac{1}{4}\right)^k \left(\frac{3}{4}\right)^{8-k}$$

For instance, for the test numbered 4 in the table, the computation is as follows:

$$\alpha = \sum_{k=0}^{2} \binom{8}{k} \left(\frac{1}{2}\right)^8 = \frac{1}{256}\left[\binom{8}{0} + \binom{8}{1} + \binom{8}{2}\right] = \frac{37}{256},$$

$$\beta = 1 - \sum_{k=0}^{2} \binom{8}{k} \left(\frac{1}{4}\right)^k \left(\frac{3}{4}\right)^{8-k} = 1 - \frac{1}{4^8}\left[\binom{8}{0}3^8 + \binom{8}{1}3^7 + \binom{8}{2}3^6\right].$$

The likelihood ratio scheme is adapted to the case of *composite* hypotheses by defining the likelihood ratio to be the ratio of the maximum likelihood in H_0 to the maximum likelihood in H_1—that is, the best explanation in each case is used as the basis of comparison:

$$\Lambda = \frac{\max_{\theta \text{ in } H_0} L(\theta)}{\max_{\theta \text{ in } H_1} L(\theta)}.$$

The critical region used is again of the form $\Lambda < K$, calling for rejection of H_0 if the best explanation in H_0 is much less likely than the best explanation in H_1.

EXAMPLE 8-e. Consider again a normal population with unit variance and unknown mean, and the problem of testing $\mu = \mu_0$ against the alternative $\mu \neq \mu_0$. Since H_0 is simple, the numerator in Λ is just the value of the likelihood function at $\mu = \mu_0$: $L(\mu_0)$. For the denominator one must maximize $L(\mu)$ or $\log L(\mu)$ over the set of values of μ different from μ_0. Examination of the graph of $\log L(\mu)$ shows that whether μ_0 is admitted or not in the maximization makes no difference, if $\mu_0 \neq \bar{X}$, and the maximum is $L(\bar{X})$. If μ_0 happens to equal $\bar{X}$, and this point is not permitted in the maximization, then the maximum does not exist; in such a case (which occurs often in using Λ) one replaces the notion of maximum by "least upper bound," which in the case at hand is again $L(\bar{X})$. Thus, the denominator in Λ is $L(\bar{X})$:

$$\Lambda = \frac{L(\mu_0)}{L(\bar{X})} = \frac{e^{-\Sigma(X_i - \mu_0)^2/2}}{e^{-\Sigma(X_i - \bar{X})^2/2}}.$$

and

$$\log \Lambda = -\frac{n}{2}[\mu_0^2 - \bar{X}^2 - 2\bar{X}(\mu_0 - \bar{X})] = -\frac{n}{2}(\mu_0 - \bar{X})^2.$$

The critical region $\Lambda < K$ is then seen to be equivalent to

$$|\bar{X} - \mu_0| > K,$$

with a change in definition of K. This is intuitively quite appealing.

As in the above example, it is often the case that the maximum or least upper bound over H_1 is the same as over all states of nature, so that the denominator of the likelihood ratio is $L(\hat{\theta})$, where $\hat{\theta}$ is the maximum likelihood state.

The maximum likelihood principle and its modification usually lead to good procedures, but there is no guarantee of this. It can be shown that they have desirable properties for large samples under fairly general conditions, but their only real basis lies in intuition. At any rate, the method does give a procedure—that can then be studied as to the associated risks.

8.3   Maximization of power

In the realm of hypothesis-testing problems, a widely used principle assumes that one kind of error is more crucial than the other and should be controlled closely, doing as best one can for the other type of error. The more important error is called "type I," which can be made the probability of rejecting H_0 when H_0 is true by suitably labeling the hypotheses. The principle used is that in a class of tests having the same size of type I error, the test with greatest power (or smallest size of type II error) is the best test.

When the alternative hypothesis is not simple, but made up of many simple hypotheses, it can easily happen that a test that maximizes power for one alternative does not maximize the power for another alternative. However, when the alternative is simple, as well as the null hypothesis, the likelihood ratio test introduced in the preceding section actually is most powerful when compared with all other tests with the same α. This fact is known as the "Neyman-Pearson lemma," and will be illustrated in the following example.

EXAMPLE 8-f.   Consider testing $p_0 = 1/2$ against $p_1 = 1/4$ on the basis of four independent trials of a Bernoulli experiment with probability p of success at each trial. The likelihood ratio test calls for rejecting $p = 1/2$ (and accepting $p = 1/4$) if Y, the number of successes in the four trials, is smaller than a given constant. For example, the critical region $Y = 0$ or 1 is a likelihood ratio test, of size

$$\alpha = P_{p=1/2}(Y = 0 \text{ or } 1) = (1/2)^4 + 4(1/2)^3(1/2)^1 = 5/16.$$

Another test of the same size is defined by the critical region $Y = 1$ or 4:

$$\alpha^* = P_{p=1/2}(Y = 1 \text{ or } 4) = 4(1/2)^3(1/2)^1 + (1/2)^4 = 5/16.$$

Denoting by β the size of the type II error for the likelihood ratio critical region $\{0, 1\}$ and by β^* the size of the type II error for the region $\{1, 4\}$, one finds

$$\begin{aligned}
\beta^* - \beta &= P_{1/4}(\{0, 2, 3\}) - P_{1/4}(\{2, 3, 4\}) \\
&= P_{1/4}(\{0\}) - P_{1/4}(\{4\}) \geq C[P_{1/2}(\{0\}) - P_{1/2}(\{4\})].
\end{aligned}$$

The inequality follows from the fact that since 0 is in the likelihood ratio critical region,

$$\varLambda(0) = \frac{P_{1/2}(Y = 0)}{P_{1/4}(Y = 0)} < C,$$

and since $Y = 4$ is not in that region, $\varLambda(4) \geq C$. Continuing, one has

$$\beta^* - \beta \geq C[P_{1/2}(\{0, 1\}) - P_{1/4}(\{1, 4\})] = C(\alpha^* - \alpha) = 0,$$

showing that $\beta^* \geq \beta$. This means that the likelihood ratio critical region $\{0, 1\}$ is at least as powerful as the region $\{1, 4\}$, which has the same α.

The computation in the above example can be generalized to a proof. Suppose that R is a critical region defined by $f_0(x)/f_1(x) < C$, for some C, and that $P_0(R) = \alpha$. (Let the subscript i on P denote that the probability is calculated under hypothesis $H_i : f(x) = f_i(x)$.) If S is any other critical region for which $P_0(S) = \alpha$, then

$$P_1(R) - P_1(S) = \sum_R f_1(x) - \sum_S f_1(x)$$
$$= \sum_{R \cap S^c} f_1(x) - \sum_{R^c \cap S} f_1(x)$$

(since the terms in $R \cap S$ in the first sum cancel the terms over $R \cap S$ in the second). Now because $R \cap S^c \subset R$, it follows that in the first term on the right one has $f_1(x) \geq C f_0(x)$; and because $R^c \cap S \subset R^c$, it follows that in the second term $-f_1(x) \geq -C f_0(x)$. Hence

$$P_1(R) - P_1(S) = \sum_{R \cap S^c} C f_0(x) - \sum_{R^c \cap S} C f_0(x)$$
$$= C[P_0(R) - P_0(S)] = 0.$$

Thus, $P_1(R) \geq P_1(S)$, which says that R is at least as powerful as S. This (for discrete cases) is the Neyman-Pearson lemma: A likelihood ratio test for $f_0(x)$ against $f_1(x)$ is at least as powerful as any other test with the same size type I error.

When the alternative H_1 is composite, the situation is that a test which maximizes power for one simple hypothesis in H_1 may not do so for another simple hypothesis in H_1. When a test does maximize power for all alternatives simultaneously, it is said to be *uniformly most powerful* (UMP); but such tests do not always exist and at any rate are beyond the scope of this discussion. (They often *do* exist in one-sided testing problems, and usually do *not* in two-sided cases.)

EXAMPLE 8-g. A test with critical region of the form $Y < K$, where Y denotes the number of successes in a sequence of n independent Bernoulli trials, is most powerful for testing $p = .5$ against $p = .1$, because given $Y = j$, the likelihood ratio is

$$\Lambda(j) = \frac{(.5)^j (.5)^{n-j}}{(.1)^j (.9)^{n-j}} = 9^j (5/9)^n,$$

an increasing function of j. The same would be true if in place of $p = .1$ one had used any $p_1 < .5$, and therefore the test $Y < K$ is uniformly most powerful for $p = .5$ against $p < .5$.

Problems

8-6. In testing the hypothesis that a population is normal with mean 0 and variance 1 against the alternative that it is normal with mean 1 and variance 1, based on a random sample of size n, show that the likelihood ratio test (that is, of the form $\varLambda <$ const.) can be expressed as having a critical region of the form $\bar{X} > K$. Determine K for an α of .05 and a sample of size 25. [Recall: $\bar{X}$ is normal with mean EX and variance σ^2/n.]

8-7. It is desired to test whether X has the probability function $f_0(x)$ or the probability function $f_1(x)$, where these are given in the following table:

x	$f_0(x)$	$f_1(x)$
0	.3	.5
1	.6	.3
2	.1	.2

For each x compute $\varLambda$, and so arrange the X-values in order of increasing $\varLambda$; then list the four possible critical regions that are equivalent to $\varLambda < K$, for some K.

8-8. Construct the likelihood ratio test of the hypothesis that a population density is e^{-x} $(x > 0)$ against the alternative that it is $.5e^{-.5x}$ $(x > 0)$, based on a random sample of size n. Show that the critical region of the form $\varLambda <$ const. is equivalent to a region of the form $\bar{X} > K$.

8-9.† Determine the likelihood ratio test for $v = v_0$ against $v = v_1$ for a normal family with unknown mean and variance v, based on a random sample of size n.

8-10. Let M denote the number of white beads in a bag containing four beads, from which two are selected at random. Construct a table whose columns give the five distributions of the number Y of white beads in the selection of two, corresponding to $M = 0, 1, \ldots, 4$. For each value of Y, the likelihood function values are then the rows of this array. For each Y-value, determine the corresponding likelihood ratio for testing $M = 2$ against $M \neq 2$, as the ratio of $L(2)$ to the maximum of $L(0)$, $L(1)$, $L(3)$, and $L(4)$. From these values of $\varLambda$ the Y-values can be arranged according to increasing $\varLambda$; construct the three possible likelihood ratio tests.

8-11. Referring to Problem 8-6, plot the error sizes (α, β) for each test corresponding to several choices of K as a point in an $\alpha\beta$-plane, and connect these with a smooth curve. According to the Neyman-Pearson lemma, where would the (α, β) points corresponding to all other tests lie relative to this curve? In particular, plot (α, β) for the critical region $\bar{X} < .5$, and note the β-value as compared with that of the likelihood ratio test with the same α.

8.4   Sequential testing

In the tests considered so far it has been assumed that a sample size is fixed before the experimentation begins and that the decision between the two

† Requires calculus.

available actions is not made until all the results are in. It often happens that the results of the sample are such that the decision variable has a value near the boundary between the critical set and its complement, so that the decision is not terribly clear-cut. In such a case there is a temptation to continue the sampling—to gather more data and see if the case can be made stronger, even though to achieve certain error sizes or power it was agreed to make the decision when the sample of given size had been obtained. And then sometimes it happens that in the process of gathering the data, there is an early indication as to which action is correct—long before the entire sample of agreed on size is gathered. The concept of *sequential* testing has arisen partly to take into account these disconcerting features of testing with fixed sample sizes.

A sequential test is a procedure that provides after each observation (or possibly after each group of observations) the opportunity to decide between the actions at that stage, with the alternative of continuing the sampling process if the indications are not yet clear. For such tests the number of observations used in making a decision depends on the values observed and so it is a random variable; it may be smaller than or greater than the number of observations used in a test of fixed sample size and comparable sensitivity.

The *sequential likelihood ratio test* is designed for testing between two simple hypotheses—in the case of a Bernoulli population, between $H_0 : p = p_0$ and $H_1 : p = p_1$. As implied by the name, this test is based on the value of the likelihood ratio computed after each observation for all of the observations obtained up to that point:

$$\Lambda_n = \frac{L(p_0)}{L(p_1)} = \frac{p_0{}^k (1 - p_0)^{n-k}}{p_1{}^k (1 - p_1)^{n-k}},$$

assuming k successes in the first n observations. The test is specified by two numbers A and B; after n observations the sampling is continued if the likelihood ratio lies between A and B:

$$A < \Lambda_n < B;$$

but if it exceeds B, this is taken as reason to choose p_0, and if it falls below A, this is taken as a basis for selecting p_1. Having selected p_0 or p_1, one would then cease sampling.

The error sizes α and β for the test depend on the constants A and B that are used, of course. If B is small, for instance, the test will be more apt to accept H_0 when it is false than if B is large. However, the exact relationships between A and B and the resulting error sizes are not simple. Fortunately approximate relationships have been found which permit specification of A and B in terms of desired error sizes, as follows:

$$A = \frac{\alpha}{1 - \beta}, \qquad B = \frac{1 - \alpha}{\beta}.$$

That is, if certain values α and β are desired, the test given by the A and B from these formulas should be used; the actual error sizes achieved are not then exactly α and β, but are close enough for practical purposes if α and β are not too large.

EXAMPLE 8-h.   Suppose it is desired to test between $H_0:p = .5$ and $H_1:p = .7$ with specified error sizes $\alpha = .05$ and $\beta = .10$. The inequality for continuing sampling is then defined by the constants

$$A = \frac{.05}{1 - .10} = \frac{1}{18}, \qquad B = \frac{1 - .05}{.10} = 9.5.$$

After n observations the likelihood ratio is

$$\Lambda_n = \left(\frac{.5}{.7}\right)^k \left(\frac{.5}{.3}\right)^{n-k},$$

and the value of Λ_{n+1} can be obtained from Λ_n by multiplying in the factor 5/7 if the $(n + 1)$st observation is success, or the factor 5/3 if it is failure. Thus, if a sequence of observations is as follows: $H, T, T, H, H, H, T, T, H, H, T, T, T, H,$ $H, T, T, T, H, H, \ldots$, the first few Λ's are

$$\Lambda_1 = \frac{5}{7}, \qquad \Lambda_2 = \frac{5}{7}\frac{5}{3}, \qquad \Lambda_3 = \frac{5}{7}\frac{5}{3}\frac{5}{3}, \qquad \Lambda_4 = \frac{5}{7}\frac{5}{3}\frac{5}{3}\frac{5}{7}, \ldots$$

Continuing in this manner one would find $\Lambda_{18} = 11$, which exceeds 9.5 (for the first time in the sequence), and so after eighteen observations $p = .5$ is accepted in preference to $p = .7$. (The remaining two observations given need not be obtained, of course.)

The computations, as the sampling proceeds, can be made a little less tedious by rewriting the inequality for continuing sampling in terms of k, the number of successes. This is done by taking the logarithms of each term in the inequality (which preserves the order):

$$\log A < k \log \frac{p_0}{p_1} + (n - k) \log \frac{1 - p_0}{1 - p_1} < \log B,$$

and manipulating further to obtain, for $p_0 > p_1$:

$$\frac{\log A - n \log \dfrac{1 - p_0}{1 - p_1}}{\log \dfrac{p_0}{p_1} - \log \dfrac{1 - p_0}{1 - p_1}} < k < \frac{\log B - n \log \dfrac{1 - p_0}{1 - p_1}}{\log \dfrac{p_0}{p_1} - \log \dfrac{1 - p_0}{1 - p_1}}.$$

The extremes of this extended inequality are linear functions of n, easily computed and graphed once and for all at the beginning of the test; the value of k can then be plotted as the test proceeds, and when it strays outside the region between the two straight lines, the test stops, the decision depending on which line is crossed. In case $p_0 < p_1$, the inequalities above are reversed.

EXAMPLE 8-i.   Consider the problem of Example 8-h above. Since $p_0 = .5$ and is less than $p_1 = .7$, the inequality for continued sampling is

$$\frac{\log 18}{\log (7/3)} + n\frac{\log (5/3)}{\log (7/3)} > k > -\frac{\log 9.5}{\log (7/3)} + n\frac{\log (5/3)}{\log (7/3)}$$

or

$$3.41 + .603n > k > -2.63 + .603n.$$

The graphs of the linear functions of n in the extremes of this inequality are shown (as though n were continuous) in Figure 8-1, along with a record of the number of successes as given in the sequence of outcomes of Example 8-h. Notice that

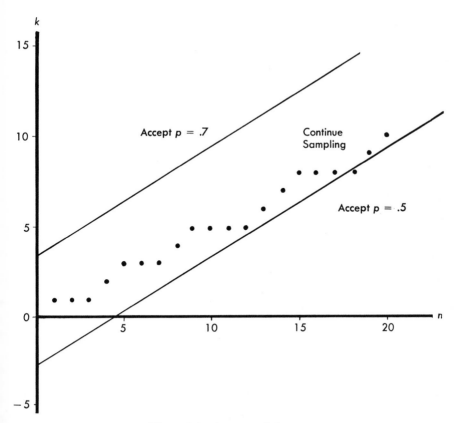

Figure 8-1   A sequential test.

the lower line (corresponding to the right member of the above inequality) is crossed with the eighteenth observation, calling for acceptance of $H_0(p = .5)$ at that point in the sequence.

Carrying out a sequential test such as above, one might well wonder whether in some cases the test might never terminate, with Λ_n remaining indefinitely between A and B. It was shown by A. Wald, in his pioneering book *Sequential Analysis* (John Wiley and Sons, 1947), that the test will terminate with probability one. Moreover, the number of observations required to reach a decision (a random variable) has an expected value that is usually less than needed for a test with comparable detecting power based on a fixed sample size. In individual cases, of course, a sequential test *can* require a great many observations.

It can be shown that the expected number n of observations required for a decision using a sequential likelihood ratio test is

$$E(n) = \frac{E(\log \Lambda_n)}{EZ},$$

where Z is the logarithm of the likelihood ratio for a single observation, and where the numerator is given approximately by

$$E(\log \Lambda_n) \doteq (\log A)P(\text{reject } H_0) + (\log B)P(\text{accept } H_0).$$

For the Bernoulli population, given the observation x,

$$\log \frac{L(p_0|x)}{L(p_1|x)} = \log \left(\frac{p_0}{p_1}\right)^x \left(\frac{1 - p_0}{1 - p_1}\right)^{1-x}$$

$$= x \log \frac{p_0(1 - p_1)}{p_1(1 - p_0)} + \log \frac{1 - p_0}{1 - p_1},$$

for $x = 0, 1$. This function of x defines a function of the Bernoulli random variable X, and this is what was called Z above. Thus,

$$EZ = p \log \frac{p_0(1 - p_1)}{p_1(1 - p_0)} + \log \frac{1 - p_0}{1 - p_1}.$$

EXAMPLE 8-j.   Referring again to the situation in Examples 8-h and 8-i, one finds the following expected sample sizes. Under H_0,

$$E_{H_0}(n) \doteq \frac{-.05 \log 18 + .95 \log 9.5}{.5 \log (3/7) + \log (5/3)} \doteq 26,$$

and under H_1,

$$E_{H_1}(n) \doteq \frac{-.9 \log 18 + .1 \log 9.5}{.7 \log (3/7) + \log (5/3)} \doteq 31.$$

It is of interest to observe that for a sample of fixed size 26 and an α of .05, the corresponding β is .173, considerably larger than the .10 of the above sequential test.

The sequential likelihood ratio test is constructed for testing p_0 against p_1, given the desired sizes of the type I and type II errors. But as in the case of fixed-size tests, the test constructed for choosing between two simple hypotheses can also be used in testing between composite hypotheses in the one-sided case: $p \leq p^*$ versus $p > p^*$. The power function of the test defined by the inequality $A < \Lambda_n < B$ (as the criterion for continuing the sampling), although nontrivial to derive, can easily be roughly sketched using five points, as follows. First, of course, it should be realized that the notation Λ_n has been used as denoting the likelihood ratio corresponding to p-values p_0 and p_1. What is usually done is to select arbitrarily a p_0 in H_0 ($p \leq p^*$) and a p_1 in H_1 ($p > p^*$) and to specify α and β such that

$$\begin{cases} \alpha = P(\text{reject } H_0 | p_0) \\ \beta = P(\text{accept } H_0 | p_1). \end{cases}$$

The power function $\pi(p)$ of the test so specified has these† values:

$$\pi(0) = 0,$$
$$\pi(1) = 1,$$
$$\pi(p_0) = \alpha,$$
$$\pi(p_1) = 1 - \beta,$$
$$\pi(p_2) = \frac{\log B}{\log B - \log A},$$

where

$$p_2 = -\frac{\log\left[(1 - p_0)/(1 - p_1)\right]}{\log\left(p_0/p_1\right) - \log\left[(1 - p_0)/(1 - p_1)\right]}.$$

EXAMPLE 8-k.   If it is desired to conduct a sequential test between $p \leq .6$ and $p > .6$, one might specify that the test is to reject $p \leq .6$ with probability .05 when $p = .5$ and to accept $p \leq .6$ with probability .10 when $p = .7$. This reduces the problem to that of Examples 8-h, 8-i, and 8-j, with $p_0 = .5$, $p_1 = .7$, $\alpha = .05$, and $\beta = .10$. The power function of the test for this situation, as given in Example 8-h, has the values $\pi(0) = 0$, $\pi(1) = 1$, $\pi(.5) = .05$, $\pi(.7) = .90$; for the fifth point, in the above notation,

$$p_2 = \frac{\log 5/3}{\log (5/3) - \log (5/7)} = .603,$$

and

$$\pi(p_2) = \frac{\log 9.5}{\log 9.5 - \log (1/18)} = .438.$$

Figure 8-2 shows the power function as sketched from these five points on its graph.

† The derivation of these results can be found in B. W. Lindgren, *Statistical Theory* (2nd Ed.), Macmillan, 1968.

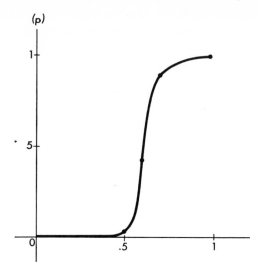

Figure 8-2   Power function of the sequential test of Example 8-k.

Problems

8-12.   Toss a coin repeatedly to test between $p = .5$ and $p = .7$ with the aid of the graph given in Example 8-i. (Let $p = P(\text{Heads})$.)

8-13.   How many tosses would be required to make the decision between $p = .5$ and $p = .7$, if the coin used has two Heads? Two Tails?

8-14.   Construct the sequential likelihood ratio test for $H_0:p = .5$ against $H_1:p = .1$, using $\alpha = \beta = .2$. Use a coin to carry out the test, with $p = P(\text{Heads})$. Carry out the test again using a die, with $p = P(1 \text{ or } 2)$.

8-15.   Determine the expected number of trials necessary to reach a decision in Problem 8-14, under H_0 and under H_1.

8-16.   Sketch the power function for the test of Problem 8-14 using the five point method illustrated in Example 8-k. (Because $p_1 < p_0$, it is necessary to make slight changes: $\pi(0) = 1$, $\pi(1) = 0$.)

8.5   The minimax principle

It is sometimes instructive to treat a problem of statistical inference as a problem of *statistical decision theory*. It is assumed that the statistician must choose one from a set of available actions, but that his choice must be made in ignorance of the actual state of nature, educated only to the extent that the information in a finite sample can do so. It is assumed further that there is given a *loss function*, a function $l(\theta, a)$ whose value measures (on a numerical scale) the loss or cost involved when action a is taken and nature is in state θ.

It is seldom easy in any decision problem to determine this loss function, and yet it is felt by some that without a determination of losses one can hardly expect to be able to make rational decision, or to assess the cost of the decisions he might make. At any rate, the loss function is assumed to be known.

A *decision rule*, or *statistical decision function*, is simply a specification of what action to take corresponding to each possible result of the sampling upon which a decision is to be based. If the sample outcome or "datum" is $Z = z$, the rule assigns an action $a = d(z)$ to that outcome, which action is then taken if one observes $Z = z$. Following such a rule, the action taken is random, being a function $d(Z)$ of the random variable Z, and so the loss incurred is also random: $l(\theta, d(Z))$. The performance of a given rule $d(\cdot)$ will be studied on the basis of the expected value of the loss, called the *risk function*:

$$R(\theta, d) = E[l(\theta, d(Z))].$$

Thus, corresponding to each state of nature and each decision rule there is a measure of cost, that is, the value of the risk function.

EXAMPLE 8-1.   Flash bulbs come off the production line in batches of 102 bulbs; two are selected from the 102 and tested (which ruins them). The remaining lot of 100 bulbs is then either rejected (and junked) at a cost of $1, or passed and sold, for 15¢ each with a "double your money back" guarantee. The state of "nature," or the state of the lot of 100 that is to be passed or rejected, is described by the number of defectives in it, or by p, the proportion of defectives in it. The actions are to sell (S) or junk (J), and the losses are computed as follows:

$$L(p, J) = 1$$
$$L(p, S) = -.15 \times 100 + .30 \times 100p = 15(2p - 1),$$

as measured in dollars lost (a negative loss is a gain). The data available is the number of bulbs that test "defective" among the two that are tested, with distribution given by

$$f(x; p) = P(x \text{ def. among } 2|p) = \binom{2}{x} p^x (1 - p)^{2 - x},$$

for $x = 0, 1, 2$. A decision rule assigns either action J or action S to each of these values, which can be done in $2^3 = 8$ ways, listed in the following table (with arbitrary numbering)

x	$d_1(x)$	$d_2(x)$	$d_3(x)$	$d_4(x)$	$d_5(x)$	$d_6(x)$	$d_7(x)$	$d_8(x)$
2	S	J	S	S	J	J	S	J
1	S	S	J	S	J	S	J	J
0	S	S	S	J	S	J	J	J

That is, rule d_3 says to junk the lot if 1 of the two bulbs tested is defective, otherwise pass the lot. The risk function for a given rule is a weighted average, or expected value, of the losses:

$$R(p, d) = L(p, J)P(\text{rule calls for } J) + L(p, S)P(\text{rule calls for } S).$$

Thus, for example,

$$\begin{aligned} R(p, d_2) &= 1 \cdot P(X = 2) + 15(2p - 1)P(X = 1 \text{ or } 0) \\ &= p^2 + 15(2p - 1)(1 - p^2), \end{aligned}$$

and

$$\begin{aligned} R(p, d_6) &= 1 \cdot P(X = 2 \text{ or } 0) + 15(2p - 1) \cdot P(X = 1) \\ &= p^2 + (1 - p)^2 + 15(2p - 1) \cdot 2p(1 - p). \end{aligned}$$

The risks for the other six rules, as functions of the state p, can be computed similarly.

When the risk function for the various possible decision rules has been computed, one is still faced with the problem of picking a decision rule not knowing the state of nature. And of course the rule best for one state of nature is not generally best for another. The *minimax principle* for choosing a decision rule calls for determining the maximum loss for each rule, and then to pick the rule with the smallest maximum loss.

EXAMPLE 8-m.   Suppose that one is given the following table of risks, in a problem involving just two states of nature and five decision rules:

	d_1	d_2	d_3	d_4	d_5
θ_1	2	3	4	1	0
θ_2	5	0	1	2	4
Max	5	3	4	2	4

A row has been added to the table of risks showing, for each rule, the maximum loss for the two states of nature. The smallest of these maxima is 2, corresponding to rule d_4; this rule is the minimax rule.

A graphical construction, possible when there are only two states of nature, is interesting. For each rule, let R_i denote the risk under θ_i, and consider the plot of the points (R_1, R_2) corresponding to the various decision rules. This is shown in Figure 8-3. For any point (or rule) above the line $R_1 = R_2$, the maximum risk is the R_2-coordinate, and for a point below the line $R_1 = R_2$, the maximum risk is the R_1-coordinate. The minimum maximum occurs for the lowest point among those above $R_1 = R_2$ and for the left-most point among those below $R_1 = R_2$; the minimax rule thus is obtained graphically by moving a wedge with vertex on $R_1 = R_2$ and with edges parallel to the axes upward along $R_1 = R_2$ until the wedge first strikes one of the points representing the decision rules. The one first encountered is the minimax rule, and this is illustrated in Figure 8-3.

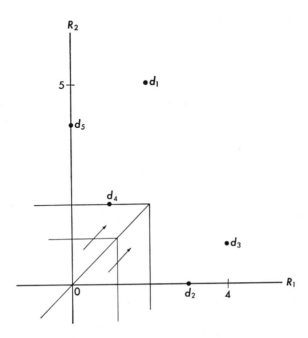

Figure 8-3 Graph of decision rules according to risks.

EXAMPLE 8-n.   The graphical approach of the preceding example can be applied in particular to a problem of the testing of a simple hypothesis H_0 against a simple alternative H_1. Consider then testing the hypothesis that a population is normal with mean 0 and variance 4 against the alternative that it is normal with mean 1 and variance 4, on the basis of the mean of a sample of size 4 from the population. Under H_0, $\bar{X}$ is normal with mean 0 and variance 1; under H_1 it is normal with mean 1 and variance 1. Let losses be given as in the following table:

		Reject H_0	Accept H_0
	H_0	2	0
State			
	H_1	0	1

A decision rule is defined by a critical region C for $\bar{X}$:

$$d(\bar{X}) = \begin{cases} \text{Reject } H_0 \text{ if } \bar{X} \text{ falls in } C, \\ \text{Accept } H_0 \text{ if } \bar{X} \text{ does not fall in } C. \end{cases}$$

The risk function for a given critical region C is the expected loss:

$$R(H_0, C) = 2 \times P(\text{rule rejects } H_0 | H_0) + 0 \times P(\text{rule accepts } H_0 | H_0)$$
$$= 2 \times P(\bar{X} \text{ falls in } C | H_0) = 2\alpha,$$

$$R(H_1, C) = 0 \times P(\text{rule rejects } H_0 | H_1) + 1 \times P(\text{rule accepts } H_0 | H_1)$$
$$= P(\bar{X} \text{ does not fall in } C | H_1) = \beta.$$

Thus, the plot of $(R_0, \dot{R}_1)$, where R_i is the risk under H_i, is closely related to a plot of (α, β). The likelihood ratio rules for this problem have critical regions of the form $\bar{X} > K$, and the corresponding error sizes are

$$\alpha = P(\bar{X} > K | \mu = 0) = 1 - \Phi(K - 0) = \Phi(-K),$$
$$\beta = P(\bar{X} < K | \mu = 1) = \Phi(K - 1).$$

The points (R_0, R_1) corresponding to these rules are shown in Figure 8-4; since the Neyman-Pearson lemma asserts that no rule has a smaller β for a given α, there would be no points (that is, no rules) below the curve representing all likelihood ratio rules (for the various K, $-\infty < K < \infty$). Hence, the minimax rule for this problem is that first encountered by the wedge technique (as in the preceding example) among those of the type $\bar{X} > K$. This minimax rule would then be represented by the point for which $2\alpha = \beta$, or $2\Phi(-K) = \Phi(K - 1)$, which is satisfied by $K \doteq .803$.

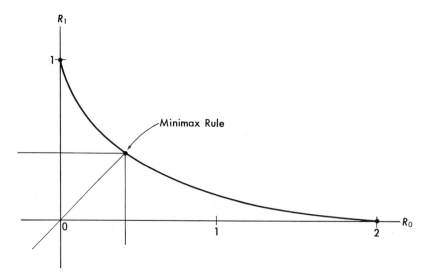

Figure 8-4   Likelihood ratio rules for Example 8-n.

The minimax principle is pessimistic, in that for each action it essentially asks what is the worst that can happen, and then minimizes that worst. It assumes that the statistician is playing a game with nature, and that nature is consciously trying to outsmart him. Aside from this feature, which makes the minimax principle somewhat unattractive—especially when the most un-favorable state of nature against which it guards may well be in some sense far-fetched or unlikely—minimax procedures are not often easy to determine, particularly when more than two states of nature are involved. However, there is a relation between determining a minimax procedure and the problem of "linear programming"; the simplex technique of linear programming has been used to compute minimax solutions to statistical decision problems, a matter that is discussed, for instance, in *Statistical Decision Theory*, by L. Weiss (McGraw-Hill, 1961).

Problems

8-17. Referring to Problem 8-7, with two states of nature, two actions, and three possible values of a decision variable X, list all of the possible decision rules. Given zero losses for the correct action and losses of 1 for the incorrect actions, plot the point (R_0, R_1) corresponding to each rule, where R_i is the risk under state $f_i(x)$. Observe the location of the likelihood ratio rules as determined in Problem 8-7.

8-18. Determine the minimax rule for Problem 8-17. Determine also the mini-max rule for the modified problem in which the type I error is three times as costly as the type II error.

8-19. Determine the minimax critical region for Problem 8-6, assuming zero losses for correct actions and losses of 1 for incorrect actions.

8-20. Compute $R(p, d_i)$ for $i = 1, 3, 4, 5, 7, 8$ for the problem of Example 8-l. For each such risk, find a p-value such that the risk exceeds 1—except for $R(p, d_8)$, which is identically 1. What can you then conclude about the minimax rule?

8-21. Determine the minimax rule for the problem of Example 8-n, but modified so that the losses for incorrect actions are equal.

8.6 Bayesian inference

Another device for assigning a measure of goodness to decision rules, so that a "best" rule can be chosen, is that of weighting the states of nature according to one's prior convictions or beliefs. The *Bayes risk* for a rule d is then the "expected" risk—an average computed with respect to the prior weights:

$$B(d) = \sum_{\theta} R(\theta, d)g(\theta),$$

where $R(\theta, d)$ is the risk using Rule d when nature is in state θ and $g(\theta)$ is the weight assigned to θ. (If the set of state of nature is not discrete, weights have to be assigned according to a density function, and the averaging carried out by integration.) Having thus assigned a single number $B(d)$ to each rule d one selects the rule with the *smallest* Bayes risk; this is called a *Bayes procedure*, corresponding to the assumed prior weighting $g(\theta)$.

The weights $g(\theta)$ are often thought of as probabilities (in which case they are normalized to total 1), and are said to describe the *prior distribution* of θ, which implies that θ is conceived of as random. This does not mean that nature is believed to be accidental, but rather that a probabilistic model for partial knowledge or beliefs about the unknown state of nature is useful in devising a rational rule for behavior. The probability $g(\theta)$ assigned to the state θ would naturally be quite personal or subjective—different people would have different $g(\theta)$'s, leading them to different choices of a decision rule. (But surely a rule that is rational for one person's experience is not necessarily so for another's.)

EXAMPLE 8-o. Consider again the simple table of risks, with two states of nature, given in Example 8-m and repeated below. If one assumes a prior distribution that assigns weights .4 to θ_1 and .6 to θ_2, the average risk for each action is just

$$E[R(\theta, d)] = .4R(\theta_1, d) + .6R(\theta_2, d).$$

These are shown as entries in the last row of the table. The smallest of these is 1.2, obtained by using d_2, which is then the Bayes rule corresponding to the given prior distribution.

	d_1	d_2	d_3	d_4	d_5
θ_1	2	3	4	1	0
θ_2	5	0	1	2	4
Av.	3.8	1.2	2.2	1.6	2.4

Again a graphical plot is helpful, in terms of the (R_1, R_2) representation introduced in Example 8-m. It is desired to minimize $.4R_1 + .6R_2$, and points for which this combination is equal to a given constant K lie on a line, $.4R_1 + .6R_2 = K$, with slope $-2/3$. And the larger the K the higher the line, so what is wanted is the point among those representing the available rules that lies on the member of this family of lines corresponding to the smallest K, that is, the point on the lowest line. This can be thought of as being obtained by moving a line with slope $-2/3$

up from below the set of rules until it first strikes one; that one is the Bayes rule, as illustrated in Figure 8-5. The effect of using different priors, each of which determines a slope for a family of lines, can easily be studied from the figure. In particular, observe that d_1 and d_3 could not be Bayes solutions for any prior distribution.

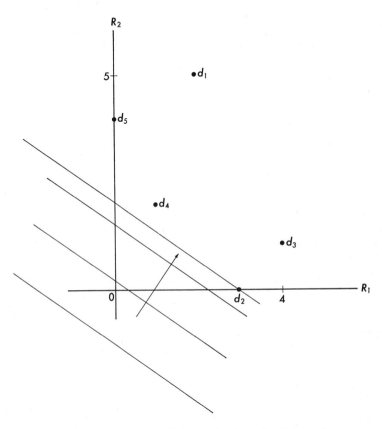

Figure 8-5   Geometrical determination of a Bayes rule.

EXAMPLE 8-p.   The decision problem of Example 8-1 is one in which a prior distribution is rather natural. That is, the lot proportion defective p is $M/100$, where M is the number of defectives among 100; this number may well be thought of as the number of "successes" in 100 trials, where each trial consists of producing one flash bulb. Thus, for instance, if the production process is "in control" with a probability .1 that a given flash bulb is defective, the number defective in a lot of 100 would be binomially distributed (100, 0.1), or approximately Poisson with mean 10. Then $E(M) = 10$, $E(M^2) = 110$, and $E(M^3) = 1310$. From these, one can compute the expected values of p, p^2, and p^3 with respect to the prior

220   *Selection of Procedures* [*Ch. 8*]

distribution, and can therewith average $R(p, d)$ with respect to the distribution on p. For instance, $R(p, d_1) = 15(2p - 1)$, and so $ER(p, d_1) = 15(2 \times .1 - 1) = -12$, a gain of \$12. On the other hand, $R(p, d_8) = 1$, so $ER(p, d_8) = 1$, a loss of \$1; so with the given prior distribution, selling (no matter what X is) is a better rule than junking (no matter what X is). But the minimax rule is to junk for all X.

Problems

8-22. Referring to Example 8-o, the risk table for a decision problem is as follows:

	d_1	d_2	d_3	d_4	d_5
θ_1	2	3	4	1	0
θ_2	5	0	1	2	4

Assume a prior distribution with probabilities $g(\theta_1) = \gamma$ and $g(\theta_2) = 1 - \gamma$ and compute the expected risk for each rule d_i as a function of γ. Plot these five functions of γ on a simple graph and note which rule gives the smallest expected risk for each γ ($0 \le \gamma \le 1$). Give the Bayes rule for prior distributions defined by γ according to subintervals of $0 \le \gamma \le 1$. Compare the results with those obtained from the graphical method of Example 8-o.

8-23. Determine the Bayes rules for the decision problem given in Problems 8-7 and 8-17, and verify that they are precisely the likelihood ratio rules.

8-24. Assuming equal prior probabilities for $\mu = 0$ and $\mu = 1$, determine the Bayes critical region for Problem 8-6, observing first that only the likelihood ratio rules will be Bayes. Assume zero losses for correct actions and equal (positive) losses for incorrect actions.

8-25. Determine the Bayes critical region for the testing problem in Example 8-n corresponding to prior probabilities $g(H_0) = g(H_1) = 1/2$. [Notice first that only regions of the form $\bar{X} > K$ would be Bayes, and then use the fact that the locus of the points $(2\alpha, \beta)$ for such regions has slope $-\Phi'(K - 1)/\Phi'(-K)$, where $\Phi'(x)$ is $\phi(x)$ as given in Example 4c, page 101.]

8.7 Posterior distributions

In the model in which the state of nature is considered random it is perhaps consistent to use capital theta for this quantity: Θ. The conditional distribution for the data Z, given the state of nature, and the prior distribution of the state of nature together determine the joint distribution of Z and Θ:

$$P(\Theta = \theta \text{ and } Z = z) = f(z|\theta)\, g(\theta),$$

and the "marginal" distribution of Z is obtained by summing this over the values of Θ:

$$P(Z = z) = \sum_{\theta} f(z|\theta) g(\theta).$$

(This is different from the probability assigned to $Z = z$ in the conditional distribution given the state of nature.) The conditional distribution of Θ given $Z = z$ is called the *posterior distribution*, defined by

$$h(\theta|z) = P(\Theta = \theta|Z = z) = \frac{P(\Theta = \theta \text{ and } Z = z)}{P(Z = z)}$$

$$= \frac{f(z|\theta) g(\theta)}{\sum_{\theta} f(z|\theta) g(\theta)}.$$

(This shift from a conditional probability given θ to a conditional probability given z is essentially what is called Bayes' theorem.)

So the information in the data Z can be thought of as a means intelligently altering one's prior beliefs about the state of nature to those expressed by the posterior probabilities.

EXAMPLE 8-q. Consider the probability distributions under states θ_0 and θ_1 for a decision variable Y which can take on values 0, 1, 2 as given in the following table:

	State	
	θ_0	θ_1
$Y = 2$	.49	.01
$Y = 1$	.42	.18
$Y = 0$	.09	.81

(The entry under θ_i and opposite y_j is $f(y_j|\theta_i)$.) Suppose that one has past experience and convictions expressed in prior probabilities $g_0 = .3$ and $g_1 = .7$. Then

$$P(Y = 2) = f(2|\theta_0) g_0 + f(2|\theta_1) g_1$$
$$= .49 \times .3 + .01 \times .7 = .154,$$

and similar computations yield $P(Y = 1) = .252$, $P(Y = 0) = .594$. (Notice that these add to 1.) And then

$$h(\theta_0|2) = \frac{.49 \times .3}{.154} = \frac{21}{22},$$

and

$$h(\theta_1|2) = \frac{.01 \times .7}{.154} = \frac{1}{22}.$$

If $Y = 2$, the prior probability of .3 is increased to a posterior probability of $21/22$. Similar modifications could be computed given $Y = 1$ or $Y = 0$.

Posterior probabilities can be used to simplify the determination of a Bayes rule. Given a loss function $l(\theta, a)$ and corresponding risk function $R(\theta, d)$ for the rule $a = d(z)$, the Bayes risk is

$$
\begin{aligned}
B(d) &= \sum_\theta R(\theta, d) \, g(\theta) \\
&= \sum_\theta \sum_z l(\theta, d(z)) \, g(\theta) f(z|\theta) \\
&= \sum_z \left\{ \sum_\theta l(\theta, d(z)) \, h(\theta|z) \right\} P(Z = z).
\end{aligned}
$$

From this it is clear that to minimize (Bd) it suffices to choose an action a given $Z = z$ such that

$$\sum_\theta l(\theta, a) \, h(\theta|z)$$

is a minimum. That is, the Bayes action given $Z = z$ can be determined by applying the Bayes technique with the posterior distribution and the loss table (rather than with the prior distribution and the risk table). This procedure has the advantage that one need only determine the action appropriate to a value z that is actually observed—rather than prepare the whole decision rule in advance. Mathematically, the simplification is the replacement of minimization with respect to an unknown function $d(z)$ by minimization with respect to a single variable a.

EXAMPLE 8-r.   Continuing the problem of the preceding example, assume a loss table for actions A and B as follows:

	A	B
θ_0	0	4
θ_1	1	0

The expected loss using the posterior probabilities $21/22$ and $1/22$, determined in Example 8-q for θ_0 and θ_1 respectively, is as follows:

$$\text{For action } A: \quad 0 \times \frac{21}{22} + 1 \times \frac{1}{22} = \frac{1}{22},$$

$$\text{For action } B: \quad 4 \times \frac{21}{22} + 0 \times \frac{1}{22} = \frac{82}{22}.$$

Thus, the observation $Y = 2$ which led to these posterior probabilities calls for action A according to the principle of Bayes, since action A has the smaller expected posterior loss.

8.8 Bayes estimates

In estimation problems, in which one's "action" is to choose (for an announcement) one of the states of nature, a frequently used loss function is quadratic:

$$l(\theta, a) = (\theta - a)^2,$$

where θ is the actual parameter value being estimated and a is the value announced. A Bayes estimate would be obtained by minimizing this loss function with respect to the posterior distribution on the state of nature, that is, by minimizing:

$$E(\Theta - a)^2 = \sum_\theta (\theta - a)^2 h(\theta|x),$$

where h denotes the posterior probability of state θ when the observation $X = x$ is obtained from a sample. But this is simply the second moment of a random variable Θ about a number a, which is known to be minimized when that number a is the mean value of θ. Thus, the Bayes estimate of θ is the mean of the posterior distribution:

$$a = E(\Theta) = \sum_\theta \theta\, h(\theta|x).$$

EXAMPLE 8-S. It is desired to estimate M, the number of white beads in a container with 10 beads, some white and some black, on the basis of X, the number of white beads in a random selection of two from the container. Suppose that two beads are selected and it is observed that one is white, that is, $X = 1$. Suppose further that the prior distribution assumed for M is that $P(M = 0) = P(M = 1) = 1/2$, as might be the case if white beads are symbolic of defective items in a production process of high quality. Then, since

$$f(x|m) = P(X = x|M = m) = \begin{cases} \dfrac{(10 - m)(9 - m)}{90}, & \text{if } x = 0, \\[2mm] \dfrac{2m(10 - m)}{90}, & \text{if } x = 1, \\[2mm] \dfrac{m(m - 1)}{90}. & \text{if } x = 2, \end{cases}$$

it follows that

$$P(X = 1) = 0 \cdot P(M = 0) + \frac{1}{5} P(M = 1) = \frac{1}{10}.$$

The posterior probabilities are the ratios of the terms in this sum to the sum, namely, $h(0|1) = 0$ and $h(1|1) = 1$; thus, if the only prior possibilities are $M = 0$ and $M = 1$, the observation $X = 1$ rules out $M = 0$ as impossible. If, on the other hand, the selection of two contains *no* white beads, the appropriate probability is

$$P(X = 0) = 1 \cdot P(M = 0) + \frac{8}{10} P(M = 1) = \frac{9}{10},$$

and the posterior probabilities are

$$h(0|0) = \frac{1 \cdot \frac{1}{2}}{9/10} = \frac{5}{9} \quad \text{and} \quad h(1|0) = \frac{\frac{8}{9} \cdot \frac{1}{2}}{9/10} = \frac{4}{9}.$$

The Bayes estimate of M is then its expected value with respect to this posterior distribution:

$$0 \cdot \frac{5}{9} + 1 \cdot \frac{4}{9} = \frac{4}{9}.$$

EXAMPLE 8-t. Suppose that it is desired to estimate a Bernoulli parameter p on the basis of three independent trials, and suppose further that two successes are observed in the three trials. If one assumes a "uniform" prior distribution for p, that is, a constant density $g(p) = 1$ for $0 \le p \le 1$, the absolute probability of two successes is obtained by averaging

$$f(x|p) = 3p^2(1 - p)$$

with respect to that constant density:

$$f(x) = \int_0^1 f(x|p) \, g(p) \, dp = \int_0^1 3p^2(1 - p) \cdot 1 \, dp = 1/4.$$

The posterior density of p is then

$$h(p|2) = f(x|p) \, g(p)/f(x) = 12p^2(1 - p).$$

The Bayes estimate of p is the mean of p with respect to this posterior density:

$$E(p) = \int_0^1 p \, h(p|2) \, dp = \int_0^1 12p^3(1 - p) \, dp = 3/5.$$

Problems

8-26. Compute the posterior distributions corresponding to $Y = 0$ and $Y = 1$ for Example 8-q. What are the corresponding Bayes actions, using the loss table of Example 8-r?

8-27. Compute $h(\theta|z)$ for the prior distribution that assigns probability 1 to θ_1 and probability 0 to all other θ's. (And so show that prior convictions amounting to certainty are not changed by data.)

8-28. Suppose that $f(z_i|\theta) = a_i$, the same for all θ. Show that $h(\theta|z_i) = g(\theta)$. (A prior distribution is unaltered by data that have nothing to do with the state of nature.)

8-29. Referring to the estimation problem of Example 8-s, determine the Bayes estimate of M given the observation $X = 2$ and the prior distribution that is uniform (equal probabilities) on $M = 0, 1, 2, 3$, and zero for $M \geq 4$.

8-30.† Referring to Example 8-t, determine the Bayes estimates of p corresponding to each of $X = 0, 1, 3$ where X is the number of successes in three independent trials.

† Requires calculus.

9

SOME NONPARAMETRIC

PROCEDURES

Most of the problems studied thus far have involved parametric families—families of distributions indexed by a finite number (one or two, in the examples considered) of real parameters. Procedures for these problems, called *parametric* procedures, are appropriate as long as one can be sure that the possible states of nature can be indexed in this way and knows the form of the distribution except for the values of the parameters. However, it is certainly desirable to have procedures that are valid when this much is *not* known about the state of nature.

Nonparametric problems of hypothesis testing frequently involve null hypotheses that are composite; in some cases in which the null hypothesis is simple, this null distribution may be a particular one of a large class of distributions. In either case, to be useful a procedure should be based on a statistic whose distribution does not depend on the particular null distribution that may be governing or that is tested. Such a statistic is said to be *distribution-free*, and when one uses procedures based on such statistics, a single table suffices for determining a critical level from a given α, no matter which particular null distribution may be true.

Mention of power characteristics will be minimal, primarily because the study of power is quite complex, and frequently can be done only empirically, owing to the highly composite nature of the class of alternatives.

226

In this chapter are presented some nonparametric procedures that are commonly employed in dealing with problems of comparing locations, randomness, and goodness-of-fit.

9.1 The population median

The median of a probability distribution is in a sense a parameter of the distribution, one that relates to the location of the distribution on the axis of values; but it is not commonly used to index the family of states of nature that are admitted in a given problem, and so the term nonparametric might be considered appropriate.

For some continuous distributions the median is uniquely defined, and it is ordinarily in this case that the median is useful. If X has a unique median, the median is that number m such that

$$P(X > m) = P(X < m) = 1/2.$$

Observations on X can be classed according to whether they fall to the left or to the right of the median, thus defining a Bernoulli distribution (say, 1 if X falls to the left and 0 if to the right) with parameter $p = .5$. The variable that is 1 or 0 according as X falls to the left or right of any *other* given value is similarly of the Bernoulli type, but with a p that is different from .5. And then the number of observations that fall to one side of that given value is binomially distributed, a convenient statistic related to the location of the distribution of X.

Suppose then that it is desired to test $m = m_0$. The number of observations to the left of m_0 is binomial with $p = .5$ if m_0 is actually the median—if H_0 is true, and binomial with some other p if m_0 is not the median. The critical region used would depend on the alternative; if the alternative is $m \neq m_0$, a critical region consisting of too many or too few observations to the left of m_0 is appropriate, since an equivalent formulation of this alternative is $p \neq .5$. Similarly, the alternative $m > m_0$ is equivalent to $p < .5$, and the null hypothesis that $p = .5$ is rejected if there are too few observations to the left of the value m_0.

If Y denotes the number of observations to the left of m_0, the critical region $Y \leq K$, say, has the power function:

$$\pi(p) = P(Y \leq K|p) = \sum_{i=0}^{K} \binom{n}{i} p^i (1 - p)^{n-i},$$

where n is the number of observations in the sample and $p = P(X < m_0)$. For large samples this can be approximated by using the normal distribution.

EXAMPLE 9-a. In testing the hypothesis that the median m of a continuous distribution is 32 against the alternative that $m \neq 32$ it is decided to reject $m = 32$ if more than fifteen or less than five observations out of twenty are greater than 32. This critical region has, under the null hypothesis, the probability

$$\left[\binom{20}{0} + \cdots + \binom{20}{4} + \binom{20}{16} + \cdots + \binom{20}{20}\right]\left(\frac{1}{2}\right)^{20} = .012.$$

This is α, or the significance level of the test. Given the following twenty observations (taken again from Table 5.2)

37.0, 31.4, 34.4, 33.3, 34.9, 31.6, 31.6, 31.3, 34.6, 32.6,
36.2, 31.0, 33.5, 33.7, 33.4, 33.4, 32.1, 33.3, 32.7, 31.5,

one finds fourteen of them greater than 32, not significantly different from ten (the expected number) to call for rejection of $m = 32$ at $\alpha = .012$. Sometimes the data are transformed into plus and minus signs according as an observation is greater or less than the value tested (here $m = 32$):

+ − + + + − − − + +
+ − + + + + + + + −

The test statistic can then be thought of as the number of plus signs, and the test is sometimes called a *sign test*.

A confidence interval for the population median can be constructed as follows. Let $X_{(1)}, \ldots, X_{(n)}$ denote the observations in a random sample arranged in *numerical* order (rather than in the order drawn). Then if $r < s$,

$P(X_{(r)} < m < X_{(s)})$

$= P(\text{exactly } r \text{ or } r + 1 \text{ or} \cdots \text{or } s - 1 \text{ observations are } \leq m)$

$$= \sum_{k=r}^{s-1} \binom{n}{k}\left(\frac{1}{2}\right)^n.$$

Thus, the random interval from the rth observation to the sth, in numerical order, is a confidence interval for m with confidence coefficient given by the above sum of binomial probabilities.

EXAMPLE 9-b. In the case of twenty observations, the interval from the fourth to the sixteenth observation in order will include m with probability .993, according to the calculation in the preceding example. For the twenty observations given in that example, $X_{(4)} = 31.5$, and $X_{(16)} = 34.6$. These are 99.3 percent confidence limits.

Problems

9-1. In a certain table of "random normal numbers" constructed by sampling from a population with expectation 2 and variance 1, it is found that 88 out of 150 entries are larger than 2. Would you accept $\mu = 2$ on this basis? [Note: The mean and median of a symmetric population coincide, so tests about μ can be thought of as about the median.]

9-2. Compute the size of type I error for the rule that rejects $H_0 : m = 20$ in favor of $H_1 : m > 20$ if more than eight out of ten observations are larger than twenty. Determine the power function of the test, and from it the probability that H_0 is accepted when $p = P(X > 20) = 2/3$.

9-3. Determine the probability that m is included between the fortieth and sixtieth observations, in numerical order, of a random sample of 100 observations.

9.2   The sign test

If independent random variables X and Y have identical continuous distributions, the probability that an observation from one exceeds an observation from the other is one-half:

$$P(Y > X) = 1/2.$$

If the distributions are not identical, this probability is generally not equal to $1/2$, but is some other number between 0 and 1, say, p. The number of times in a sequence of independent pairs $(X_1, Y_1), \ldots, (X_n, Y_n)$ the second observation exceeds the first is then binomially distributed with parameters n and p. This number is often counted by recording a plus sign $(+)$ when $Y_i > X_i$ and a minus sign $(-)$ when $Y_i < X_i$ and counting the number of plus signs; hence, the name *sign test* for testing the hypothesis of identical distributions by testing $p = 1/2$. Tests concerning the value of p in a Bernoulli population by using the binomially distributed sample sum were discussed in detail in Chapter 4. (Observe that the test of the preceding section concerning the population median was also reduced to the Bernoulli problem and is also a sign test.)

It is important to observe that the distribution of the test statistic is not dependent on the distributions of X and Y and is therefore "distribution-free."

Application of the sign tests requires a single sample of pairs—paired data; and if the data are not naturally paired, the linking of the ith X with the ith Y provides a pairing when the X's and the Y's each form a random sample. It is not necessary, however, that within each pair the X and Y be independent; the test can be used in comparing twins, or right- and left-hand characteristics in an individual, or two sides of a tire, and so on. All that is required is that $P(Y > X)$ remain fixed from pair to pair and that the pairs be independent.

EXAMPLE 9-c.   In the following table, the first twenty observations from Table 5.2 are taken as a sample $(X_1, \ldots, X_{20})$ from one population and the last twenty as a sample ($Y_1, \ldots, Y_{20}$) from a possibly different population. If the alternative to $P(X < Y) = 1/2$ is $P(X < Y) < 1/2$, the appropriate test is to reject the null hypothesis of identical distributions if there are too few plus signs. If "too few" means, say, fewer than six, the type I error size of this test is

$$P(\text{fewer than 6 plus signs} \mid p = 1/2) \doteq \Phi\left(\frac{5.5 - 10}{\sqrt{5}}\right) = .022.$$

Since there is in fact just one plus sign in the following table, the hypothesis of identical populations is rejected at $\alpha = .022$.

X_i	Y_i	Sign of $Y_i - X_i$
37.0	31.0	−
31.4	31.3	−
34.4	30.7	−
33.3	32.8	−
34.9	30.6	−
36.2	30.0	−
31.0	29.5	−
33.5	30.8	−
33.7	31.3	−
33.4	31.3	−
34.8	29.2	−
30.8	29.0	−
32.9	31.6	−
34.3	31.4	−
33.3	30.6	−
34.5	32.5	−
30.0	30.3	+
32.8	32.7	−
35.9	30.7	−
32.4	31.7	−

In some instances, such as in the above example, a *t*-test can be used if the populations can be assumed to be normal (and to have equal variances). When it is applicable, a *t*-test is generally more efficient than a sign test; however, the sign test is much simpler to apply and has the distinct advantage of not requiring the assumption of normality. (It might be mentioned that if the data come paired so that the X's and Y's do not by themselves form random samples, the number of degrees of freedom of the *t*-statistic is $n - 1$, since the differences constitute a sample of size n from the population $Y - X$, rather than the $m + n - 2$ used in comparing two samples.)

Although if the population distributions are continuous the probability of a *tie* ($X_i = Y_i$) is zero, ties do occur in practice because of round-off. The best procedure for treating ties seems to be to ignore tied pairs and to base the test on only those pairs of observations in which there is a discernible difference. With this understanding, there is no harm in allowing the populations to be discrete; under the null hypothesis the probability of $Y > X$ would equal the probability of $Y < X$ but would be less than 1/2. However, the conditional probabilities are 1/2:

$$P(Y > X \mid Y \neq X) = P(Y < X \mid Y \neq X) = 1/2$$

under the null hypothesis.

An important situation in which populations are discrete is that in which one compares individuals from the two populations without making a numerical measurement. This is illustrated in the following example.

EXAMPLE 9-d.   Two dozen tomatoes of variety A and two dozen of variety B are selected at random and compared in pairs as to the quality (pulpiness, taste, and so on). Suppose that there are six ties and that variety A scores higher than variety B in thirteen of the remaining eighteen pairs. The probability of five or fewer minus signs or five or fewer plus signs is (using the binomial formula) about .096. Hence, the given result would call for rejection of equality of the varieties at the 10 percent significance level, against the alternative that there is a difference. If the alternative had been that variety A is of better quality than variety B, a one-sided test would be appropriate; and the test which calls for rejection of equal qualities when thirteen or more plus signs out of eighteen occur has an α of .048.

Problems

9-4.   Apply the sign test to the data of Problem 7-27.

9-5.   To compare two alloys with respect to resistance to corrosion, pipes are buried in pairs, one of each alloy, to avoid the influencing of results by differences in composition of the earth—extraneous factors are different from pair to pair but the same for each pair. Out of 50 such pairs, it is decided (after inspection following a period of time) that alloy 1 showed more resistance in 17 of the pairs and alloy 2 showed more resistance in 12 of the pairs. (In the remaining pairs they were judged to be of about equal resistance.) Test the hypothesis that the alloys are equivalent with respect to corrosion against the hypothesis that alloy 1 is superior.

9-6.   Test the hypothesis of no change using a two-sided critical region with $\alpha = .10$ on the basis of the following data from populations A and B:

A. $+4, +1, +6, -1, -1, -1, -2, +3, -4, +4, -1, 0, +6, 0, -2, 0,$
$+5, -2, 0, -3, -3, -1, -3, 0, -2, 0, -2, -7, -4, -1, -2, +1,$
$+3, +3, +1, +1, -5, +6, +2, +1$

B. $+2, -3, +1, 0, -2, -10, +2, +1, 0, -4, +6, 0, -10, -1, +1,$
     $-5, -3, -3, -3, 0, +1, -1, -5, +3, 0, -1, +3, 0, +4, +5, -2,$
     $0, -1, +4, -2, +1, -9, +1, +4, +1$

9-7.   Determine the power function (as a function of p, the probability that
$Y > X$) for the test that rejects identical distributions if fewer than two or more
than eight of ten comparisons result in $+$.

9.3   The median test

Another nonparametric test for a difference in locations is the *median test*.
The observations from the two samples, one from X and one from Y, are
arranged in numerical order, and the median of the combined data is determined. When the populations are identical, one would expect roughly as
many observations from X and observations from Y on each side of the
median; and the occurrence of too much unbalance in this pattern is taken
as evidence that the populations are not identical. To interpret "too much
unbalance" it is necessary to know the probability distribution of the possible
patterns under the null hypothesis of identical populations.

Suppose that the samples are of size m from X and of size n from Y, and
(for convenience) that $m + n = 2a$, an even number. There are then exactly
a observations on each side of the median of the combined sample when the
populations are assumed to be continuous. The test statistic Z is the number
of observations from X among the a observations to the left of the median.
(It could equally well be the number of observations from Y to the left, or
observations from X to the right, or observations from Y to the right; any
of these four numbers determines the other three.)

Under the null hypothesis the combined sample can be thought of as a
single sample of size $2a$ from the common population, and the same set of
ordered observations used in determining the median could have been
obtained from any of $(2a)!$ different such combined samples, corresponding
to the $(2a)!$ orderings of $2a$ distinct objects. It can be shown that these $(2a)!$
samples are equally likely to have produced a given set of ordered observations; so to compute the probability that $Z = k$ it is only necessary to count
the number of those $(2a)!$ arrangements in which $Z = k$ and divide by $(2a)!$.
(This is actually a conditional probability, given the ordered observations;
but since it is the same for any given set of ordered observations, it is also an
absolute probability.) To make an arrangement of $(2a)!$ observations in
which exactly k from X are to the left of the median, one can first pick k of
the m X's and $a - k$ of the n Y's and then arrange the a numbers to the left

and the remaining a numbers to the right of the median; this can be done in $\binom{m}{k}\binom{n}{a-k}a!a!$ ways. The desired probability is then

$$\frac{\binom{m}{k}\binom{n}{a-k}a!a!}{(2a)!} = \frac{\binom{m}{k}\binom{n}{a-k}}{\binom{2a}{a}}.$$

So Z has a hypergeometric distribution, under H_0, and from this one can determine the relation between the critical region and the size of the type I

Table 9.1   Data for Example 9-e (below)

Sample 1	Sample 2
37.0	
36.2	
35.9	
34.9	
34.8	
34.5	
34.4	
34.3	
33.7	
33.5	
33.4	
33.3, 33.3	
32.9	
32.8	32.8
	32.7
	32.5
32.4	
	31.7

—Overall median

Sample 1	Sample 2
	31.6
31.4	31.4
	31.3, 31.3, 31.3
31.0	31.0
30.8	30.8
	30.7, 30.7
	30.6, 30.6
	30.3
30.0	30.0
	29.5
	29.2
	29.0

error. (The hypergeometric distribution is approximately normal for large samples, and a rule of thumb says to use this approximation if the variance of the distribution exceeds 9.)

EXAMPLE 9-e.   Given above are the data used in Example 9-c, only this time arranged in numerical order. Let Z denote the number of observations in sample 2 to the right of the median. The critical region $Z \leq 7$ (appropriate in protecting for an alternative that says that population 1 is to the right of population 2) has the following probability under the null hypothesis:

$$\sum_{0}^{7} \binom{20}{k} \binom{20}{20-k} \bigg/ \binom{40}{20} = .056.$$

With this as size of type I error, the data calls for rejection of the null hypothesis, since $Z = 4$.

9.4   The Wilcoxon-Mann-Whitney test

Again consider independent random samples $(X_1, \ldots, X_m)$ and $(Y_1, \ldots, Y_n)$ for testing the null hypothesis of identical populations against the alternative of a shift in location. After arranging the observations in numerical order in a combined sample, identification of the observations, according to the sample they came from, yields a sequence of X's and Y's. In this sequence, one *inversion* is counted for each X that precedes a given Y in the sequence, and the statistic on which the test is to be based is the total number of inversions for the n Y's. This number can also be counted as follows; for each pair of observations (X_i, Y_j) define

$$Z_{ij} = \begin{cases} 1, & \text{if } X_i < Y_j; \\ 0, & \text{if } X_i > Y_j, \end{cases}$$

and let

$$U = \sum_{i=1}^{m} \sum_{j=1}^{n} Z_{.j}.$$

Under the null hypotheses, Z_{ij} is a Bernoulli variable with $p = 1/2$, and hence

$$EU = \sum_{i=1}^{m} \sum_{j=1}^{n} EZ_{ij} = \frac{mn}{2}.$$

It can also be shown that U is asymptotically normal, and that the variance of U is

$$\text{var } U = mn(m + n + 1)/12.$$

Knowing U is equivalent to knowing the *rank sums*: Let each of the observations be assigned ranks according to their position in the combined set of ordered observations, the smallest being assigned rank 1, the next smallest rank 2, and so forth. If the smallest Y_j has rank r_1, there are $r_1 - 1$ corresponding inversions; if the rank of the next smallest Y_j is r_2, there are $r_2 - 2$ corresponding inversions, and so on, so that

$$U = (r_1 - 1) + \cdots + (r_n - n) = \sum_{j=1}^{n} r_j - n(n + 1)/2.$$

Thus, with R_y denoting the *sum* of the Y-ranks r_j,

$$R_y = U_y + n(n + 1)/2.$$

(U_y, of course, is the total number of inversions for the Y's.) And similarly,

$$R_x = U_x + m(m + 1)/2.$$

Notice that

$$ER_x = EU_x + m(m + 1)/2 = [mn + m(m + 1)]/2,$$

and that

$$\text{var } R_x = \text{var } U_x.$$

If the alternative hypothesis is that the X and Y distributions are not identical, the null hypothesis is rejected if U_y (or R_y, or U_x, or R_x) is either too large or too small. If the X distribution is to the right of the Y distribution, the X values tend to appear to the right of the Y values, and U_x is then large; for such an alternative, reject H_0 if U_x exceeds a value depending on the significance level. These tests are especially sensitive to differences in *location*, as opposed to differences in variability.

Table VIII, page 278, gives rejection limits for sample sizes up to 10. They are given as lower rejection limits, so that, for example, if H_1 is that the X distribution is to the right of the Y distribution (which would tend to make U_y small), the test would reject H_0 if U_y is less than or equal to the indicated rejection limit. The same table can be used to obtain two-sided rejection limits, the upper limit being mn minus the lower rejection limit, provided the level is doubled.

The statistic U (either U_x or U_y) is asymptotically normal, and the probability distribution of the standardized statistic (with a continuity correction thrown in)

$$Z = \frac{U + 1/2 - mn/2}{\sqrt{mn(m + n + 1)/12}}$$

is approximately the standard normal distribution for large m and n. At the point where Table VIII leaves off the approximation is only fair, and a better approximation† to $P(U \leq u)$ is given by

$$\Phi(z) - \frac{m^2 + n^2 + mn + m + n}{20mn(m + n + 1)} \phi^{(3)}(z),$$

where $\Phi(z)$ is given in Table I, $\phi^{(3)}(z)$ is the third derivative‡ of the standard normal density, and z comes from u in the same way as Z is given in terms of U above.

Because of round-off, ties can occur (in ordering the x and y values) even though the populations of interest are continuous. It is customary to use a randomization process in such cases—pick an order at random from the possible ones. The effect of this is involved, and it will not be discussed here.

EXAMPLE 9-f.   Five observations are taken from X and four from Y. According to Table VIII,

$$P(2 < U < 18 \mid H_0) = .936,$$

where U could be either U_x or U_y. Thus, the rejection region consisting of U values exceeding 17 or less than 3 has a type I error size of 6.4 percent.

Given the observations

$$10, 15, 13, 17, 8 \text{ (from } X), \quad \text{and} \quad 16, 12, 9, 11 \text{ (from } Y),$$

the combined sequence of ordered observations is

$$8, 9, 10, 11, 12, 13, 15, 16, 17,$$

or, noting only which numbers came from X and which from Y:

$$X, Y, X, Y, Y, X, X, Y, X.$$

There are $1 + 3 + 3 + 4 = 11$ inversions of the X's and the rank sum of the X's is $1 + 3 + 6 + 7 + 9 = 26 = 11 + 5 \times 6/2$. Since the number of inversions is between two and eighteen, the null hypothesis of no difference is accepted at $\alpha = .064$.

EXAMPLE 9-g.   From the tabulation in Example 9-e one can easily compute the number of inversions. For sample 1 it is about 354, depending on how ties are broken. The expected number is

$$mn/2 = 400/2 = 200,$$

---

† See "Significance Probabilities of the Wilcoxon Test," *Annals of Math. Stat.*, XXVI (1955), 301–312, by E. Fix and J. L. Hodges, Jr.

‡ Available, for instance, in the *Mathematical Tables from Handbook of Chemistry and Physics*, Chemical Rubber Publishing Co.

and the variance is

$$mn(m + n + 1)/12 \doteq (37)^2.$$

Thus, 354 corresponds to

$$Z = \frac{354 - 200}{37} \doteq 4,$$

calling for rejection of the null hypothesis even at $\alpha = .01$, and whether the alternative is one or two-sided. (Notice that the conclusion would not be different if the ties were broken differently).

Problems

9-8. Apply the median test and Wilcoxon-Mann-Whitney test to the data of Problem 7-27.

9-9. Apply the median test and Wilcoxon-Mann-Whitney test to the data of Problem 9-6.

9-10. The following observations were obtained from the same process from which those labeled A in Problem 9-6 were obtained. Test the hypothesis that there has not been a shift in population center after the first forty observations

   (a) using the sign test (necessarily discarding twenty of the forty observations so that the rest can be paired);
   (b) using the median test;
   (c) using the Mann-Whitney test.

$$3, \; -1, \; 6, \; -7, \; 1, \; 1, \; 3, \; -8, \; 3, \; 3, \; 1, \; 9, \; -4, \; 1, \; 0, \; 1, \; 2, \; 5, \; 6, \; -1$$

9.5   Testing goodness-of-fit

For testing the hypothesis

H_0:   The population distribution function is $F_0(x)$

against the alternative

H_1:   The population distribution function is not $F_0(x)$,

two tests will be given. Notice that although the hypothesis H_0 (often called the "null hypothesis") is simple, the alternative H_1 is quite composite—there is an endless number of distribution functions that are not the same as the null distribution, $F_0(x)$. Thus, although the size of the type I error is uniquely defined for a given test:

$$\alpha = P(\text{reject } H_0 \mid H_0 \text{ is true}),$$

the probability that H_0 is rejected under H_1 depends on which of the multitude of alternative distributions is assumed.

The *Kolmogorov-Smirnov test* is based on the sample distribution function $F_n(x)$, defined in Section 5.3; the statistic used is the maximum absolute deviation of $F_n(x)$ from $F_0(x)$:

$$D_n = \max_{-\infty < x < \infty} |F_n(x) - F_0(x)|.$$

(To be mathematically accurate, the word "sup"—for *supremum* or least upper bound—should be used in place of "max," but it is not assumed that the reader is aware of this fine point.) The distribution of the random variable D_n, which is indeed a statistic and varies from sample to sample, has been computed under the assumption that the null hypothesis holds. The results are given in Table VI for sample sizes up to $n = 20$, for various preselected values of α, called *significance levels*. It happens that the distribution does not depend on what $F_0(x)$ is, so the same table can be used in all such problems. For large values of n there are given asymptotic formulas.

The test is defined by a critical region of the type $D_n >$ constant; that is, $F_0(x)$ is rejected if the sample distribution function differs from it (in the sense defined by D_n) by too much. Since

$$P(D_n > k) = 1 - F_{D_n}(k),$$

it follows that the table entry under, say, $\alpha = .10$ is really the ninetieth percentile of the distribution of D_n under H_0.

EXAMPLE 9-h.   Consider the ten observations: 31.0, 31.4, 33.3, 33.4, 33.5, 33.7, 34.4, 34.9, 36.2 (which happen to be the first ten observations in Table 5.2). The corresponding sample distribution function is sketched in Figure 9-1 along with the normal distribution whose mean is 32 and whose standard deviation is 1.8. To test the hypothesis that the population distribution is normal with $\mu = 32$ and $\sigma = 1.8$, the maximum deviation between the two curves is determined; it is

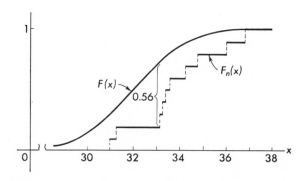

Figure 9-1   Sample distribution function for Example 9-h.

about .56, as shown on the graph. In Table VI the 95th percentile of D_{10} is seen to be .409; so the test with $\alpha = .05$ rejects the given null distribution.

Although the power of the Kolmogorov-Smirnov test is not easily studied, because of the number of possible alternatives to $F_0(x)$, a lower bound for power has been obtained in terms of the maximum (vertical) distance between $F_0(x)$ and the alternative distribution function being considered. This distance is defined as follows:

$$\Delta = \Delta(F_0, F) = \max_{-\infty < x < \infty} |F(x) - F_0(x)|.$$

(Again "sup" is more appropriate.) Figure 9-2 shows two curves giving the lower bound of the power, one for $\alpha = .05$ and the other for $\alpha = .01$.

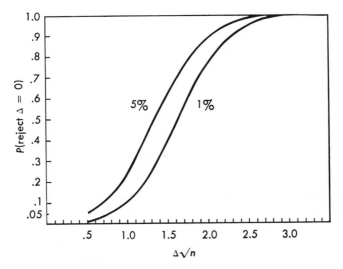

Figure 9-2 Lower bounds for power of *K-S* test. Reproduced from "The Kolmogorov-Smirnov Test for Goodness of Fit," by F. J. Massey, Jr., *Journal of the American Statistical Association*, 46 (1951), 68–78.

EXAMPLE 9-i.   Suppose it is desired to know how powerful the Kolmogorov-Smirnov test is in detecting the alternative $F_1(x)$, a normal distribution function with mean 34 and standard deviation 1.8, when D_y is computed using the null distribution function $F_0(x)$ of Example 9-h (that is, normal with mean 32 and standard deviation 1.8). Since $F_1(x)$ is congruent to $F_0(x)$ and simply displaced by 2 units, it is clear (sketch the two graphs to see this) that the maximum deviation between them occurs at $x = 33$. At this point,

$$F_0(33) = \Phi\left(\frac{33 - 32}{1.8}\right) = .7107,$$

and

$$F_1(33) = \Phi\left(\frac{33 - 34}{1.8}\right) = .2893.$$

Then $\varDelta = .7107 - .2893 = .4214$. With a sample of size $n = 10$, one enters the graph at $\varDelta\sqrt{10} = 1.33$; the power of the test is then at least about .52, for $\alpha = .05$.

The *chi-square test* of goodness of fit (devised by K. Pearson about 1900) is really a test for a discrete population and is applied to the continuous case through the discrete approximation represented by a frequency distribution for the sample to be used. It is a "large sample" test, in that the distribution of the statistic used is usefully simple only as the sample size becomes infinite— approximated by the case of a "large" sample.

Suppose that an experiment of chance has k possible outcomes, $E_1, E_2, \ldots,$ E_k with probabilities, respectively, $p_1, p_2, \ldots, p_k$ such that $p_1 + \cdots + p_k = 1$. Data resulting from n independent trials of the experiment can be put into the form of frequencies f_1 for $E_1, \ldots,$ and f_k for E_k, where $f_1 + \cdots + f_k = n$. To test the particular distribution represented by given specific probabilities $p_1 = p_{01}, \ldots, p_k = p_{0k}$, the following statistic is used, based on the differences $f_i - np_{0i}$ between the observed and expected frequencies:

$$\chi^2 = \sum_{i=1}^{k} \frac{(f_i - np_{0i})^2}{np_{0i}}.$$

The exact distribution of this statistic is not simple and it depends on the p_0's in the null distribution (H_0); but it was found that this dependence disappears as the sample size becomes infinite, and that the distribution for $n = \infty$ can be computed. It is, when H_0 is true, a "chi-square distribution with $k - 1$ degrees of freedom" and is given in Table II, page 271.

The test for H_0 (that the probabilities of the E_i's are the specified p_0's) against H_1 (that the p_0's are not exactly right) calls for rejection of H_0 if the statistic χ^2 is "too large." That is, the *critical region* (the set of values of a statistic calling for rejection of H_0 under a given rule) is taken to be of the form

$$\chi^2 > \text{const},$$

the constant being chosen to achieve a specified α, or probability of rejecting H_0 when it is true. For a given constant M (called the rejection limit), the corresponding α is as follows:

$$\begin{aligned}\alpha &= P(\text{reject } H_0 \,|\, H_0)\\ &= P(\chi^2 > M \,|\, H_0) = 1 - F_{\chi^2}(M).\end{aligned}$$

So M is the $100(1 - \alpha)$ percentile of the distribution of χ^2, and this is approximated for large samples by the same percentile of the chi-square distribution with $k - 1$ degrees of freedom as given in Table II.

EXAMPLE 9-j. To test the equal likelihood of the six faces of a die, it is cast 120 times, with the following resulting frequencies of the six faces: 18, 23, 16, 21, 18, 24. Is the die "straight"?
The expected frequencies are all 20, and the value of χ^2 is readily computed:

$$\chi^2 = \frac{1}{20} [(18 - 20)^2 + (23 - 20)^2 + \cdots + (24 - 20)^2] = 2.5.$$

Reference to Table II shows the 90th percentile of the chi-square distribution with $6 - 1 = 5$ degrees of freedom to be about 9.2. Since $2.5 < 9.2$, the chi-square test with $\alpha = .10$ calls for acceptance of the hypothesis that the six faces of the die are equally likely.

To apply the test to a continuous population with density $f(x)$ and distribution function $F(x)$, the x-axis is divided into class intervals $E_1, E_2, \ldots, E_k$, reading left to right along the axis. Let $a_0, a_1, \ldots, a_k$ denote the endpoints of the class intervals, in order; the probability of E_i is then

$$p_i = P(a_{i-1} < X < a_i) = \text{Area under } f(x) \text{ between } a_{i-1} \text{ and } a_i$$
$$= F(a_i) - F(a_{i-1}).$$

The probabilities p_{0i} come from the distribution function under H_0; let this be denoted by $F_0(x)$:

$$p_{0i} = F_0(a_i) - F_0(a_{i-1}).$$

The chi-square test then proceeds as described above for the discrete case, to test $p_i = p_{0i}$. Notice that the chi-square test does not test $F_0(x)$ but only the p_0's. In particular, then, the natural order of the class intervals does not enter the test; moreover, F_0 is not the only distribution function having the p_0's obtained from F_0. Yet, despite these minor objections, the chi-square test is frequently used in testing a continuous distribution.

EXAMPLE 9-k. The data given in the frequency tabulation of Table 5.3 can be used to test the hypothesis that the population from which they are taken is normal with mean 32 and standard deviation 1.8 against the alternative hypothesis that this is not the correct population distribution. Necessary computations are given in the following table:

Class interval	p_{0i}	$200p_{0i}$	f_i	$(f_i - 200p_{0i})^2$
< 27.85	.0105	2.10	3	.81
27.85–28.95	.0346	6.92	7	.0064
28.95–30.05	.0943	18.86	25	37.65
30.05–31.15	.1791	35.82	42	38.10
31.15–32.25	.2388	47.76	56	67.9
32.25–33.35	.2161	43.22	30	174.5
33.35–34.45	.1399	27.98	22	35.8
34.45–35.55	.0624	12.48	11	2.19
35.55–36.65	.0195	3.90	3	.81
> 36.65	.0048	.96	1	.0016

To illustrate the computations, the entry .1791 under p_{0i} is obtained from the normal distribution function, Table I:

$$P(30.05 < X < 31.15) = \Phi\left(\frac{31.15 - 32}{1.8}\right) - \Phi\left(\frac{30.05 - 32}{1.8}\right) = .1791.$$

The statistic χ^2 is now obtained by summing the quotients of the entries in the last column by the corresponding entries $200p_{0i}$, with the result $\chi^2 \doteq 10.6$. This does not exceed the 95th percentile of the appropriate chi-square distribution, that is, the one with $10 - 1 = 9$ "degrees of freedom." (According to Table II this percentile is 16.9.) The chi-square test therefore calls for accepting the null distribution on the basis of the given data.

One reason for the popularity of the chi-square test is that it turns out to be readily adaptable to test the composite hypothesis

H_0:   the population density is one of the family $f(x; \theta)$,

where $f(x; \theta)$ is a density depending on a parameter θ which therefore serves to index the family of densities. For instance, one might wish to test the hypothesis that a population is normal (without specifying the mean and variance) against the alternative that it is not normal. Of course the probability p_{0i} of the ith class interval cannot be computed unless the null distribution F_0 is specified completely; what is done is to obtain an "F_0" using the sample, by estimating θ from the sample and using this estimate in $f(x; \theta)$ to determine p_0's for computation of χ^2. Since selecting a null distribution on the basis of the sample tends to make the fit close, one might expect that for a given α the rejection limit should be smaller—he would be more willing to reject H_0 for a given degree of misfit since using the sample has worked to make the fit better. And this turns out to be the case; the asymptotic distribution of χ^2 is again of the chi-square type but with a new parameter—the number of degrees of freedom is now reduced from $k - 1$ by the number of parameters being estimated—provided the estimate used has certain properties. Suffice it to say here that in the normal case the sample mean and sample variance are estimators of population mean and population variance, respectively, of the type needed. (More generally, a maximum likelihood estimator will usually be of this type.)

EXAMPLE 9-l. Consider again (as in Example 9-k) the frequency distribution of Table 5.3. The mean and standard deviation of this sample distribution were found in Example 5-m to be 31.7 and 1.81, respectively. Using these to compute the p_0's, one obtains, for example,

$$p_{06} = P(32.25 < X < 33.35)$$
$$= \Phi\left(\frac{33.35 - 31.7}{1.81}\right) - \Phi\left(\frac{32.25 - 31.7}{1.81}\right) = .1940.$$

Completing the computations in this way, one finds $\chi^2 = 4.35$. Notice that this is considerably less than the 10.6 obtained using as a null distribution the normal distribution with mean 32 and standard deviation 1.8; this reduction comes from using a normal distribution that is in a sense the *best*-fitting normal distribution for the given data. The rejection limit now comes from the chi-square distribution with $10 - 1 - 2 = 7$ degrees of freedom (two parameters were estimated from the sample). The ninety-fifth percentile is 14.1, so at an α of .05 the hypothesis of normality would be accepted.

It was implicit in writing the formula defining the statistic χ^2 that none of the probabilities p_{0i} could be zero, and in applying the technique to a continuous distribution the class intervals must be chosen so that no one has zero probability. Moreover, if any p_{0i} is quite small, a single observation falling in the corresponding class would give rise to a very large term in the sum defining χ^2; class intervals must then be chosen so that their probabilities are not too small. One rule of thumb often quoted is that the expected frequencies of the class intervals should be at least five, but it has been found that this is a bit conservative. One or two class intervals with expected frequencies near 1 can be tolerated, without jeopardizing the validity of the test.

Problems

9-11. A coin falls Heads 230 times in 400 tosses. Test for $p = 1/2$ at the 1 percent level using the chi-square test.

9-12. Assuming that applying the acceptance limits in Table VI in a case in which the population is discrete results in a test with an α no larger than that given (which *is* true), use the data of Problem 9-11 to test $p = 1/2$ using the Kolmogorov-Smirnov test at $\alpha = .10$. (It is necessary to code the outcomes; try it both ways that are possible.)

9-13.   Consider the data given in the following table:

x_i	f_i
−2.5	1
−2.0	3
−1.5	5
−1.0	10
−0.5	17
0	19
0.5	19
1.0	12
1.5	7
2.0	7

(a) Use the data to test the hypothesis that the population from which the sample was taken is normal with mean 0 and variance 1, using the chi-square test at the 10 percent significance level.

(b) Use the data to test the hypothesis that the population is normal, using the chi-square test, with $\alpha = .10$.

(c) Use the data to test the hypothesis that the population is standard normal with the Kolmogorov-Smirnov test at the 10 percent level.

9-14.   Apply the Kolmogorov-Smirnov test at the 20 percent level to the sample consisting of the last ten observations in Table 5.2, to test the hypothesis that the population is normal with mean 32 and standard deviation 1.8. (Use the last two subgroups of five in the bottom row of subgroups.)

9-15.   Apply the Kolmogorov-Smirnov test to test equal probabilities of the six faces of a die which was cast 120 times with the following results: the six faces turned up with these frequencies, 18, 23, 16, 21, 18, 24. (Again a coding must be assigned; try it with the code 1, 2, 3, 4, 5, 6 for the faces corresponding to the frequencies in the given order, and then try it again with the coding 2, 5, 1, 4, 3, 6.)

9.6   Tests for randomness

It has been essential, for the theory behind many of the methods presented thus far, that the sample on which an inference is based be a random sample— a set of independent, identically distributed observations, each with the distribution of the "population." A sampling process will be said to be *in statistical control* if a random sample is obtained by using it.

In the process of gathering data, however, it may happen that the population changes in one or more of its characteristics, so that the observations are not from the same population. It is also possible that dependence is inadvertently introduced among the sample observations. Thus, it is often wise, before proceeding with a test designed for random samples, to test the hypothesis that the sampling process is in control. In this section are described a few of the many tests that have been proposed, referred to as tests of *randomness*.

It is essential, in testing for randomness, that the original data, in the order of observation, be on hand. It is not possible to detect, say, a "trend" (a continually changing population characteristic) if the original order of observations of the data is lost.

Consider then a sample $(X_1, \ldots, X_n)$, in which the observation X_i is the ith observation in the order obtained. For each observation record an "a" or "b" according as it lies above or below the median of the sample. So doing results in a sequence of a's and b's, such as:

$$a, b, a, a, a, b, b, a, b, a, b, b.$$

(There will be as many a's as b's, by definition of the median.) Each string of a's or of b's, uninterrupted by the other letter, is called a *run*. In the above sequence there are eight runs:

$$(a), (b), (a, a, a), (b, b), (a), (b), (a), (b, b).$$

The total number of runs is a random variable; let it be denoted by r. It can be shown that

$$E(r) = \frac{1}{2}(n + 2), \qquad \text{var } r = \frac{n(n - 2)}{4(n - 1)},$$

and that r is approximately normally distributed for large samples. (The formulas are exact only if n is even, and the population is continuous.) Here, "large" may be taken to mean $n > 25$. For such samples, then, the pth fractile of the distribution of r can be obtained from the relation

$$p = P(r < r_p) \doteq \Phi\left(\frac{r_p + \frac{1}{2} - \frac{1}{2}(n + 2)}{\sqrt{\dfrac{n(n - 2)}{4(n - 1)}}}\right),$$

where Φ is the standard normal distribution function (Table I) and the $\frac{1}{2}$ is added in as a "continuity correction," such as was employed in approximating binomial by normal probabilities. The quantity in parentheses after Φ must be the standard normal percentile z_p:

$$r_p \doteq \frac{1}{2}\left(n + 1 + z_p\sqrt{\frac{n(n - 2)}{n - 1}}\right) \doteq \frac{1}{2}(n + 1 + z_p\sqrt{n - 1}).$$

The type of critical region to be used will depend on the alternative hypothesis. For instance, if there is a shift in the mean as the sampling proceeds, one expects to find fewer runs, the earlier observations tending to be below and the later ones above the median (or vice versa). An excessively large number of runs, on the other hand, would suggest a systematic, bouncing back and forth (from one observation to the next) from one side of the median to the other—a type of dependence among the observations.

Another type of run test is based on what are called "runs up and down." The statistic used is the total number of runs of $+$'s and $-$'s in the sequence of $n - 1$ signs of the differences $X_i - X_{i-1}$. (A sequence of increasing values yields a sequence of $+$'s, for example.) Denoting this statistic by s, we can show

$$E(s) = \frac{1}{3}(2n - 1), \qquad \text{var } s = \frac{1}{90}(16n - 29),$$

and that the large sample distribution of s is again normal. The type of critical region to use depends again on the type of alternative to randomness that the test is intended to detect.

EXAMPLE 9-m.   Consider the following thirty observations taken from a table of what are called "random digits." (They are supposed to constitute a random sample.)

$$15, 71, 01, 64, 69, 59, 48, 40, 81, 16, 60, 20, 00, 84, 22,$$
$$28, 26, 46, 66, 36, 86, 66, 17, 34, 49, 85, 40, 51, 40, 10$$

The sample median is 43, and the corresponding sequence of a's and b's is as follows:

$$b, a, b, a, a, a, a, b, a, b, a, b, b, a, b,$$
$$b, b, a, a, b, a, a, b, b, a, a, b, a, b, b$$

Here there are 20 runs, whereas the 10th percentile of r is

$$r_{.10} \doteq \tfrac{1}{2}(31 - 1.28\sqrt{29}) \doteq 12.05.$$

Since $r > 12.05$, one would accept randomness against the alternative of the presence of a trend at the 10 percent level.

The sequence of signs of $X_i - X_{i-1}$ is the following:

$$+ - + + ? - - + - + - - + -$$
$$+ - + + - + - - + + + - + - -$$

Here there are also 20 runs, counting the tie (?) either as $+$ or $-$. For $n = 30$, one has

$$E(s) = 59/3, \qquad \text{var } s = 451/90 = 5.01.$$

The observed s is thus standardized as follows:

$$\frac{20 - 59/3}{\sqrt{5.01}} = .149$$

That is, it is .149 standard deviations above the expected value, surely no cause to reject randomness at any reasonable level, using a critical region of the form $s < K$. (An α of .10 would give a rejection limit of $K = 16.8$.)

Another type of test for randomness is based on *ranks*. For a given sample $(X_1, \ldots, X_n)$ let t_i denote the rank of X_i, that is, the position X_i occupies in the list of numerically ordered observations. For each such order statistic there are $n!$ permutations of the numbers in it that might have been the original sample; these permutations are equally likely, under the null hypothesis, to have produced that order statistic. Putting as many permutations as possible into a critical set according to the value of the statistic

$$T = \sum_{i=1}^{n} it_i$$

until there are k permutations in the critical set with $k/n! \leq \alpha$, one obtains a test of size α. If the alternative to randomness is a trend, a large value of T suggests that randomness should be rejected.

EXAMPLE 9-n. Consider the observations (1, 3, 9, 4, 7) from a continuous population. Given below are some of the 120 rank permutations and the value of $T = \sum it_i$ in each case. Notice that a sequence such as (1, 3, 4, 7, 9) which might point to a trend gives rise to an extreme value of T. Because under H_0 the 120 permutations are equally likely, a test of size $\alpha = .10$ would be obtained by putting the 12 permutations with smallest and largest T values into the critical set. Since the given sample corresponds to the rank sequence (1, 2, 5, 3, 4) and so has $T = 52$, one accepts randomness at $\alpha = .05$.

Permutations of Ranks	$\sum it_i$
1 2 3 4 5	55
2 1 3 4 5	54
1 2 4 3 5	54
1 3 2 4 5	54
1 2 3 5 4	54
2 1 3 5 4	53
1 3 2 5 4	53
2 1 4 3 5	53
⋮	⋮
4 5 3 1 2	37
4 5 3 2 1	36
5 4 2 3 1	36
5 3 4 2 1	36
5 4 3 1 2	36
5 4 3 2 1	35

Problems

9-16.   Apply the run test to the data of Table 5.2 on page 135, first, assuming that the data were recorded left to right, and second, assuming that the data were recorded top to bottom, in the order of occurrence.

9-17.   Apply the run tests to the data in Problem 5-8, given that the data were recorded, as it was obtained, in columns.

9-18.   Use the rank test of Example 9-n to test for randomness against an upward trend in level, at $\alpha = .01$, on the basis of the observations (13, 16, 19.3, 14, 21, 19).

10

LINEAR MODELS

Among the most fruitful of the notions of statistical analysis are those dealing with the means of several populations, where those populations arise as the result of several "treatments" (controlled contributing factors). The models used are usually of a type called linear, so named because of the way the factors are assumed to enter, as will be seen in the particular cases to be taken up.

This area of statistics has been extensively developed, and the discussion here will be but the barest introduction to some of the concepts and techniques. Some regression models will be considered first; in these, contributions to the mean are assumed to enter as functions of one or more controlled variables, and the interest centers on the form of the functions and on inference about parameters in the assumed functional form. In the other type of model to be considered the contributing factors that are controlled are given at certain "levels," not necessarily ordered, and a principal aim is to study the effect of one or more factors in the presence of others.

10.1 Regression

A theory for the isothermal relation between pressure and temperature in a fixed volume of gas suggests that these quantities are linearly related.

However, actually measured pressures p_i corresponding to several temperatures T_i involve random components, and the points (p_i, T_i) do not fall on a straight line. Thus, even though pressure and temperature are linearly related, the *measured* pressure and temperature may not be so because of random elements in the measured pressure. The measured pressure can be thought of as an "actual" pressure plus a random error with mean zero. One problem is this: How can one extract the correct linear relationship from data that do not fall on a line? Another problem is to determine whether or not one is justified in assuming at the outset a *linear* relationship.

Problems of this sort occur in a variety of situations that are studied under the general heading of "regression" analysis. In these, several random variables (the measured pressures, in the above example) are indexed according to values of a controlled or systematic variable (temperature), although often, the controlled variable is controlled only in a relative sense.† Of interest is the functional relation between the expectation of the random variable (the actual pressure) and the controlled variable (temperature). It may be desired to confirm that the relationship is linear, or some other given type of functional relation—according to theoretical considerations. And it is usually desired to determine the coefficients in the functional relation, given its type (the constant of proportionality in $p = kT$).

The symbol x will refer to the controlled variable, and $x_1, x_2, \ldots, x_n$ will denote particular values used in a given experiment; these are *not* random. The dependent variable under study, which includes the randomness, will be denoted by $Y(x)$, or more simply by Y. The observations on Y corresponding to $x_1, \ldots, x_n$ will be denoted by $Y_1, Y_2, \ldots, Y_n$; that is, $Y_i = Y(x_i)$. The expected value EY depends on x; the function defined by this dependence is called the *regression* function. Only the special type of regression function that depends *linearly* on x will be considered in detail:

$$E[Y(x)] = \alpha + \beta x.$$

For the particular observations used, then,

$$E(Y_i) = \alpha + \beta x_i, \qquad i = 1, \ldots, n.$$

It will be assumed that the observations $Y_1, \ldots, Y_n$ are *uncorrelated* random variables. With this simplifying assumption the applicability of the model is restricted but still quite wide. It will be assumed further that the observations have the same variance:

$$\text{var } Y_i = \sigma^2, \qquad i = 1, \ldots, n.$$

† The situation is considerably more complicated when the supposedly controlled variable is subject to chance fluctuations approaching, in order of magnitude, those of the variable under observation.

Again this does not leave the model without application. A much more restrictive assumption is made in the development of statistical inference for the model, namely, that the observations are *normally* distributed. The reasons are essentially those given at the beginning of Chapter 7 to explain the prevalence of normal theory throughout much of statistics.

The data $\{(x_i, Y_i), i = 1, \ldots, n\}$ in a regression problem can be represented graphically by plotting each pair (x_i, Y_i) as a point in the plane having those numbers as rectangular coordinates, as shown in Figure 10-1. Also shown in

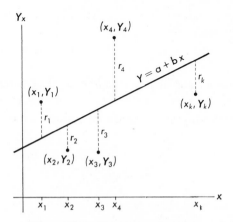

Figure 10-1   Regression function.

that figure is a line $y = a + bx$ which may or may not be the actual regression line, $y = \alpha + \beta x$. For each such possible regression line, one defines *residuals* r_i, shown in the figure and defined as follows:

$$r_i = Y_i - (a + bx_i).$$

These are the amounts, measured vertically, by which the data points miss falling on the line, positive if the point in question falls above, and negative if it falls below the line $y = a + bx$. Different linear functions enjoy different degrees of success in passing through the data points; and a line that passes through or near certain points may not come close to others. The principle of *least squares* calls for the selection of that line that minimizes the sum of squares residuals:

$$R(a, b) = \sum_{i=1}^{n} r_i^2 = \sum_{i=1}^{n} (Y_i - a - bx_i)^2.$$

This number, which depends on the intercept and slope constants a and b, is a measure of success in fitting a line to points that do not lie on a line—

but not the only conceivable measure. It is, however, eminently tractable and widely used.

To minimize a function of two variables, simply observe that if it is a minimum for $a = \hat{\alpha}$ and $b = \hat{\beta}$, it is then a minimum as a function of a at $a = \hat{\alpha}$ when b is held fixed at $\hat{\beta}$, and it is also a minimum as a function of b at $\hat{\beta}$ when a is held fixed at $\hat{\alpha}$. To apply these conditions, write $R(a, b)$ in the following forms indicating the dependence on a and on b, after squaring the residuals and collecting terms:

$$R(a, b) = na^2 - 2a\left\{\sum_{i=1}^{n} (Y_i - bx_i)\right\} + \text{(other terms, with no } a\text{)}$$
$$= \left\{\sum_{i=1}^{n} x_i^2\right\}b^2 - 2b\left\{\sum_{i=1}^{n} x_i(Y_i - a)\right\} + \text{(terms with no } b\text{)}.$$

Thus, R is quadratic in a and quadratic in b; using the fact (derived in algebra by completing the square) that $ca^2 - 2da + k$ has a minimum at $a = d/c$, one obtains the following as necessary conditions for $(\hat{\alpha}, \hat{\beta})$ to maximize $R(a, b)$:

$$\hat{\alpha} = \frac{1}{n}\sum_{i=1}^{n} (Y_i - \hat{\beta}x_i)$$
$$\left\{\sum_{i=1}^{n} x_i^2\right\}\hat{\beta} = \sum_{i=1}^{n} x_i(Y_i - \hat{\alpha}).$$

These equations, often called the *normal equations* of the least squares method, will have a unique solution if and only if the determinant of the coefficients does not vanish:

$$0 = \begin{vmatrix} 1 & \bar{x} \\ n\bar{x} & \sum x_i^2 \end{vmatrix} = \sum x_i^2 - n\bar{x}^2 = ns_x^2,$$

where $\bar{x}$ and s_x^2 are the mean and variance, respectively, of the numbers $x_1, \ldots, x_n$. (These symbols are used even though the x_i's are not observations on a random variable but are selected values of the controlled variable.) This determinant, then, is *not* zero when the values $x_1, \ldots, x_n$ are not identical; it will be assumed henceforth that this is the case.

The solutions of the normal equation can be expressed in the following form:

$$\hat{\beta} = s_{xY}/s_x^2, \qquad \hat{\alpha} = \bar{Y} - \hat{\beta}\bar{x},$$

where

$$s_{xY} = \frac{1}{n}\sum_{i=1}^{n} x_i Y_i - \bar{x}\bar{Y},$$

which is the covariance of the sets of numbers $(x_1, \ldots, x_n)$ and $(Y_1, \ldots, Y_n)$, although it should be kept in mind that the x's are not random.

EXAMPLE 10-a.   The following five points are given: (1, 3), (2, 3), (4, 7), (5, 6), (8, 12), the first coordinates being values of a controlled variable and the second, observations on the dependent variable (random) corresponding to the values of the controlled variable. Determination of the least squares regression line (that is, estimate of the actual regression line based on the given data and the least squares principle) proceeds as follows:

	x_i	Y_i	x_i^2	$x_i Y_i$
	1	3	1	3
	2	3	4	6
	4	7	16	28
	5	6	25	30
	8	12	64	96
Sums:	20	31	110	163

$$\bar{x} = 20/5 = 4, \qquad \bar{Y} = 31/5, \qquad \hat{\beta} = \frac{163/5 - 124/5}{110/5 - 16} = 13/10,$$
$$\hat{\alpha} = 31/5 - (13/10)4 = 1.$$

The desired line is then

$$y = 1.3x + 1.$$

The least squares line derived above is a "best" fit for given data—and would be different for each sample of observations. It can be thought of as an estimate of the true regression line $\alpha + \beta x$, and the coefficients can be considered as estimates of the true regression coefficients. It can be shown, indeed, that if the observations $Y_1, \ldots, Y_n$ are assumed to be *normally* distributed about the true regression line, the estimates $\hat{\alpha}$ and $\hat{\beta}$ result from applying the principle of maximum likelihood (cf. Section 8.1); it turns out further that the estimate of the common variance σ^2 resulting from that approach is just the average sum of squared residuals about the least squares regression line:

$$\hat{\sigma}^2 = \frac{1}{n} \sum_{i=1}^{n} (Y_i - \hat{\alpha} - \hat{\beta} x_i)^2.$$

These estimates then can be shown to approach in probability (cf. Section 6.1) the corresponding parameters.

The first two moments of $\hat{\alpha}$ and $\hat{\beta}$ can be calculated as follows. They are both linear combinations of the observations, and can be written in the slightly modified forms:

$$\hat{\beta} = \frac{1}{ns_x^2} \sum_{i=1}^{n} (x_i - \bar{x}) Y_i$$

$$\hat{\alpha} = \frac{1}{n} \sum_{i=1}^{n} Y_i[1 - \bar{x}(x_i - \bar{x})/s_x^2].$$

The terms in these sums are independent, so not only the means but also the variances are readily computed:

$$E(\hat{\beta}) = \frac{1}{ns_x^2} \sum_{i=1}^{n} (x_i - \bar{x})(\alpha + \beta x_i) = \beta,$$

$$E(\hat{\alpha}) = \frac{1}{n} \sum_{i=1}^{n} (\alpha + \beta x_i)[1 - \bar{x}(x_i - \bar{x})/s_x^2] = \alpha,$$

$$\text{var } \hat{\beta} = \frac{1}{(ns_x^2)^2} \sum_{i=1}^{n} (x_i - \bar{x})^2 \text{ var } Y_i = \frac{\sigma^2}{ns_x^2},$$

$$\text{var } \hat{\alpha} = \frac{1}{n^2} \sum_{i=1}^{n} (\text{var } Y_i)[1 - \bar{x}(x_i - \bar{x})/s_x^2]^2 = \frac{\sigma^2}{n} (1 + \bar{x}^2/s_x^2).$$

The estimates are seen to be *unbiased* (they have distributions centered at the parameters estimated in each case); and a well-known result going back to Gauss is that among unbiased linear combinations of the observations, the least squares estimates have the smallest variances. (Cf. the "Gauss-Markov theorem" in more advanced texts, for example, *The Analysis of Variance*, by H. Scheffé, Wiley, 1959, p. 14.)

Notice that the formulas for $\hat{\alpha}$ and for its variance would both simplify considerably if $\bar{x}$ were zero, and it is often convenient to choose the origin on the x-axis so that this is the case. A further simplification resulting from this choice (which in effect changes the definition of the intercept coefficient α) is that the estimates $\hat{\alpha}$ and $\hat{\beta}$ turn out to be uncorrelated (zero covariance).

The formula for the variance of the slope coefficient estimate shows that choosing x_i's to be widely spaced makes this variance small; an optimum allocation of observations from the point of view of precision of this slope estimate would be to put half of the observations as far to the left and half as far to the right as possible.

Because $\hat{\alpha}$ and $\hat{\beta}$ are each linear combinations of $Y_1, \ldots, Y_n$, the assumption of normality of the Y's implies that $\hat{\alpha}$ and $\hat{\beta}$ are normally distributed. If n is large enough so that $\hat{\sigma}^2$ can be taken as a good approximation to σ^2, large sample tests and confidence intervals for α and β can be constructed as in the following example.

EXAMPLE 10-b. Suppose that calculations based on a given set of 100 points (x_i, Y_i) yield $s_x^2 = 9.7$, $\hat{\alpha} = 1.1$, $\hat{\beta} = .02$, and $\hat{\sigma}^2 = .0036$. Then starting with the approximate equality

$$P\left(|\hat{\beta} - \beta| < 1.645 \frac{\hat{\sigma}}{s_x\sqrt{n}}\right) \doteq .90,$$

one obtains the following 90 percent confidence limits for β:

$$\hat{\beta} \pm 1.645 \frac{\hat{\sigma}}{s_x\sqrt{n}},$$

or for the given data,

$$.02 \pm 1.645 \frac{.06}{10\sqrt{9.7}}$$

which interval then extends from .0168 to .0232.

Rejecting $\beta = \beta_0$ if this value does not fall in the above confidence interval is a test of $\beta = \beta_0$ against the two-sided alternative $\beta \neq \beta_0$ at the 10 percent level. The power function is

$$P(\text{reject } \beta_0 \mid \beta) = P\left(\left|\frac{\hat{\beta} - \beta_0}{\hat{\sigma}/\sqrt{ns_x^2}}\right| > 1.645\right)$$

$$\doteq 1 - \Phi\left(\frac{\beta_0 - \beta}{\hat{\sigma}/\sqrt{ns_x^2}} + 1.645\right) + \Phi\left(\frac{\beta_0 - \beta}{\hat{\sigma}/\sqrt{ns_x^2}} - 1.645\right).$$

When the number of sample points is not large enough for the normal approximation and for replacement of σ^2 by $\hat{\sigma}^2$, a small sample modification similar to that used in Section 7.2 can be used, if the "population" is itself normal (that is, if the Y_i's are normal). The essential difference lies in the fact that the distribution of $n\hat{\sigma}^2/\sigma^2$ is chi-square with $n - 2$ degrees of freedom; it is said that "two degrees of freedom are used up in estimating α and β." Thus, the ratio used in tests about β:

$$\frac{\hat{\beta} - \beta_0}{\hat{\sigma}/\sqrt{ns_x^2}}$$

has a t-distribution with $n - 2$ degrees of freedom, if $\beta = \beta_0$. If $\beta \neq \beta_0$, it has a "noncentral" t-distribution; this must be used in constructing power functions.

Having considered the problem of linear regression, we mention briefly other types of regression functions. Whenever the assumed regression function depends linearly on its parameters, the corresponding "normal equations" are linear equations in those parameters. For instance, if it is assumed that

$$EY = ax^3 + bx^2 + cx + d,$$

(which, though cubic in x, is linear in a, b, c, and d), the minimization of the sum of squared residuals leads to a system of four linear equations in a, b, c, and *d*. The solution of this system yields the least squares estimates of the four parameters.

Certain types of relationships among physical variables are not linearly dependent on parameters. However, if a suitable transformation is made, such cases can sometimes be handled. For example, if pressure and temperature are connected by the relation $p = KT^\alpha$, their logarithms are related as follows:

$$\log p = \log K + \alpha \log T.$$

The parameters $\log K$ and α are involved linearly, and the least squares method can be applied to data in the form $(\log p_i, \log T_i)$. It must be realized, on the other hand, that the assumption of equal variances and normality would then have to be made about the *logarithms* of the measured pressures.

The principle of least squares can also be extended to cases in which the random variable of interest depends on more than one controlled variable, but these multiple regression problems will not be treated here.

Problems

10-1.   Determine the line which best fits the following points in the least squares sense: (0, 2), (1, 1), (4, 3), (5, 2).

10-2.   The independent, normal random variables Y_x are assumed to have variance σ^2 independent of x and mean $E(Y_x) = \alpha + \beta x$. Fifty observations (x_i, y_i) are obtained, with these results:

$$\bar{x} = 8.2, \qquad s_x^2 = 10.24, \qquad \hat{\alpha} = 6.31, \qquad \hat{\beta} = .092, \qquad \hat{\sigma}^2 = 4.6.$$

Construct a 95 percent confidence interval for β. Would you accept $\beta = 0$ at the 5 percent level, against $\beta \neq 0$? (Observe that this is a test of equality of means of several populations.)

10-3.   Suppose that the origin is selected on the x-axis so that the *new* $\bar{x} = 0$, for the data given in Problem 10-2. Compute the new values of s_x^2, $\hat{\alpha}$, $\hat{\beta}$, and $\hat{\sigma}^2$ and from these construct 95 percent confidence intervals for the new α and β.

10-4.   Construct a 95 percent confidence interval for σ^2, assuming a normal distribution for Y, using the data given in Problem 10-2.

10-5.   Construct a confidence interval for β, with a confidence coefficient of 80 percent, using the four points of Problem 10-1 and assuming that the Y's are normal.

10.2   Comparison of several means

The idea of *analysis of variance* provides a means of comparing the means of several populations, corresponding to responses to several treatments. The technique is briefly as follows: The total variability of all the observations in the samples from the several populations (thought of as a single sample) is broken into two components, one associated with the variability in measurement (assumed to be the same for all populations being considered) and the other associated with the variation arising because the population means are not the same. The size of the latter relative to the former is taken as the basis for deciding whether or not the population means can be considered equal.

Regression problems also deal with the means of several populations, corresponding to several values of a controlled variable, but here it is not assumed that the treatments are so indexed—or even ordered. On the other hand, analysis of variance techniques can be applied to some extent to regression problems. But their real power begins to be evident only in the next section, in which treatments result from combinations of two factors, which can then be studied simultaneously.

Suppose then that a sample is obtained from each of k populations, corresponding to k treatments; in the ith sample ($i = 1, 2, \ldots, k$) let the observations be $X_{i1}, X_{i2}, \ldots, X_{in_i}$, their mean be $\bar{X}_i$, and their variance be s_i^2. (The size of the ith sample is n_i.) It is supposed further that all $n = \sum n_i$ of the observations are *independent*, *normal*, and have *equal variances*. Let the mean of all of the observations be

$$\bar{X} = \frac{1}{n} \sum_{i=1}^{k} \sum_{j=1}^{n_i} X_{ij} = \frac{1}{n} \sum_{i=1}^{k} n_i \bar{X}_i,$$

which can be thought of as a weighted mean of the sample means. Consider now the sum of squared deviations about $\bar{X}$, decomposed as follows:

$$\sum_{i=1}^{k} \sum_{j=1}^{n_i} (X_{ij} - \bar{X})^2 = \sum_{i=1}^{k} \sum_{j=1}^{n_i} [(X_{ij} - \bar{X}_i) + (\bar{X}_i - \bar{X})]^2$$

$$= \sum_{i=1}^{k} \sum_{j=1}^{n_i} (X_{ij} - \bar{X}_i)^2 + \sum_{i=1}^{k} \sum_{j=1}^{n_i} (\bar{X}_i - \bar{X})^2$$

$$+ 2 \sum_{i=1}^{k} \sum_{j=1}^{n_i} (X_{ij} - \bar{X}_i)(\bar{X}_i - \bar{X})$$

$$= \sum_{i=1}^{k} \sum_{j=1}^{n_i} (X_{ij} - \bar{X}_i)^2 + \sum_{i=1}^{k} n_i(\bar{X}_i - \bar{X})^2 + 0.$$

(The value 0 for the third term results from the fact that the average deviation of $X_{i1}, \ldots, X_{in_i}$ about their mean $\bar{X}_i$ is zero.) Notice that the first term on the right in the last expression is essentially the "pooled variance" of Section 7.4, except for the divisor:

$$\bar{s}^2 = \frac{1}{n - k} \sum_{i=1}^{k} \sum_{j=1}^{n_i} (X_{ij} - \bar{X}_i)^2.$$

It is used to estimate the common population variance σ^2 and is based on the variability within samples. The second term on the right arises because the sample means differ, and is referred to as the "between samples" variation.

EXAMPLE 10-c. Consider the data of Example 7-j, repeated in the following table:

	n_i	Observations X_{ij}	$\bar{X}_i$	$\sum\limits_{j=1}^{n_i} (X_{ij} - \bar{X}_i)^2$
Sample 1	4	11, 9, 13, 11	11	8
Sample 2	6	33, 25, 28, 31, 27, 30	29	42
Sample 3	5	19, 23, 19, 21, 20	20.4	11.2
	$n = 15$			61.2

The "grand mean" $\bar{X}$ is

$$\bar{X} = (4\bar{X}_1 + 6\bar{X}_2 + 5\bar{X}_3)/15 = 21\tfrac{1}{3},$$

and the total sum of squared deviations about this is

$$845\tfrac{1}{3} = 61\tfrac{1}{3} + 784\tfrac{2}{15},$$

the indicated breakup being, as described above, into within samples and between samples variations. Notice that the second term is quite large; how large is too large will be discussed below.

An examination of the data shows what is happening. The variability of the data about $\bar{X}$ is clearly caused by a difference in population levels—one probably would not even bother with a statistical test to make this conclusion, but the test to be discussed below will of course confirm it.

It should be realized that even if the population means are identical, there will still be some between-samples variation, since the *sample* means will not be identical; and the between-samples variation measures the variance of the sample means about the grand mean. It can be shown that under the null hypothesis of no differences in sample means, the expected values of total, within-sample, and between-samples sums of squares are the terms in the following relation (in that order):

$$(n - 1)\sigma^2 = (n - k)\sigma^2 + (k - 1)\sigma^2.$$

Hence, the expected values of

$$\frac{1}{n - 1} \sum_{i=1}^{k} \sum_{j=1}^{n_i} (X_{ij} - \bar{X})^2, \qquad \frac{1}{n - k} \sum_{i=1}^{k} \sum_{j=1}^{n_i} (X_{ij} - \bar{X}_i)^2,$$

and

$$\frac{1}{k-1} \sum_{i=1}^{k} n_i(\bar{X}_i - \bar{X})^2$$

are each equal to σ^2 under the null hypothesis H_0 of equality of means. But the expected value of the second of these (that is, of the pooled variance) is σ^2 even when the population means are *not* equal. Thus, it is reasonable to take the ratio

$$\frac{\dfrac{1}{k-1} \sum_{i=1}^{k} n_i(\bar{X}_i - \bar{X})^2}{\dfrac{1}{n-k} \sum_{i=1}^{k} \sum_{j=1}^{n_i} (X_{ij} - \bar{X}_i)^2}$$

as a statistic useful in detecting inequality of the population means. If the ratio is near 1, it is assumed that the between-samples variation is of a size that might be expected even when the population means are equal, and the null hypothesis (of equal means) is accepted; if the ratio is large, this is taken as evidence that the population means are not equal and gives rise to an unusually large between-samples variation, and the null hypothesis is rejected. A critical value of the ratio—such that a larger ratio is taken as reason to reject the null hypothesis—is determined by a given α (size of type I error, or probability of rejecting H_0 when it is true) together with the distribution of the ratio under H_0. This ratio can be shown to have an F-distribution (Table IV) under H_0, and is the ratio of two independent chi-square variates, each divided by its number of degrees of freedom. The parameters of the F-distribution to be used (called *degrees of freedom*) are just the numbers of degrees of freedom in the numerator and denominator of the ratio, namely, $k-1$ and $n-k$, respectively.

EXAMPLE 10-d.   Continuing with the data of Example 10-c, note first that $k=3$ and $n=15$, so that the degrees of freedom of the between-samples and within-samples variations are respectively 2 and 12. The estimates of σ^2 from these two sources are then

$$\frac{784.133}{2} \doteq 392 \quad \text{and} \quad \frac{61.2}{12} = 5.1,$$

the latter being the pooled variance. The F-ratio is $392/5.1 = 77$, which is far in excess of, say, the 95th percentile of the F-distribution with 2 and 12 degrees of freedom in numerator and denominator respectively:

$$77 > 3.89 = F_{.95}(2, 12).$$

A test at the 5 percent level thus calls for rejection of the hypothesis of the equality of the population means.

When the population means can be considered equal (and the populations therefore identical), the grand mean $\bar{X}$ would be used as an estimate of their common value, since the samples can then be considered as making up a single sample of size n. The variance of this sample is based on the total sum of squares—obtained by putting back together the between-samples and within-samples sums of squares. However, if there is a temptation to use the same sample for tests about the common population mean as was used to test the hypothesis of equal means, it should be pointed out that the test statistics are not independent and that the apparent significance level for the t-test would not really be correct. It is better to base the tests on different sets of data.

It is helpful to think of the mathematical model for the above single classification problem in the following way. With $\mu_i = EX_i$ and μ related to the μ_i's as $\bar{X}$ is to the $\bar{X}_i$'s:

$$\mu = \frac{1}{n} \sum_{i=1}^{k} n_i \mu_i,$$

let $\theta_i = \mu_i - \mu$. This can be thought of as a contribution to μ_i associated with the ith treatment, whereas μ is common to all treatments. The observations are then composed of the common part μ, a contribution of the particular treatment, and a random element with mean zero, ϵ_{ij}:

$$X_{ij} = \mu + \theta_i + \epsilon_{ij}.$$

Testing equality of means is then equivalent to testing $\theta_1 = \cdots = \theta_k = 0$. Natural estimates of μ_i, μ, and θ_i are (respectively) $\bar{X}_i$, $\bar{X}$, and $\bar{X}_i - \bar{X}$; notice that

$$E\bar{X}_i = \frac{1}{n_i} \sum_{j=1}^{n_i} EX_{ij} = \mu_i, \qquad E\bar{X} = \frac{1}{n} \sum_{i=1}^{k} n_i E\bar{X}_i = \mu,$$

and therefore

$$E(\bar{X}_i - \bar{X}) = \mu_i - \mu = \theta_i.$$

These considerations are part of the motivation in breaking up the sum of squared deviations as was done:

$$(X_{ij} - \bar{X})^2 = [(X_{ij} - \bar{X}_i) + (\bar{X}_i - \bar{X})]^2.$$

In the above test for equality of means, the critical region was established by using the distribution of the test statistic under the null hypothesis. A power function (or operating characteristic function, which is 1 minus the power function) can be determined for the test, but this requires a knowledge of the distribution of the test statistic under the alternative hypothesis (that the means are *not* equal). The distribution has been studied and tabulated; tables of operating characteristic functions for the above problem and other analysis of variance tests are given in *Techniques of Statistical Analysis*, by Eisenhart, Hastay, and Wallis (eds.), McGraw-Hill, 1947.

Problems

10-6. Samples of size three are obtained from each of three normal populations with results as follows: 3, 5, 4; 11, 10, 12; 16, 21, 17. Test the hypothesis that the population means are the same at $\alpha = .05$.

10-7. A tensile test measures the quality of a spot-weld of an aluminum clad material. To determine there is a "machine effect" when welding a material of specified gage, the following samples from three machines are obtained:

> Machine A: 3.2, 4.1, 3.5, 3.0, 3.1,
> Machine B: 4.9, 4.5, 4.5, 4.0, 4.2,
> Machine C: 3.0, 2.9, 3.7, 3.5, 4.2.

Is there a significant difference among the machines? Estimate the (common) process variance. (Assume normality, independence, and equal variances.)

10-8. Four analysts determine the yield of a given process. For convenience eighty was subtracted from the original data to give the following table of values:

	Analyst		
1	2	3	4
8	7	4	1
5	12	−2	6
−1	5	1	10
6	3		8
5	10		
3			

(a) Do the analysts differ significantly in their determinations of yield?

(b) Estimate the variance in determinations of yield, assuming that it is the same for all analysts.

(c) Would the conclusions in (a) and (b) have been different if the eighty had not been subtracted in giving the data?

10.3 A two-factor problem

A simple extension of the problem of the preceding section permits two factors that might be influencing a response variable (as, for example, both

fertilizer type and brand of seed might influence the yield per unit area of a
certain crop). If factor A enters in p levels (for example, p types of fertilizer)
and factor B in q levels (for example, q brands of seed), there are pq combinations of a level of factor A and a level of factor B. Each of these is a "treatment" or population from which a sample might be drawn. The simplest
situation is that in which only one observation is obtained for each treatment;
the discussion here will be restricted to that case. The observations will be
given in two-way table, and each treatment or combination of levels of the
two factors is a "cell" in this table; the observation in the cell corresponding
to level i for factor A and level j for factor B will be denoted by X_{ij} ($i = 1, \ldots,$
p, and $j = 1, \ldots, q$).

It is assumed that the X_{ij}'s are independent and normally distributed, and
that they all have the same variance, σ^2. Calling the mean of the population
in the ij-cell $\mu_{ij} = EX_{ij}$, one defines

$$\mu_{i\cdot} = \frac{1}{q} \sum_{j=1}^{q} \mu_{ij}, \qquad \mu_{\cdot j} = \frac{1}{p} \sum_{i=1}^{p} \mu_{ij},$$

and

$$\mu = \frac{1}{q} \sum_{j=1}^{q} \mu_{\cdot j} = \frac{1}{p} \sum_{i=1}^{p} \mu_{i\cdot} = \frac{1}{pq} \sum_{j=1}^{q} \sum_{i=1}^{p} \mu_{ij}.$$

The factor contributions to μ_{ij} are thought of as

$$\theta_i = \mu_{i\cdot} - \mu, \qquad \phi_j = \mu_{\cdot j} - \mu,$$

and the observations then have the following structure

$$X_{ij} = \mu + \theta_i + \phi_j + \gamma_{ij} + \epsilon_{ij},$$

where ϵ_{ij} is a random component with mean zero and variance σ^2 and γ_{ij}
is the difference between μ_{ij} and $\mu + \theta_i + \phi_j$, conceived of as an "interaction" contribution, present when level i of factor A is used with level j
of factor B. In the present discussion, with just one observation per cell
it is necessary to *assume* that the interaction term is zero: $\gamma_{ij} \equiv 0$, but with
more observations per cell it could be tolerated.

Relevant sample means are defined to correspond to the above parameters,
as follows:

$$\bar{X}_{i\cdot} = \frac{1}{q} \sum_{j=1}^{q} X_{ij}, \qquad \bar{X}_{\cdot j} = \frac{1}{p} \sum_{i=1}^{p} X_{ij},$$

$$\bar{X} = \frac{1}{pq} \sum_{j=1}^{q} \sum_{i=1}^{p} X_{ij} = \frac{1}{q} \sum_{j=1}^{q} \bar{X}_{\cdot j} = \frac{1}{p} \sum_{i=1}^{p} \bar{X}_{i\cdot},$$

whose expected values are easily computed:

$$E\bar{X}_{i\cdot} = \mu_{i\cdot}, \qquad E\bar{X}_{\cdot j} = \mu_{\cdot j}, \qquad E\bar{X} = \mu.$$

Clearly then,

$$E(\bar{X}_{i\cdot} - \bar{X}) = \theta_i \qquad \text{and} \qquad E(\bar{X}_{\cdot j} - \bar{X}) = \phi_j.$$

These estimates suggest the following decomposition of the sum of squared deviations of the observations about the grand mean:

$$\sum\sum (X_{ij} - \bar{X})^2 = \sum\sum [X_{ij} - (\bar{X}_{i\cdot} - \bar{X}) - (\bar{X}_{\cdot j} - \bar{X}) - \bar{X}]^2 \\ + \sum\sum (\bar{X}_{i\cdot} - \bar{X})^2 + \sum\sum (\bar{X}_{\cdot j} - \bar{X})^2.$$

(It must of course be shown that the several cross products that arise do sum to zero, in establishing this identity. Thus, for instance,

$$\sum\sum (\bar{X}_{i\cdot} - \bar{X})[X_{ij} - (\bar{X}_{i\cdot} - \bar{X}) - (\bar{X}_{\cdot j} - \bar{X}) - \bar{X}] \\ = \sum_i \left\{ (\bar{X}_{i\cdot} - \bar{X}) \sum_j [X_{ij} - \bar{X} - (\bar{X}_{i\cdot} - \bar{X}) - (\bar{X}_{\cdot j} - \bar{X})] \right\} = 0,$$

and the others are treated similarly.)

Under the null hypothesis of no effect from either factor, the expected values of the terms in the above decomposition are as follows, keeping the same order:

$$(pq - 1)\sigma^2 = (p - 1)(q - 1)\sigma^2 + (p - 1)\sigma^2 + (q - 1)\sigma^2.$$

Then the quantity

$$\frac{1}{p - 1} \sum\sum (\bar{X}_{i\cdot} - \bar{X})^2 = \frac{q}{p - 1} \sum_{i=1}^{p} (\bar{X}_{i\cdot} - \bar{X})^2$$

can be used as an estimate of σ^2, provided $\theta_i = 0$, $i = 1, \ldots, p$. But if factor A introduces significant differences (not all $\theta_i = 0$), the differences $(\bar{X}_{i\cdot} - \bar{X})$ tend to be abnormally large in magnitude, the above sum of squares results in something too much larger than σ^2. On the other hand, the first term in the decomposition (having in effect the factor contributions taken out) provides a reasonable estimate of σ^2 even when the factors do have an effect; the ratio

$$\frac{\dfrac{q}{p - 1} \sum (\bar{X}_{i\cdot} - \bar{X})^2}{\dfrac{1}{(p - 1)(q - 1)} \sum\sum (X_{ij} - \bar{X}_{i\cdot} - \bar{X}_{\cdot j} + \bar{X})^2}$$

is then useful as a means of determining whether factor A has an effect. The null hypothesis that factor A has no effect (that is, has the same effect at all levels used) is rejected if this ratio is too large; the critical value is determined from a specified α and the fact that under the null hypothesis the distribution of the ratio is an F-distribution with $p - 1$ and $(p - 1)(q - 1)$ degrees of freedom in numerator and denominator, respectively.

A test for the presence of a factor B effect is constructed similarly, with the same denominator as in the above ratio, using

$$\frac{p}{q - 1} \sum (\bar{X}_{.j} - \bar{X})^2$$

in the numerator. It is important to notice that one can test for the effect of factor A even though factor B influences the response, and conversely. This is in contrast to a common belief that to determine whether a given factor has an effect all other factors must be held constant.

The design in such an experiment permits testing for the influence of one factor in the presence of another factor. However, the two test statistics, for the effect of factor A and the effect of factor B, are not independent, and a *joint* conclusion concerning the presence of the two factors does not have the reliability indicated by a simple combination of significance levels of the individual tests. For instance, if one test is conducted at the 2 percent level and the other at the 5 percent level, the significance level of the joint test is not necessarily $1 - (.98)(.95) \doteq 7$ percent, as would be the case if the test statistics were independent.

EXAMPLE 10-e.   Consider two factors with three levels each, and assume that one observation per cell is obtained, with the results in the following array:

Factor A	Factor B			$\bar{X}_{i.}$	$\bar{X}_{i.} - \bar{X}$
	Level 1	Level 2	Level 3		
Level 1	3	5	4	4	-7
Level 2	11	10	12	11	0
Level 3	16	21	17	18	7
$\bar{X}_{.j}$	10	12	11	$\bar{X} = 11$	
$\bar{X}_{.j} - \bar{X}$	-1	1	0		

The breakup in the sum of squared deviations about $\bar{X}$ is easily computed to be as follows:

$$312 = 12 + 294 + 6.$$

The test ratio (for the effect of factor A) is then

$$\frac{294/(3-1)}{12/(3-1)(3-1)} = 49.$$

This is considerably greater than 6.94, the 95th percentile of the F-distribution with 2 and 4 degrees of freedom in numerator and denominator respectively.

Observe that had we been interested in testing for the effect of factor B, the corresponding test ratio would have been 1, which does not call for rejection of $\phi_j = 0$.

Problems

10-9. The data in the following table refer to the purity of a product determined by a given method. The four levels of factor A represent boiling times. The two levels of factor B represent the solvents used. Low values of the given results correspond to high purity.

Level of Factor B	Level of factor A			
	1	2	3	4
1	3.1	2.7	3.3	3.0
2	4.7	3.5	3.9	3.6

(a) Is the purity significantly affected by differences in boiling time?

(b) Is it a matter of indifference whether solvent 1 or solvent 2 is used?

10-10. A wear testing machine consists of four weighted brushes under which samples of fabric are fixed, in order to measure their resistances to abrasion. The loss of weight of the material after a given number of cycles is used as a measure of the resistance to abrasion. The data denote the loss of weight of four fabrics tested.

Fabric	Brush position			
	1	2	3	4
A	1.93	2.38	2.20	2.25
B	2.55	2.72	2.75	2.70
C	2.40	2.68	2.31	2.28
D	2.33	2.40	2.28	2.25

(a) Is there a significant amount of variation associated with brush position?
(b) Are there significant differences in the resistance to abrasion among the four fabrics?

The material in this chapter is but a brief introduction to a very broad, important, and extensively developed area of statistics. Reference is made to the following for further study:

N. Johnson and F. Leone, *Statistics and Experimental Design*, Vol. II. John Wiley and Sons, 1964.

O. Kempthorne, *The Design and Analysis of Experiments*. John Wiley and Sons, 1952.

F. Graybill, *An Introduction to Linear Statistical Models*. McGraw-Hill Book Company, 1961.

H. Scheffé, *The Analysis of Variance*. John Wiley and Sons, 1959.

LIST OF TABLES

Table I. Values of the standard normal distribution function

$$\Phi(z) = \int_{-\infty}^{z} \frac{1}{\sqrt{2\pi}} e^{-u^2/2}\, du = P(Z \le z)$$

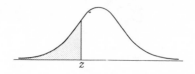

z	0	1	2	3	4	5	6	7	8	9
−3.	.0013	.0010	.0007	.0005	.0003	.0002	.0002	.0001	.0001	.0000
−2.9	.0019	.0018	.0017	.0017	.0016	.0016	.0015	.0015	.0014	.0014
−2.8	.0026	.0025	.0024	.0023	.0023	.0022	.0021	.0020	.0020	.0019
−2.7	.0035	.0034	.0033	.0032	.0031	.0030	.0029	.0028	.0027	.0026
−2.6	.0047	.0045	.0044	.0043	.0041	.0040	.0039	.0038	.0037	.0036
−2.5	.0062	.0060	.0059	.0057	.0055	.0054	.0052	.0051	.0049	.0048
−2.4	.0082	.0080	.0078	.0075	.0073	.0071	.0069	.0068	.0066	.0064
−2.3	.0107	.0104	.0102	.0099	.0096	.0094	.0091	.0089	.0087	.0084
−2.2	.0139	.0136	.0132	.0129	.0126	.0122	.0119	.0116	.0113	.0110
−2.1	.0179	.0174	.0170	.0166	.0162	.0158	.0154	.0150	.0146	.0143
−2.0	.0228	.0222	.0217	.0212	.0207	.0202	.0197	.0192	.0188	.0183
−1.9	.0287	.0281	.0274	.0268	.0262	.0256	.0250	.0244	.0238	.0233
−1.8	.0359	.0352	.0344	.0336	.0329	.0322	.0314	.0307	.0300	.0294
−1.7	.0446	.0436	.0427	.0418	.0409	.0401	.0392	.0384	.0375	.0367
−1.6	.0548	.0537	.0526	.0516	.0505	.0495	.0485	.0475	.0465	.0455
−1.5	.0668	.0655	.0643	.0630	.0618	.0606	.0594	.0582	.0570	.0559
−1.4	.0808	.0793	.0778	.0764	.0749	.0735	.0722	.0708	.0694	.0681
−1.3	.0968	.0951	.0934	.0918	.0901	.0885	.0869	.0853	.0838	.0823
−1.2	.1151	.1131	.1112	.1093	.1075	.1056	.1038	.1020	.1003	.0985
−1.1	.1357	.1335	.1314	.1292	.1271	.1251	.1230	.1210	.1190	.1170
−1.0	.1587	.1562	.1539	.1515	.1492	.1469	.1446	.1423	.1401	.1379
− .9	.1841	.1814	.1788	.1762	.1736	.1711	.1685	.1660	.1635	.1611
− .8	.2119	.2090	.2061	.2033	.2005	.1977	.1949	.1922	.1894	.1867
− .7	.2420	.2389	.2358	.2327	.2297	.2266	.2236	.2206	.2177	.2148
− .6	.2743	.2709	.2676	.2643	.2611	.2578	.2546	.2514	.2483	.2451
− .5	.3085	.3050	.3015	.2981	.2946	.2912	.2877	.2843	.2810	.2776
− .4	.3446	.3409	.3372	.3336	.3300	.3264	.3228	.3192	.3516	.3121
− .3	.3821	.3783	.3745	.3707	.3669	.3632	.3594	.3557	.3520	.3483
− .2	.4207	.4168	.4129	.4090	.4052	.4013	.3974	.3936	.3897	.3859
− .1	.4602	.4562	.4522	.4483	.4443	.4404	.4364	.4325	.4286	.4247
− .0	.5000	.4960	.4920	.4880	.4840	.4801	.4761	.4721	.4681	.4641

Table I. Values of the standard normal
distribution function (*continued*)

z	0	1	2	3	4	5	6	7	8	9
.0	.5000	.5040	.5080	.5120	.5160	.5199	.5239	.5279	.5319	.5359
.1	.5398	.5438	.5478	.5517	.5557	.5596	.5363	.5675	.5714	.5753
.2	.5793	.5832	.5871	.5910	.5948	.5987	.6026	.6064	.6103	.6141
.3	.6179	.6217	.6255	.6293	.6331	.6368	.6406	.6443	.6480	.6517
.4	.6554	.6591	.6628	.6664	.6700	.6736	.6772	.6808	.6844	.6879
.5	.6915	.6950	.6985	.7019	.7054	.7088	.7123	.7157	.7190	.7224
.6	.7257	.7291	.7324	.7357	.7389	.7422	.7454	.7486	.7517	.7549
.7	.7580	.7611	.7642	.7673	.7703	.7734	.7764	.7974	.7823	.7852
.8	.7881	.7910	.7939	.7967	.7995	.8023	.8051	.8078	.8106	.8133
.9	.8159	.8186	.8212	.8238	.8264	.8289	.8315	.8340	.8365	.8389
1.0	.8413	.8438	.8461	.8485	.8508	.8531	.8554	.8577	.8599	.8621
1.1	.8643	.8665	.8686	.8708	.8729	.8749	.8770	.8790	.8810	.8830
1.2	.8849	.8869	.8888	.8907	.8925	.8944	.8962	.8980	.8997	.9015
1.3	.9032	.9049	.9066	.9082	.9099	.9115	.9131	.9147	.9162	.9177
1.4	.9192	.9207	.9222	.9236	.9251	.9265	.9278	.9292	.9306	.9319
1.5	.9332	.9345	.9357	.9370	.9382	.9394	.9406	.9418	.9430	.9441
1.6	.9452	.9463	.9474	.9484	.9495	.9505	.9515	.9525	.9535	.9545
1.7	.9554	.9564	.9573	.9582	.9591	.9599	.9608	.9616	.9625	.9633
1.8	.9641	.9648	.9656	.9664	.9671	.9678	.9686	.9693	.9700	.9706
1.9	.9713	.9719	.9726	.9732	.9738	.9744	.9750	.9756	.9762	.9767
2.0	.9772	.9778	.9783	.9788	.9793	.9798	.9803	.9808	.9812	.9817
2.1	.9821	.9826	.9830	.9834	.9838	.9842	.9846	.9850	.9854	.9857
2.2	.9861	.9864	.9868	.9871	.9874	.9878	.9881	.9884	.9887	.9890
2.3	.9893	.9896	.9898	.9901	.9904	.9906	.9909	.9911	.9913	.9916
2.4	.9918	.9920	.9922	.9925	.9927	.9929	.9931	.9932	.9934	.9936
2.5	.9938	.9940	.9941	.9943	.9945	.9946	.9948	.9949	.9951	.9952
2.6	.9953	.9955	.9956	.9957	.9959	.9960	.9961	.9962	.9963	.9964
2.7	.9965	.9966	.9967	.9968	.9969	.9970	.9971	.9972	.9973	.9974
2.8	.9974	.9975	.9976	.9977	.9977	.9978	.9979	.9979	.9980	.9981
2.9	.9981	.9982	.9982	.9983	.9984	.9984	.9985	.9985	.9986	.9986
3.	.9987	.9990	.9993	.9995	.9997	.9998	.9998	.9999	.9999	1.0000

Note 1: If a normal variable X is not "standard," its values must be "standardized": $Z = (X - \mu)/\sigma$. That is, $P(X \leq x) = \Phi\left(\dfrac{x - \mu}{\sigma}\right)$.

Note 2: For "two-tail" probabilities, see Table Ib.
Note 3: For $z \geq 4$, $\Phi(x) = 1$ to four decimal places; for $z \leq -4$, $\Phi(z) = 0$ to four decimal places.
Note 4: The entries opposite $z = 3$ are for 3.0, 3.1, 3.2, etc.

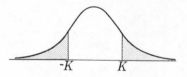

$P(Z \leq z)$	z
.001	−3.09
.005	−2.58
.01	−2.33
.02	−2.05
.03	−1.88
.04	−1.75
.05	−1.64
.10	−1.28
.15	−1.04
.20	− .84
.30	− .52
.40	− .25
.50	0
.60	.25
.70	.52
.80	.84
.85	1.04
.90	1.28
.95	1.645
.96	1.75
.97	1.88
.98	2.05
.99	2.33
.995	2.58
.999	3.09

K	$P(|Z| > K)$
1.04	.30
1.15	.25
1.28	.20
1.44	.15
1.645	.10
1.70	.09
1.75	.08
1.81	.07
1.88	.06
1.96	.05
2.05	.04
2.17	.03
2.33	.02
2.58	.01
2.81	.005
3.09	.002
3.29	.001

Table II. Percentiles of the chi-squared distribution

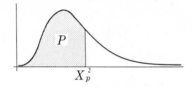

Degrees of freedom	$\chi^2_{.005}$	$\chi^2_{.01}$	$\chi^2_{.025}$	$\chi^2_{.05}$	$\chi^2_{.10}$	$\chi^2_{.20}$	$\chi^2_{.30}$	$\chi^2_{.50}$	$\chi^2_{.70}$	$\chi^2_{.80}$	$\chi^2_{.90}$	$\chi^2_{.95}$	$\chi^2_{.975}$	$\chi^2_{.99}$	$\chi^2_{.995}$
1	.000	.000	.001	.004	.016	.064	.148	.455	1.07	1.64	2.71	3.84	5.02	6.63	7.88
2	.010	.020	.051	.103	.211	.446	.713	1.39	2.41	3.22	4.61	5.99	7.38	9.21	10.6
3	.072	.115	.216	.352	.584	1.00	1.42	2.37	3.66	4.64	6.25	7.81	9.35	11.3	12.8
4	.207	.297	.484	.711	1.06	1.65	2.20	3.36	4.88	5.99	7.78	9.49	11.1	13.3	14.9
5	.412	.554	.831	1.15	1.61	2.34	3.00	4.35	6.06	7.29	9.24	11.1	12.8	15.1	16.7
6	.676	.872	1.24	1.64	2.20	3.07	3.83	5.35	7.23	8.56	10.6	12.6	14.4	16.8	18.5
7	.989	1.24	1.69	2.17	2.83	3.82	4.67	6.35	8.38	9.80	12.0	14.1	16.0	18.5	20.3
8	1.34	1.65	2.18	2.73	3.49	4.59	5.53	7.34	9.52	11.0	13.4	15.5	17.5	20.1	22.0
9	1.73	2.09	2.70	3.33	4.17	5.38	6.39	8.34	10.7	12.2	14.7	16.9	19.0	21.7	23.6
10	2.16	2.56	3.25	3.94	4.87	6.18	7.27	9.34	11.8	13.4	16.0	18.3	20.5	23.2	25.2
11	2.60	3.05	3.82	4.57	5.58	6.99	8.15	10.3	12.9	14.6	17.3	19.7	21.9	24.7	26.8
12	3.07	3.57	4.40	5.23	6.30	7.81	9.03	11.3	14.0	15.8	18.5	21.0	23.3	26.2	28.3
13	3.57	4.11	5.01	5.89	7.04	8.63	9.93	12.3	15.1	17.0	19.8	22.4	24.7	27.7	29.8
14	4.07	4.66	5.63	6.57	7.79	9.47	10.8	13.3	16.2	18.2	21.1	23.7	26.1	29.1	31.3
15	4.60	5.23	6.26	7.26	8.55	10.3	11.7	14.3	17.3	19.3	22.3	25.0	27.5	30.6	32.8
16	5.14	5.81	6.91	7.96	9.31	11.2	12.6	15.3	18.4	20.5	23.5	26.3	28.8	32.0	34.3
17	5.70	6.41	7.56	8.67	10.1	12.0	13.5	16.3	19.5	21.6	24.8	27.6	30.2	33.4	35.7
18	6.26	7.01	8.23	9.39	10.9	12.9	14.4	17.3	20.6	22.8	26.0	28.9	31.5	34.8	37.2
19	6.83	7.63	8.91	10.1	11.7	13.7	15.4	18.3	21.7	23.9	27.2	30.1	32.9	36.2	38.6
20	7.43	8.26	9.59	10.9	12.4	14.6	16.3	19.3	22.8	25.0	28.4	31.4	34.2	37.6	40.0
21	8.03	8.90	10.3	11.6	13.2	15.4	17.2	20.3	23.9	26.2	29.6	32.7	35.5	38.9	41.4
22	8.64	9.54	11.0	12.3	14.0	16.3	18.1	21.3	24.9	27.3	30.8	33.9	36.8	40.3	42.8
23	9.26	10.2	11.7	13.1	14.8	17.2	19.0	22.3	26.0	28.4	32.0	35.2	38.1	41.6	44.2
24	9.89	10.9	12.4	13.8	15.7	18.1	19.9	23.3	27.1	29.6	33.2	36.4	39.4	43.0	45.6
25	10.5	11.5	13.1	14.6	16.5	18.9	20.9	24.3	28.2	30.7	34.4	37.7	40.6	44.3	46.9
26	11.2	12.2	13.8	15.4	17.3	19.8	21.8	25.3	29.2	31.8	35.6	38.9	41.9	45.6	48.3
27	11.8	12.9	14.6	16.2	18.1	20.7	22.7	26.3	30.3	32.9	36.7	40.1	43.2	47.0	49.6
28	12.5	13.6	15.3	16.9	18.9	21.6	23.6	27.3	31.4	34.0	37.9	41.3	44.5	48.3	51.0
29	13.1	14.3	16.0	17.7	19.8	22.5	24.6	28.3	32.5	35.1	39.1	42.6	45.7	49.6	52.3
30	13.8	15.0	16.8	18.5	20.6	23.4	25.5	29.3	33.5	36.2	40.3	43.8	47.0	50.9	53.7
40	20.7	22.1	24.4	26.5	29.0	32.3	34.9	39.3	44.2	47.3	51.8	55.8	59.3	63.7	66.8
50	28.0	29.7	32.3	34.8	37.7	41.4	44.3	49.3	54.7	58.2	63.2	67.5	71.4	76.2	79.5
60	35.5	37.5	40.5	43.2	46.5	50.6	53.8	59.3	65.2	69.0	74.4	79.1	83.4	88.4	92.0

Note: For degrees of freedom $k > 30$, use $\chi_p^2 = \frac{1}{2}(z_p + \sqrt{2k - 1})^2$, where z_p is the corresponding percentile of the standard normal distribution.

This table is adapted from Table VIII of *Biometrika Tables for Statisticians*, Vol. 1, 1954, by E. S. Pearson and H. O. Hartley, originally prepared by Catherine M. Thompson, with the kind permission of the editor of *Biometrika*.

Table III.   Percentiles of the *t*-distribution

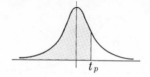

Degrees of freedom	$t_{.55}$	$t_{.60}$	$t_{.65}$	$t_{.70}$	$t_{.75}$	$t_{.80}$	$t_{.85}$	$t_{.90}$	$t_{.95}$	$t_{.975}$	$t_{.99}$	$t_{.995}$	$t_{.9995}$
1	.158	.325	.510	.727	1.00	1.38	1.96	3.08	6.31	12.7	31.8	63.7	637
2	.142	.289	.445	.617	.816	1.06	1.39	1.89	2.92	4.30	6.96	9.92	31.6
3	.137	.277	.424	.584	.765	.978	1.25	1.64	2.35	3.18	4.54	5.84	12.9
4	.134	.271	.414	.569	.741	.941	1.19	1.53	2.13	2.78	3.75	4.60	8.61
5	.132	.267	.408	.559	.727	.920	1.16	1.48	2.01	2.57	3.36	4.03	6.86
6	.131	.265	.404	.553	.718	.906	1.13	1.44	1.94	2.45	3.14	3.71	5.96
7	.130	.263	.402	.549	.711	.896	1.12	1.42	1.90	2.36	3.00	3.50	5.40
8	.130	.262	3.99	.546	.706	.889	1.11	1.40	1.86	2.31	2.90	3.36	5.04
9	.129	.261	.398	.543	.703	.883	1.10	1.38	1.83	2.26	2.82	3.25	4.78
10	.129	.260	.397	.542	.700	.879	1.09	1.37	1.81	2.23	2.76	3.17	4.59
11	.129	.260	.396	.540	.697	.876	1.09	1.36	1.80	2.20	2.72	3.11	4.44
12	.128	.259	.395	.539	.695	.873	1.08	1.36	1.78	2.18	2.68	3.06	4.32
13	.128	.259	.394	.538	.694	.870	1.08	1.35	1.77	2.16	2.65	3.01	4.22
14	.128	.258	.393	.537	.692	.868	1.08	1.34	1.76	2.14	2.62	2.98	4.14
15	.128	.258	.393	.536	.691	.866	1.07	1.34	1.75	2.13	2.60	2.95	4.07
16	.128	.258	.392	.535	.690	.865	1.07	1.34	1.75	2.12	2.58	2.92	4.02
17	.128	.257	.392	.534	.689	.863	1.07	1.33	1.74	2.11	2.57	2.90	3.96
18	.127	.257	.392	.534	.688	.862	1.07	1.33	1.73	2.10	2.55	2.88	3.92
19	.127	.257	.391	.533	.688	.861	1.07	1.33	1.73	2.09	2.54	2.86	3.88
20	.127	.257	.391	.533	.687	.860	1.06	1.32	1.72	2.09	2.53	2.84	3.85
21	.127	.257	.391	.532	.686	.859	1.06	1.32	1.72	2.08	2.52	2.83	3.82
22	.127	.256	.390	.532	.686	.858	1.06	1.32	1.72	2.07	2.51	2.82	3.79
23	.127	.256	.390	.532	.685	.858	1.06	1.32	1.71	2.07	2.50	2.81	3.77
24	.127	.256	.390	.531	.685	.857	1.06	1.32	1.71	2.06	2.49	2.80	3.74
25	.127	.256	.390	.531	.684	.856	1.06	1.32	1.71	2.06	2.48	2.79	3.72
26	.127	.256	.390	.531	.684	.856	1.06	1.32	1.71	2.06	2.48	2.78	3.71
27	.127	.256	.389	.531	.684	.855	1.06	1.31	1.70	2.05	2.47	2.77	3.69
28	.127	.256	.389	.530	.683	.855	1.06	1.31	1.70	2.05	2.47	2.76	3.67
29	.127	.256	.389	.530	.683	.854	1.05	1.31	1.70	2.04	2.46	2.76	3.66
30	.127	.256	.389	.530	.683	.854	1.05	1.31	1.70	2.04	2.46	2.75	3.65
∞	.126	.253	.385	.524	.674	.842	1.04	1.28	1.64	1.96	2.33	2.58	3.29

Note: For the lower percentiles, use the relation $t_\alpha = -t_{1-\alpha}$. In particular, $t_{.50} = -t_{.50} = 0$. For example, for 6 degrees of freedom, $t_{.35} = -t_{.65} = -.404$.

This table is abridged from Table II of Fisher and Yates, *Statistical Tables for Biological, Agricultural, and Medical Research* (5th ed.)/Fisher, *Statistical Methods for Research Workers*, published by Oliver and Boyd, Ltd., Edinburgh, by permission of the authors and publishers.

Table IVa. $F_{.95}$, 95th percentiles of the F-distribution

Denominator degrees of freedom	Numerator degrees of freedom												
	1	2	3	4	5	6	8	10	12	15	20	24	30
1	161	200	216	225	230	234	239	242	244	246	248	249	250
2	18.5	19.0	19.2	19.2	19.3	19.3	19.4	19.4	19.4	19.4	19.4	19.5	19.5
3	10.1	9.55	9.28	9.12	9.01	8.94	8.85	8.79	8.79	8.70	8.66	8.64	8.62
4	7.71	6.94	6.95	6.39	6.26	6.16	6.04	5.96	5.91	5.86	5.80	5.77	5.75
5	6.61	5.79	5.41	5.19	5.05	4.95	4.82	4.74	4.68	4.62	4.56	4.53	4.50
6	5.99	5.14	4.76	4.53	4.39	4.28	4.15	4.06	4.00	3.94	3.87	3.84	3.81
7	5.59	4.74	3.35	4.12	3.97	3.87	3.73	3.64	3.57	3.51	3.44	3.41	3.38
8	5.32	4.46	4.07	3.84	3.69	3.58	3.44	3.53	3.28	3.22	3.15	3.12	3.08
9	5.12	4.26	3.86	3.63	3.48	3.37	3.23	3.14	3.07	3.01	2.94	2.90	2.86
10	4.96	4.10	3.71	3.48	3.33	3.22	3.07	2.98	2.91	2.85	2.77	2.74	2.70
11	4.84	3.98	3.59	3.36	3.20	3.09	2.95	2.85	2.79	2.72	2.65	2.61	2.57
12	4.75	3.89	3.49	3.26	3.11	3.00	2.85	2.75	2.69	2.62	2.54	3.51	2.47
13	4.67	3.81	3.41	3.18	3.03	2.92	2.77	2.67	2.60	2.53	2.46	2.42	2.38
14	4.60	3.74	3.34	3.11	2.96	2.85	2.70	2.60	2.53	2.46	2.39	2.35	2.31
15	4.54	3.68	3.29	3.06	2.90	2.79	2.64	2.54	2.48	2.40	2.33	2.29	2.25
16	4.49	3.63	3.24	3.01	2.85	2.74	2.59	2.49	2.42	2.35	2.28	2.24	2.19
17	4.45	3.59	3.20	2.96	2.81	2.70	2.55	2.45	2.38	3.21	2.23	2.19	2.15
18	4.41	3.55	3.16	2.93	2.77	2.66	2.51	2.41	2.34	2.27	2.19	2.15	2.11
19	4.38	3.52	3.13	2.90	2.74	2.63	2.48	2.38	2.31	2.23	2.16	2.11	2.07
20	4.35	3.49	3.10	2.87	2.71	2.60	2.45	2.35	2.28	2.20	2.12	2.08	2.04
21	4.32	3.47	3.07	2.84	2.68	2.57	2.42	2.32	2.25	2.18	2.10	2.05	2.01
22	4.30	3.44	3.05	2.82	2.66	2.55	2.40	2.30	2.23	2.15	2.07	2.03	1.98
23	4.28	3.42	3.03	2.80	2.64	2.53	2.37	2.27	2.20	2.13	2.05	1.98	1.96
24	4.26	3.40	3.01	2.78	2.62	2.51	2.36	2.25	2.18	2.11	2.03	1.98	1.94
25	4.24	3.39	2.99	2.76	2.60	2.49	2.34	2.24	2.16	2.09	2.01	1.96	1.92
30	4.17	3.32	2.92	2.69	2.53	2.42	2.27	2.16	2.09	2.01	1.93	1.89	1.84
40	4.08	3.23	2.84	2.61	2.45	2.34	2.18	2.08	2.00	1.92	1.84	1.79	1.74
60	4.00	3.15	2.76	2.53	2.37	2.25	2.10	1.99	1.92	1.84	1.75	1.70	1.65

This table is adapted from Table XVIII in *Biometrika Tables for Statisticians*, Vol. I, 1954, by E. S. Pearson and H. O. Hartley, originally prepared by M. Merrington and C. M. Thompson, with the kind permission of the editor of *Biometrika*.

Table IVb. $F_{.99}$, 99th percentiles of the F-distribution

	Numerator degrees of freedom												
	1	2	3	4	5	6	8	10	12	15	20	24	30
1	4050	5000	5400	5620	5760	5860	5980	6060	6110	6160	6210	6235	6260
2	98.5	99.0	99.2	99.2	99.3	99.3	99.4	99.4	99.4	99.4	99.4	99.5	99.5
3	34.1	30.8	29.5	28.7	28.2	27.9	27.5	27.3	27.1	26.9	26.7	26.6	26.5
4	21.2	18.0	16.7	16.0	15.5	15.2	14.8	14.5	14.4	14.2	14.0	13.9	13.8
5	16.3	13.3	12.1	11.4	11.0	10.7	10.3	10.1	9.89	9.72	9.55	9.47	9.38
6	13.7	10.9	9.78	9.15	8.75	8.47	8.10	7.87	7.72	7.56	7.40	7.31	7.23
7	12.2	9.55	8.45	7.85	7.46	7.19	6.84	6.62	6.47	6.31	6.16	6.07	5.99
8	11.3	8.65	7.59	7.01	6.63	6.37	6.03	5.81	5.67	5.52	5.36	5.28	5.20
9	10.6	8.02	6.99	6.42	6.06	5.80	5.47	5.26	5.11	4.96	4.81	4.73	4.65
10	10.0	7.56	6.55	5.99	5.64	5.39	5.06	4.85	4.71	4.56	4.41	4.33	4.25
11	9.65	7.21	6.22	5.67	5.32	5.07	4.74	4.54	4.40	4.25	4.10	4.02	3.94
12	9.33	6.93	5.95	5.41	5.06	4.82	4.50	4.30	4.16	4.01	3.86	3.78	3.70
13	9.07	6.70	5.74	5.21	4.86	4.62	4.30	4.10	3.96	3.82	3.66	3.69	3.51
14	8.86	6.51	5.56	5.04	4.69	4.46	4.14	3.94	3.80	3.66	3.51	3.43	3.35
15	8.68	6.36	5.42	4.89	4.56	4.32	4.00	3.80	3.67	3.52	3.37	3.29	3.21
16	8.53	6.23	5.29	4.77	4.44	4.20	3.89	3.69	3.55	3.41	3.26	18.3	3.10
17	8.40	6.11	5.18	4.67	4.34	4.10	3.79	3.59	3.46	3.31	3.16	3.08	3.00
18	8.29	6.01	5.09	4.58	4.25	4.01	3.71	3.51	3.37	3.23	3.08	3.00	2.92
19	8.18	5.93	5.01	4.50	4.17	3.94	3.63	3.43	3.30	3.15	3.00	2.92	2.84
20	8.10	5.85	4.94	4.43	4.10	3.87	3.56	3.37	3.23	3.09	2.94	2.86	2.78
21	8.02	5.78	4.87	4.37	4.04	3.81	3.51	3.31	3.17	3.03	2.88	2.80	2.72
22	7.95	5.72	4.82	4.31	3.99	3.76	3.45	3.26	3.12	2.98	2.83	2.75	2.67
23	7.88	5.66	4.76	4.26	3.94	3.71	3.41	3.21	3.07	2.93	2.78	2.70	2.62
24	7.82	5.61	4.72	4.22	3.90	3.67	3.36	3.17	3.03	2.89	2.74	2.66	2.58
25	7.77	5.57	4.68	4.18	3.86	3.63	3.32	3.13	2.99	2.85	2.70	2.62	2.54
30	7.56	5.39	4.51	4.02	3.70	3.47	3.17	2.98	2.84	2.70	2.55	2.47	2.39
40	7.31	5.18	4.31	3.83	3.51	3.29	2.99	2.80	2.66	2.52	2.37	2.29	2.20
60	7.08	4.98	4.13	3.65	3.34	3.12	2.82	2.63	2.50	2.35	2.20	2.12	2.03

Denominator degrees of freedom

This table is adapted from Table XVIII in *Biometrika Tables for Statisticians*, Vol. I, 1954, by E. S. Pearson and H. O. Hartley, originally prepared by M. Merrington and C. M. Thompson, with the kind permission of the editor of *Biometrika*.

Table V. Distribution of the standardized range $W = R/\sigma$

(Assuming a normal population)

	Sample size										
	2	3	4	5	6	7	8	9	10	12	15
$E(W)$	1.128	1.693	2.059	2.326	2.534	2.704	2.847	2.970	3.078	3.258	3.472
σ_w	.853	.888	.880	.864	.848	.833	.820	.808	.797	.778	.775
$W_{.005}$	.01	.13	.34	.55	.75	.92	1.08	1.21	1.33	1.55	1.80
$W_{.01}$	.02	.19	.43	.66	.87	1.05	1.20	1.34	1.47	1.68	1.93
$W_{.025}$	.04	.30	.59	.85	1.06	1.25	1.41	1.55	1.67	1.88	2.14
$W_{.05}$	.09	.43	.76	1.03	1.25	1.44	1.60	1.74	1.86	2.07	2.32
$W_{.1}$	.18	.62	.98	1.26	1.49	1.68	1.83	1.97	2.09	2.30	2.54
$W_{.2}$	.36	.90	1.29	1.57	1.80	1.99	2.14	2.28	2.39	2.59	2.83
$W_{.3}$	.55	1.14	1.53	1.82	2.04	2.22	2.38	2.51	2.62	2.82	3.04
$W_{.4}$	.74	1.36	1.76	2.04	2.26	2.44	2.59	2.71	2.83	3.01	3.23
$W_{.5}$	.95	1.59	1.98	2.26	2.47	2.65	2.79	2.92	3.02	3.21	3.42
$W_{.6}$	1.20	1.83	2.21	2.48	2.69	2.86	3.00	3.12	3.23	3.41	3.62
$W_{.7}$	1.47	2.09	2.47	2.73	2.94	3.10	3.24	3.35	3.46	3.63	3.83
$W_{.8}$	1.81	2.42	2.78	3.04	3.23	3.39	3.52	3.63	3.73	3.90	4.09
$W_{.9}$	2.33	2.90	3.24	3.48	3.66	3.81	3.93	4.04	4.13	4.29	4.47
$W_{.95}$	2.77	3.31	3.63	3.86	4.03	4.17	4.29	4.39	4.47	4.62	4.80
$W_{.975}$	3.17	3.68	3.98	4.20	4.36	4.49	4.61	4.70	4.79	4.92	5.09
$W_{.99}$	3.64	4.12	4.40	4.60	4.76	4.88	4.99	5.08	5.16	5.29	5.45
$W_{.995}$	3.97	4.42	4.69	4.89	5.03	5.15	5.26	5.34	5.42	5.54	5.70

This table is adapted from Tables XX and XXII in *Biometrika Tables for Statisticians*, Vol. I, 1954, by E. S. Pearson and H. O. Hartley, with the kind permission of the editor of *Biometrika*.

Table VI. Acceptance limits for the Kolmogorov-Smirnov test of goodness of fit

Sample size (n)	Significance level				
	.20	.15	.10	.05	.01
1	.900	.925	.950	.975	.995
2	.684	.726	.776	.842	.929
3	.565	.597	.642	.708	.829
4	.494	.525	.564	.624	.734
5	.446	.474	.510	.563	.669
6	.410	.436	.470	.521	.618
7	.381	.405	.438	.486	.577
8	.358	.381	.411	.457	.543
9	.339	.360	.388	.432	.514
10	.322	.342	.368	.409	.486
11	.307	.326	.352	.391	.468
12	.295	.313	.338	.375	.450
13	.284	.302	.325	.361	.433
14	.274	.292	.314	.349	.418
15	.266	.283	.304	.338	.404
16	.258	.274	.295	.328	.391
17	.250	.266	.286	.318	.380
18	.244	.259	.278	.309	.270
19	.237	.252	.272	.301	.361
20	.231	.246	.264	.294	.352
25	.21	.22	.24	.264	.32
30	.19	.20	.22	.242	.29
35	.18	.19	.21	.23	.27
40				.21	.25
50				.19	.23
60				.17	.21
70				.16	.19
80				.15	.18
90				.14	
100				.14	
Asymptotic formula:	$\dfrac{1.07}{\sqrt{n}}$	$\dfrac{1.14}{\sqrt{n}}$	$\dfrac{1.22}{\sqrt{n}}$	$\dfrac{1.36}{\sqrt{n}}$	$\dfrac{1.63}{\sqrt{n}}$

Reject the hypothetical distribution $F(x)$ if $D_n = \max |F_n(x) - F(x)|$ exceeds the tabulated value.

(For $\alpha = .01$ and $.05$, asymptotic formulas give values which are too high—by 1.5 percent for $n = 80$.)

This table is taken from F. J. Massey, Jr., "The Kolmogorov-Smirnov Test for Goodness of Fit," *J. Amer. Stat. Assn.* (1951), **46**: 67–78, except that certain corrections and additional entries are from Z. W. Birnbaum, "Numerical Tabulation of the Distribution of Kolmogorov's Statistic for Finite Sample Size," *J. Amer. Stat. Assn.* (1952), **47**: 425–441, with the kind permission of the authors and the *J. Amer. Stat. Assn.*

Table VII. Acceptance limits for the Kolmogorov-Smirnov test of $H_0: F(x) \equiv G(x)$

Sample size n (rows) × Sample size m (columns). Upper value gives a level at most .05, lower value gives a level at most .01.

$n \backslash m$	1	2	3	4	5	6	7	8	9	10	12	15
1	* *	* *	* *	* *	* *	* *	* *	* *	* *	* *		
2		* *	* *	* *	* *	* *	* *	7/8 *	16/18 *	9/10 *		
3			* *	* *	12/15 *	5/6 *	18/21 *	18/24 *	7/9 8/9		9/12 11/12	
4				3/4 *	16/20 *	9/12 10/12	21/28 24/28	6/8 7/8	27/36 32/36	14/20 16/20	8/12 10/12	
5					4/5 4/5	20/30 25/30	25/35 30/35	27/40 32/40	31/45 36/45	7/10 8/10		10/15 11/15
6						4/6 5/6	29/42 35/42	16/24 18/24	12/18 14/18	19/30 22/30	7/12 9/12	
7							5/7 5/7	35/56 42/56	40/63 47/63	43/70 53/70		
8								5/8 6/8	45/72 54/72	23/40 28/40	14/24 16/24	
9									5/9 6/9	52/90 62/90	20/26 24/36	
10										6/10 7/10		15/30 19/30
12											6/12 7/12	30/60 35/60
15												7/15 8/15

Reject H_0 if
$D = \max |F_m(x) - G_n(x)|$
exceeds the tabulated value. The upper value gives a level at most .05 and the lower value gives a level at most .01.

Note 1: Where * appears, do not reject H_0 at the given level.

Note 2: For large values of m and n, the following approximate formulas may be used:

$$\alpha = .05: \quad 1.36 \sqrt{\frac{m+n}{mn}}$$

$$\alpha = .01: \quad 1.63 \sqrt{\frac{m+n}{mn}}$$

This table is derived from F. J. Massey, Jr., "Distribution Table for the Deviation Between Two Sample Cumulatives," *Ann. Math. Stat.* (1952), 23: 435–441. Adapted with the kind permission of the author and the *Ann. Math. Stat.* Formulas for large sample sizes were given by N. Smirnov, "Tables for Estimating the Goodness of Fit of Empirical Distributions," *Ann. Math. Stat.* (1948), **19**: 280–281.

Table VIII. Rejection limits for the Wilcoxon-Mann-Whitney test

m \ n	3	4	5	6	7	8	9	10
2						0 (2.2)	0 (1.8)	0 (1.5)
			0 (4.7)	0 (3.6)	0 (2.8)	1 (4.4)	1 (3.6)	1 (3.0)
3							0 (.45)	0 (.35)
					0 (.83)	0 (.61)	1 (.91)	1 (.70)
			0 (1.8)	1 (2.4)	1 (1.7)	2 (2.4)	3 (3.2)	3 (2.5)
	0 (5.0)	0 (2.8)	1 (3.6)	2 (4.8)	2 (3.3)	3 (4.2)	4 (5.0)	4 (3.9)
4				0 (.48)	0 (.30)	1 (.40)	1 (.28)	2 (.40)
		0 (1.4)	0 (.79)	1 (1.0)	1 (.61)	2 (.81)	3 (.98)	3 (.70)
		1 (2.9)	1 (1.6)	2 (1.9)	3 (2.1)	4 (2.4)	5 (2.5)	5 (1.8)
			2 (3.2)	3 (3.3)	4 (3.6)	5 (3.6)	6 (3.8)	7 (3.8)
5			0 (.40)	1 (.43)	1 (.25)	2 (.31)	3 (.35)	4 (.40)
			1 (.79)	2 (.82)	3 (.88)	4 .(93)	5 (.95)	6 (.97)
			2 (1.6)	3 (1.5)	5 (2.4)	6 (2.3)	7 (2.1)	8 (2.0)
			4 (4.8)	5 (4.1)	6 (3.7)	8 (4.7)	9 (4.2)	11 (5.0)
6				2 (.43)	3 (.41)	4 (.40)	5 (.38)	6 (.37)
				3 (.67)	4 (.70)	5 (.63)	7 (.88)	8 (2.0)
				5 (2.1)	6 (1.8)	8 (2.1)	10 (2.5)	11 (2.1)
				7 (4.7)	8 (3.7)	10 (4.1)	12 (4.4)	14 (4.7)
7					4 (.35)	5 (.47)	7 (.39)	9 (.48)
					6 (.87)	7 (1.0)	9 (.82)	11 (.93)
					8 (1.9)	10 (2.0)	12 (2.1)	14 (2.2)
					11 (4.9)	13 (4.7)	15 (4.5)	17 (4.4)
8						7 (.35)	9 (.39)	11 (.43)
						9 (.74)	11 (.76)	13 (.78)
						13 (2.5)	15 (2.3)	17 (2.2)
						15 (4.2)	18 (4.6)	20 (4.2)
9							11 (.39)	13 (.38)
							14 (.94)	16 (.86)
							18 (2.5)	20 (2.2)
							21 (4.7)	24 (4.7)
10								16 (.45)
								19 (.93)
								23 (2.2)
								27 (4.5)

See footnote for this table on page 265.

The four entries for each pair of sample sizes are rejection limits when it is desired to have:

a one-sided test at .5 percent or a two-sided test at 1 percent;
a one-sided test at 1 percent or a two-sided test at 2 percent;
a one-sided test at 2.5 percent or a two-sided test at 5 percent;
a one-sided test at 5 percent or a two-sided test at 10 percent.

The entries in the table are lower limits; corresponding upper limits are $mn - u$.
The number in parentheses after a value u is the probability (in percent) that $U \leq u$.

EXAMPLE   If a two-sided test at 5 percent is desired for $m = 5$ and $n = 8$, use $6 < U < 34$ as the acceptance region. For this test,

$$\alpha = P_{H_0}(U \leq 6 \text{ or } U \geq 34) = 2 \times (.023) = .046,$$

which is less than .05 as desired.

This table is adapted from those given in H. B. Mann and D. R. Whitney, "On a Test of Whether One of the Two Random Variables is Stochastically Larger than the Other," *The Annals of Mathematical Statistics* (1947). **18**: 50–60, with the kind permission of *The Annals of Mathematical Statistics*.

Table IX. Logarithms of factorials

	0	1	2	3	4	5	6	7	8	9
00	0.0000	0.0000	0.3010	0.7782	1.3802	2.0792	2.8573	3.7024	4.6055	5.5598
10	6.5598	7.6012	8.6803	9.7943	10.9404	12.1165	13.3206	14.5511	15.8063	17.0851
20	18.3861	19.7083	21.0508	22.4125	23.7927	25.1906	26.6056	28.0370	29.4841	30.9465
30	32.4237	33.9150	35.4202	36.9387	38.4702	40.0142	41.5705	43.1387	44.7185	46.3096
40	47.9116	49.5244	51.1477	52.7811	54.4264	56.0778	57.7406	59.4127	61.0939	62.7841
50	64.4831	66.1906	67.9066	69.6309	71.3633	73.1037	74.8519	76.6077	78.3712	80.1420
60	81.9202	83.7055	85.4979	87.2972	89.1034	90.9163	92.7359	94.5619	96.3945	98.2333
70	100.0784	101.9297	103.7870	105.6503	107.5196	109.3946	111.2754	113.1619	115.0540	116.9516
80	118.8547	120.7632	122.6770	124.5961	126.5204	128.4498	130.3843	132.3238	134.2683	136.2177
90	138.1719	140.1310	142.0948	144.0632	146.0364	148.0141	149.9964	151.9831	153.9744	155.9700
100	157.9700	159.9743	161.9829	163.9958	166.0128	168.0340	170.0593	172.0887	174.1221	176.1595
110	178.2009	180.2462	182.2955	184.3485	186.4054	188.4661	190.5306	192.5988	194.6707	196.7462
120	198.8254	200.9082	202.9945	205.0844	207.1779	209.2784	211.3751	213.4790	215.5862	217.6967
130	219.8107	221.9280	224.0485	226.1724	228.2995	230.4298	232.5634	234.7001	236.8400	238.9830
140	241.1291	243.2783	245.4306	247.5860	249.7443	251.9057	254.0700	256.2374	258.4076	260.5808
150	262.7569	264.9359	267.1177	269.3024	271.4899	273.6803	275.8734	278.0693	280.2679	282.4693
160	284.6735	286.8803	289.0898	291.3020	293.5168	295.7343	297.9544	300.1771	302.4024	304.6303
170	306.8608	309.0938	311.3293	313.5674	315.8079	318.0509	320.2965	322.5444	324.7948	327.0477
180	329.3030	331.5606	333.8207	336.0832	338.3480	340.6152	342.8847	345.1565	347.4307	349.7071
190	351.9859	354.2669	356.5502	358.8358	361.1236	363.4136	365.7059	368.0003	370.2970	372.5959

Table X.   Binomial coefficients $\binom{n}{k}$

n \ k	2	3	4	5	6	7	8	9	10
2	1								
3	3	1							
4	6	4	1						
5	10	10	5	1					
6	15	20	15	6	1				
7	21	35	35	21	7	1			
8	28	56	70	56	28	8	1		
9	36	84	126	126	84	36	9	1	
10	45	120	210	252	210	120	45	10	1
11	55	165	330	462	462	330	165	55	11
12	66	220	495	792	924	792	495	220	66
13	78	286	715	1287	1716	1716	1287	715	286
14	91	364	1001	2002	3003	3432	3003	2002	1001
15	105	455	1365	3003	5005	6435	6435	5005	3003
16	120	560	1820	4368	8008	11440	12870	11440	8008
17	136	680	2380	6188	12376	19448	24310	24310	19448
18	153	816	3060	8568	18564	31824	43758	48620	43758
19	171	969	3876	11628	27132	50388	75582	92378	92378
20	190	1140	4845	15504	38760	77520	125970	167960	184756

Table XI.   Exponential function

x	e^{-x}	e^x	$\log_{10}e^x$
.01	.9900	1.0101	.00434
.02	.9802	1.0202	.00869
.03	.9704	1.0305	.01303
.04	.9608	1.0408	.01737
.05	.9512	1.0513	.02171
.06	.9418	1.0618	.02606
.07	.9324	1.0725	.03040
.08	.9231	1.0833	.03474
.09	.9139	1.0942	.03909
.10	.9048	1.1052	.04343
.20	.8187	1.2214	.08686
.30	.7408	1.3499	.13029
.40	.6703	1.4918	.17372
.50	.6065	1.6487	.21715
.60	.5488	1.8221	.26058
.70	.4966	2.0138	.30401
.80	.4493	2.2255	.34744
.90	.4066	2.4596	.39087
1.00	.3679	2.7182	.43429
2.00	.1353	7.3891	.86859
3.00	.04979	20.0886	1.30288
4.00	.01832	54.598	1.73718
5.00	.00674	148.41	2.17143
6.00	.00248	403.43	2.60577
7.00	.000912	1096.6	3.04006
8.00	.000335	2981.0	3.47536
9.00	.000123	8103.1	3.90865
10.00	.000045	22026.0	4.34294

Table XII. Poisson distribution function: $F(c) = \sum_{k=0}^{c} \dfrac{m^k e^{-m}}{k!}$

m (Expected value)

c	.02	.04	.06	.08	.10	.15	.20	.25	.30	.35	.40
0	.980	.961	.942	.923	.905	.861	.819	.779	.741	.705	.670
1	1.000	.999	.998	.997	.995	.990	.982	.974	.963	.951	.938
2		1.000	1.000	1.000	1.000	1.000	.999	.999	.998	.996	.992
3							1.000	1.000	1.000	1.000	.999
4											1.000

c	.45	.50	.55	.60	.65	.70	.75	.80	.85	.90	.95
0	.638	.607	.577	.549	.522	.497	.472	.449	.427	.407	.387
1	.925	.910	.894	.878	.861	.844	.827	.809	.791	.772	.754
2	.989	.986	.982	.977	.972	.966	.959	.953	.945	.937	.929
3	.999	.998	.998	.997	.996	.994	.993	.991	.989	.987	.984
4	1.000	1.000	1.000	1.000	.999	.999	.999	.999	.998	.998	.997
5					1.000	1.000	1.000	1.000	1.000	1.000	1.000

c	1.0	1.1	1.2	1.3	1.4	1.5	1.6	1.7	1.8	1.9	2.0
0	.368	.333	.301	.273	.247	.223	.202	.183	.165	.150	.135
1	.736	.699	.663	.627	.592	.558	.525	.493	.463	.434	.406
2	.920	.900	.879	.857	.833	.809	.783	.757	.731	.704	.677
3	.981	.974	.966	.957	.946	.934	.921	.907	.891	.875	.857
4	.996	.996	.992	.989	.986	.981	.976	.970	.964	.956	.947
5	.999	.999	.998	.998	.997	.996	.994	.992	.990	.987	.983
6	1.000	1.000	1.000	1.000	.999	.999	.999	.998	.997	.997	.995
7					1.000	1.000	1.000	1.000	.999	.999	.999
8									1.000	1.000	1.000

c	2.2	2.4	2.6	2.8	3.0	3.2	3.4	3.6	3.8	4.0	4.2
0	.111	.091	.074	.061	.050	.041	.033	.027	.022	.018	.015
1	.355	.308	.267	.231	.199	.171	.147	.126	.107	.092	.078
2	.623	.570	.518	.469	.423	.380	.340	.303	.269	.238	.210
3	.819	.779	.736	.692	.647	.603	.558	.515	.473	.433	.395
4	.928	.904	.877	.848	.815	.781	.744	.706	.668	.629	.590
5	.975	.964	.951	.935	.961	.895	.871	.844	.816	.785	.753
6	.993	.988	.983	.976	.966	.955	.942	.927	.909	.889	.867
7	.998	.997	.995	.992	.988	.983	.977	.969	.960	.949	.936
8	1.000	.999	.999	.998	.996	.994	.992	.988	.984	.979	.972
9		1.000	1.000	.999	.999	.998	.997	.996	.994	.992	.989
10				1.000	1.000	1.000	.999	.999	.998	.997	.996
11							1.000	1.000	.999	.999	.999
12									1.000	1.000	1.000

Table XII. Poisson distribution function (*continued*)

c	4.4	4.6	4.8	5.0	5.2	5.4	5.6	5.8	6.0	6.2	6.4
0	.012	.010	.008	.007	.006	.005	.004	.003	.002	.002	.002
1	.066	.056	.048	.040	.034	.029	.024	.021	.017	.015	.012
2	.185	.163	.143	.125	.109	.095	.082	.072	.062	.054	.046
3	.359	.326	.294	.265	.238	.213	.191	.170	.151	.134	.119
4	.551	.513	.476	.440	.406	.373	.342	.313	.285	.259	.235
5	.720	.686	.651	.616	.581	.546	.512	.478	.446	.414	.384
6	.844	.818	.791	.762	.732	.702	.670	.638	.606	.574	.542
7	.921	.905	.887	.867	.845	.822	.797	.771	.744	.716	.687
8	.964	.955	.944	.932	.918	.903	.886	.867	.847	.826	.803
9	.985	.980	.975	.968	.960	.951	.941	.929	.916	.902	.886
10	.994	.992	.990	.986	.982	.977	.972	.965	.957	.949	.939
11	.998	.997	.996	.995	.993	.990	.988	.984	.980	.975	.969
12	.999	.999	.999	.998	.997	.996	.995	.993	.991	.989	.986
13	1.000	1.000	1.000	.999	.999	.999	.998	.997	.996	.995	.994
14				1.000	1.000	1.000	.999	.999	.999	.998	.997
15							1.000	1.000	.999	.999	.999
16									1.000	1.000	1.000

c	6.6	6.8	7.0	7.2	7.4	7.6	7.8	8.0	8.5	9.0	9.5
0	.001	.001	.001	.001	.001	.001	.000	.000	.000	.000	.000
1	.010	.009	.007	.006	.005	.004	.004	.003	.002	.001	.001
2	.040	.034	.030	.025	.022	.019	.016	.014	.009	.006	.004
3	.105	.093	.082	.072	.063	.055	.048	.042	.030	.021	.015
4	.213	.192	.173	.156	.140	.125	.112	.100	.074	.055	.040
5	.355	.327	.301	.276	.253	.231	.210	.191	.150	.116	.089
6	.511	.480	.450	.420	.392	.365	.338	.313	.256	.207	.165
7	.658	.628	.599	.569	.539	.510	.481	.453	.386	.324	.269
8	.780	.755	.729	.703	.676	.648	.620	.593	.523	.456	.392
9	.869	.850	.830	.810	.788	.765	.741	.717	.653	.587	.522
10	.927	.915	.901	.887	.871	.854	.835	.816	.763	.706	.645
11	.963	.955	.947	.937	.926	.915	.902	.888	.849	.803	.752
12	.982	.978	.973	.967	.961	.954	.945	.936	.909	.876	.836
13	.992	.990	.987	.984	.980	.976	.971	.966	.949	.926	.898
14	.997	.996	.994	.993	.991	.989	.986	.983	.973	.959	.940
15	.999	.998	.998	.997	.996	.995	.993	.992	.986	.978	.967
16	.999	.999	.999	.999	.998	.998	.997	.996	.993	.989	.982
17	1.000	1.000	1.000	.999	.999	.999	.999	.998	.997	.995	.991
18				1.000	1.000	1.000	1.000	.999	.999	.998	.996
19								1.000	.999	.999	.998
20									1.000	1.000	.999
21											1.000

Table XII. Poisson distribution function (continued)

c	10.0	10.5	11.0	11.5	12.0	12.5	13.0	13.5	14.0	14.5	15.0
2	.003	.002	.001	.001	.001	.000					
3	.010	.007	.005	.003	.002	.002	.001	.001	.000		
4	.029	.021	.015	.011	.008	.005	.004	.003	.002	.001	.001
5	.067	.050	.038	.028	.020	.015	.011	.008	.006	.004	.003
6	.130	.102	.079	.060	.046	.035	.026	.019	.014	.010	.008
7	.220	.179	.143	.114	.090	.070	.054	.041	.032	.024	.018
8	.333	.279	.232	.191	.155	.125	.100	.079	.062	.048	.037
9	.458	.397	.341	.289	.242	.201	.166	.135	.109	.088	.070
10	.583	.521	.460	.402	.347	.297	.252	.211	.176	.145	.118
11	.697	.629	.579	.520	.462	.406	.353	.304	.260	.220	.185
12	.792	.742	.689	.633	.576	.519	.463	.409	.358	.311	.268
13	.864	.825	.781	.733	.682	.628	.573	.518	.464	.413	.363
14	.917	.888	.854	.815	.772	.725	.675	.623	.570	.518	.466
15	.951	.932	.907	.878	.844	.806	.764	.718	.669	.619	.568
16	.973	.960	.944	.924	.899	.869	.835	.798	.756	.711	.664
17	.986	.978	.968	.954	.937	.916	.890	.861	.827	.790	.749
18	.993	.988	.982	.974	.963	.948	.930	.908	.883	.853	.819
19	.997	.994	.991	.986	.979	.969	.957	.942	.923	.901	.875
20	.998	.997	.995	.992	.988	.983	.975	.965	.952	.936	.917
21	.999	.999	.998	.996	.994	.991	.986	.980	.971	.960	.947
22	1.000	.999	.999	.998	.997	.995	.992	.989	.983	.976	.967
23		1.000	1.000	.999	.999	.998	.996	.994	.991	.986	.981
24				1.000	.999	.999	.998	.997	.995	.992	.989
25					1.000	.999	.999	.998	.997	.996	.994
26						1.000	1.000	.999	.999	.998	.997
27								1.000	.999	.999	.998
28									1.000	.999	.999
29										1.000	1.000

Table XIII.   Natural logarithms

N	0	1	2	3	4	5	6	7	8	9
0.0		5.395	6.088	6.493	6.781	7.004	7.187	7.341	7.474	7.592
0.1	7.697	7.793	7.880	7.960	8.034	8.103	8.167	8.228	8.285	8.339
0.2	8.391	8.439	8.486	8.530	8.573	8.614	8.653	8.691	8.727	8.762
0.3	8.796	8.829	8.861	8.891	8.921	8.950	8.978	9.006	9.032	9.058
0.4	9.804	9.108	9.132	9.156	9.179	9.201	9.223	9.245	9.266	9.287
0.5	9.307	9.327	9.346	9.365	9.384	9.402	9.420	9.438	9.455	9.472
0.6	9.489	9.506	9.522	9.538	9.554	9.569	9.584	9.600	9.614	9.629
0.7	9.643	9.658	9.671	9.685	9.699	9.712	9.726	9.739	9.752	9.764
0.8	9.777	9.789	9.802	9.814	9.826	9.837	9.849	9.861	9.872	9.883
0.9	9.895	9.906	9.917	9.927	9.938	9.949	9.959	9.970	9.980	9.990
1.0	0.00000	0995	1980	2956	3922	4879	5827	6766	7696	8618
1.1	9531	*0436	*1333	*2222	*3103	*3976	*4842	*5700	*6551	*7395
1.2	0.1 8232	9062	9885	*0701	*1511	*2314	*3111	*3902	*4686	*5464
1.3	0.2 6236	7003	7763	8518	9267	*0010	*0784	*1481	*2208	*2930
1.4	0.3 3647	4359	5066	5767	6464	7156	7844	8526	9204	9878
1.5	0.4 0547	1211	1871	2527	3178	3825	4469	5108	5724	6373
1.6	7000	7623	8243	8858	9470	*0078	*0682	*1282	*1879	*2473
1.7	0.5 3063	3649	4232	4812	5389	5962	6531	7098	7661	8222
1.8	8779	9333	9884	*0432	*0977	*1519	*2058	*2594	*3127	*3658
1.9	0.6 4185	4710	5233	5752	6269	6783	7294	7803	8310	8813
2.0	9315	9813	*0310	*0804	*1295	*1784	*2271	*2755	*3237	*3716
2.1	0.7 4194	4669	5142	5612	6081	6547	7011	7473	7932	8390
2.2	8846	9299	9751	*0200	*0648	*1093	*1536	*1978	*2418	*2855
2.3	0.8 3291	3725	4157	4587	5015	5442	5866	6289	6710	7129
2.4	7547	7963	8377	8789	9200	9609	*0016	*0422	*0826	*1228
2.5	0.9 1629	2028	2426	2822	3216	3609	4001	4391	4779	5166
2.6	5551	5935	6317	6698	7078	7456	7833	8208	8582	8954
2.7	9325	9695	*0063	*0430	*0796	*1160	*1523	*1885	*2245	*2604
2.8	1.0 2962	3318	3674	4028	4380	4732	5082	5431	5779	6126
2.9	6471	6815	7158	7500	7841	8181	8519	8856	9192	9527
3.0	9861	*0194	*0526	*0856	*1186	*1514	*1841	*2168	*2493	*2817
3.1	1.1 3140	3462	3783	4103	4422	4740	5057	5373	5688	6002
3.2	6315	6627	6938	7248	7557	7865	8173	8479	8784	9089
3.3	9392	9695	9996	*0297	*0597	*0896	*1194	*1491	*1788	*2083
3.4	1.2 2378	2671	2964	3256	3547	3837	4127	4415	4703	4990
3.5	5276	5562	5846	6130	6413	6695	6976	7257	7536	7815
3.6	8093	8371	8647	8923	9198	9473	9746	*0019	*0291	*0563
3.7	1.3 0833	1103	1372	1641	1909	2176	2442	2708	2972	3237
3.8	3500	3763	4025	4286	4547	4807	5067	5325	5584	5841
3.9	6098	6354	6609	6864	7118	7372	7624	7877	8128	8379
4.0	8629	8879	9128	9377	9624	9872	*0118	*0364	*0610	*0854
4.1	1.4 1099	1342	1585	1828	2070	2311	2552	2792	3031	3270
4.2	3508	3746	3984	4220	4456	4692	4927	5161	5395	5629
4.3	5862	6094	6326	6557	6787	7018	7247	7476	7705	7933
4.4	8160	8387	8614	8840	9065	9290	9515	9739	9962	*0185
4.5	1.5 0408	0630	0851	1072	1293	1513	1732	1951	2170	2388
4.6	2606	2823	3039	3256	3471	3687	3902	4116	4330	4543
4.7	4756	4969	5181	5393	5604	5814	6025	6235	6444	6653
4.8	6862	7070	7277	7485	7691	7898	8104	8309	8515	8719
4.9	8924	9127	9331	9534	9737	9939	*0141	*0342	*0543	*0744
5.0	1.6 0944	1144	1343	1542	1741	1939	2137	2334	2531	2782
N	0	1	2	3	4	5	6	7	8	9

Take tabular value—10 (applies to rows 0.1–0.9)

Table XIII. Natural logarithms (*continued*)

N	0	1	2	3	4	5	6	7	8	9
5.0	1.6 0944	1144	1343	1542	1741	1939	2137	2334	2531	2728
5.1	2924	3120	3315	3511	3705	3900	4094	4287	4481	4673
5.2	4866	5058	5250	5441	5632	5823	6013	6203	6393	6582
5.3	6771	6959	7147	7335	7523	7710	7896	8083	8269	8455
5.4	8640	8825	9010	9194	9378	9562	9745	9928	*0111	*0293
5.5	1.7 0475	0656	0838	1019	1199	1380	1560	1740	1919	2098
5.6	2277	2455	2633	2811	2988	3166	3342	3519	3695	3871
5.7	4047	4222	4397	4572	4746	4920	5094	5267	5440	5613
5.8	5786	5958	6130	6302	6473	6644	6815	6985	7156	7326
5.9	7495	7665	7834	8002	8171	8339	8507	8675	8842	9009
6.0	9176	9342	9509	9675	9840	*0006	*0171	*0336	*0500	*0665
6.1	1.8 0829	0993	1156	1319	1482	1645	1808	1970	2132	2294
6.2	2455	2616	2777	2938	3098	3258	3418	3578	3737	3896
6.3	4055	4214	4372	4530	4688	4845	5003	5160	5317	5473
6.4	5630	5786	5942	6097	6253	6408	6563	6718	6872	7026
6.5	7180	7334	7487	7641	7794	7947	8099	8251	8403	8555
6.6	8707	8858	9010	9160	9311	9462	9612	9762	9912	*0061
6.7	1.9 0211	0360	0509	0658	0806	0954	1102	1250	1398	1545
6.8	1692	1839	1986	2132	2279	2425	2571	2716	2862	3007
6.9	3152	3297	3442	3586	3730	3874	4018	4162	4305	4448
7.0	4591	4734	4876	5019	5161	5303	5445	5586	5727	5869
7.1	6009	6150	6291	6431	6571	6711	6851	6991	7130	7269
7.2	7408	7547	7685	7824	7962	8100	8238	8376	8513	8650
7.3	8787	8924	9061	9198	9334	9470	9606	9742	9877	*0013
7.4	2.0 0148	0283	0418	0553	0687	0821	0956	1089	1223	1357
7.5	1490	1624	1757	1890	2022	2155	2287	2419	2551	2683
7.6	2815	2946	3078	3209	3340	3471	3601	3732	3862	3992
7.7	4122	4252	4381	4511	4640	4769	4898	5027	5156	5284
7.8	5412	5540	5668	5796	5924	6051	6179	6306	6433	6560
7.9	6686	6813	6939	7065	7191	7317	7443	7568	7694	7819
8.0	7944	8069	8194	8318	8443	8567	8691	8815	8939	9063
8.1	9186	9310	9433	9556	9679	9802	9924	*0047	*0169	*0291
8.2	2.1 0413	0535	0657	0779	0900	1021	1142	1263	1384	1505
8.3	1626	1746	1866	1986	2106	2226	2346	2465	2585	2704
8.4	2823	2942	3061	3180	3298	3417	3535	3653	3771	3889
8.5	4007	4124	4242	4359	4476	4593	4710	4827	4943	5060
8.6	5176	5292	5409	5524	5640	5756	5871	5987	6102	6217
8.7	6332	6447	6562	6677	6791	6905	7020	7134	7248	7361
8.8	7475	7589	7702	7816	7929	8042	8155	8267	8380	8493
8.9	8605	8717	8830	8942	9054	9165	9277	9389	9500	9611
9.0	9722	9834	9944	*0055	*0166	*0276	*0387	*0497	*0607	*0717
9.1	2.2 0827	0937	1047	1157	1266	1375	1485	1594	1703	1812
9.2	1920	2029	2138	2246	2354	2462	2570	2678	2786	2894
9.3	3001	3109	3216	3324	3431	3538	3645	3751	3858	3965
9.4	4071	4177	4284	4390	4496	4601	4707	4813	4918	5024
9.5	5129	5234	5339	5444	5549	5654	5759	5863	5968	6072
9.6	6176	6280	6384	6488	6592	6696	6799	6903	7006	7109
9.7	7213	7316	7419	7521	7624	7727	7829	7932	8034	8136
9.8	8238	8340	8442	8544	8646	8747	8849	8950	9051	9152
9.9	9253	9354	9455	9556	9657	9757	9858	9958	*0058	*0158
10.0	2.3 0259	0358	0458	0558	0658	0757	0857	0956	1055	1154
N	0	1	2	3	4	5	6	7	8	9

Table XIV.   Four-place common logarithms

N	0	1	2	3	4	5	6	7	8	9
10	0000	0043	0086	0128	0170	0212	0253	0294	0334	0374
11	0414	0453	0492	0531	0569	0607	0645	0682	0719	0755
12	0792	0828	0864	0899	0934	0969	1004	1038	1072	1106
13	1139	1173	1206	1239	1271	1303	1335	1367	1399	1430
14	1461	1492	1523	1553	1584	1614	1644	1673	1703	1732
15	1761	1790	1818	1847	1875	1903	1931	1959	1987	2014
16	2041	2068	2095	2122	2148	2175	2201	2227	2253	2279
17	2304	2330	2355	2380	2405	2430	2455	2480	2504	2529
18	2553	2577	2601	2625	2648	2672	2695	2718	2742	2765
19	2788	2810	2833	2856	2878	2900	2923	2945	2967	2989
20	3010	3032	3054	3075	3096	3118	3139	3160	3181	3201
21	3222	3243	3263	3284	3304	3324	3345	3365	3385	3404
22	3424	3444	3464	3483	3502	3522	3541	3560	3579	3598
23	3617	3636	3655	3674	3692	3711	3729	3747	3766	3784
24	3802	3820	3838	3856	3874	3892	3909	3927	3945	3962
25	3979	3997	4014	4031	4048	4065	4082	4099	4116	4133
26	4150	4166	4183	4200	4216	4232	4249	4265	4281	4298
27	4314	4330	4346	4362	4378	4393	4409	4425	4440	4456
28	4472	4487	4502	4518	4533	4548	4564	4579	4594	4609
29	4624	4639	4654	4669	4683	4698	4713	4728	4742	4757
30	4771	4786	4800	4814	4829	4843	4857	4871	4886	4900
31	4914	4928	4942	4955	4969	4983	4997	5011	5024	5038
32	5051	5065	5079	5092	5105	5119	5132	5145	5159	5172
33	5185	5198	5211	5224	5237	5250	5263	5276	5289	5302
34	5315	5328	5340	5353	5366	5378	5391	5403	5416	5428
35	5441	5453	5465	5478	5490	5502	5514	5527	5539	5551
36	5563	5575	5587	5599	5611	5623	5635	5647	5658	5670
37	5682	5694	5705	5717	5729	5740	5752	5763	5775	5786
38	5798	5809	5821	5832	5843	5855	5866	5877	5888	5899
39	5911	5922	5933	5944	5955	5966	5977	5988	5999	6010
40	6021	6031	6042	6053	6064	6075	6085	6096	6107	6117
41	6128	6138	6149	6160	6170	6180	6191	6201	6212	6222
42	6232	6243	6253	6263	6274	6284	6294	6304	6314	6325
43	6335	6345	6355	6365	6375	6385	6395	6405	6415	6425
44	6435	6444	6454	6464	6474	6484	6493	6503	6513	6522
45	6532	6542	6551	6561	6571	6580	6590	6599	6609	6618
46	6628	6637	6646	6656	6665	6675	6684	6693	6702	6712
47	6721	6730	6739	6749	6758	6767	6776	6785	6794	6803
48	6812	6821	6830	6839	6848	6857	6866	6875	6884	6893
49	6902	6911	6920	6928	6937	6946	6955	6964	6972	6981
50	6990	6998	7007	7016	7024	7033	7042	7050	7059	7067
51	7076	7084	7093	7101	7110	7118	7126	7135	7143	7152
52	7160	7168	7177	7185	7193	7202	7210	7218	7226	7235
53	7243	7251	7259	7267	7275	7284	7292	7300	7308	7316
54	7324	7332	7340	7348	7356	7364	7372	7380	7388	7396
N	0	1	2	3	4	5	6	7	8	9

Table XIV. Four-place common logarithms (*continued*)

N	0	1	2	3	4	5	6	7	8	9
55	7404	7412	7419	7427	7435	7443	7451	7459	7466	7474
56	7482	7490	7497	7505	7513	7520	7528	7536	7543	7551
57	7559	7566	7574	7582	7589	7597	7604	7612	7619	7627
58	7634	7642	7649	7657	7664	7672	7679	7686	7694	7701
59	7709	7716	7723	7731	7738	7745	7752	7760	7767	7774
60	7782	7789	7796	7803	7810	7818	7825	7832	7839	7846
61	7853	7860	7868	7875	7882	7889	7896	7903	7910	7917
62	7924	7931	7938	7945	7952	7959	7966	7973	7980	7987
63	7993	8000	8007	8014	8021	8028	8035	8041	8048	8055
64	8062	8069	8075	8082	8089	8096	8102	8109	8116	8122
65	8129	8136	8142	8149	8156	8162	8169	8176	8182	8189
66	8195	8202	8209	8215	8222	8228	8235	8241	8248	8254
67	8261	8267	8274	8280	8287	8293	8299	8306	8312	8319
68	8325	8331	8338	8344	8351	8357	8363	8370	8376	8382
69	8388	8395	8401	8407	8414	8420	8426	8432	8439	8445
70	8451	8457	8463	8470	8476	8482	8488	8494	8500	8506
71	8513	8519	8525	8531	8537	8543	8549	8555	8561	8567
72	8573	8579	8585	8591	8597	8603	8609	8615	8621	8627
73	8633	8639	8645	8651	8657	8663	8669	8675	8681	8686
74	8692	8698	8704	8710	8716	8722	8727	8733	8739	8745
75	8751	8756	8762	8768	8774	8779	8785	8791	8797	8802
76	8808	8814	8820	8825	8831	8837	8842	8848	8854	8859
77	8865	8871	8876	8882	8887	8893	8899	8904	8910	8915
78	8921	8927	8932	8938	8943	8949	8954	8960	8965	8971
79	8976	8982	8987	8993	8998	9004	9009	9015	9020	9025
80	9031	9036	9042	9047	9053	9058	9063	9069	9074	9079
81	9085	9090	9096	9101	9106	9112	9117	9122	9128	9133
82	9138	9143	9149	9154	9159	9165	9170	9175	9180	9186
83	9191	9196	9201	9206	9212	9217	9222	9227	9232	9238
84	9243	9248	9253	9258	9263	9269	9274	9279	9284	9289
85	9294	9299	9304	9309	9315	9320	9325	9330	9335	9340
86	9345	9350	9355	9360	9365	9370	9375	9380	9385	9390
87	9395	9400	9405	9410	9415	9420	9425	9430	9435	9440
88	9445	9450	9455	9460	9465	9469	9474	9479	9484	9489
89	9494	9499	9504	9509	9513	9518	9523	9528	9533	9538
90	9542	9547	9552	9557	9562	9566	9571	9576	9581	9586
91	9590	9595	9600	9605	9609	9614	9619	9624	9628	9633
92	9638	9643	9647	9652	9657	9661	9666	9671	9675	9680
93	9685	9689	9694	9699	9703	9708	9713	9717	9722	9727
94	9731	9736	9741	9745	9750	9754	9759	9763	9768	9773
95	9777	9782	9786	9791	9795	9800	9805	9809	9814	9818
96	9823	9827	9832	9836	9841	9845	9850	9854	9859	9863
97	9868	9872	9877	9881	9886	9890	9894	9899	9903	9908
98	9912	9917	9921	9926	9930	9934	9939	9943	9948	9952
99	9956	9961	9965	9969	9974	9978	9983	9987	9991	9996
N	0	1	2	3	4	5	6	7	8	9

ANSWERS

Chapter 1

1-1	{Match, Don't match}	**1-19**	38
1-2	{0, 1, 2, ...}	**1-20**	720
1-3	{0, 1, 2, ...}	**1-21**	720
1-5	{0, 1, 2}	**1-22**	2^n
1-6	{0, .01, .02, .03, ...}	**1-23**	184,756
1-7	2^6, 2^3	**1-24**	121
1-8	1/4, 5/12, 2/3, 2/3	**1-25**	121/184756
1-9	3/4, 7/12, 1/3, 1/3	**1-26**	2/3
1-10	{5, 6}, {2, 4}, Empty set, {1, 6}	**1-27**	1/2, 1/3, 2/3
1-11	(a), (b), (c): {1, 2, 4, 5, 6}	**1-28**	1/2
	(d): {1, 2, 3, 4, 5}	**1-29**	$(1/6)^3$, 5/18
1-12	$P(E \cap F) = 1/6$	**1-30**	1, 105, 1, 15, 1035, 2598960
1-13	Not general	**1-31**	36
1-14	Use $F = E \cup (F \cap E^c)$	**1-32**	$n^2 - n$
1-15	8, 2^n, 243, m^k, 6^n	**1-33**	2,118,760; 2,036,265
1-16	64	**1-35**	$495p^8q^4$, $\binom{35}{15}x^{20}(2y)^{15}$
1-17	24		
1-18	24	**1-36**	5/8, 7/8. 6/8

1-37	3/8, 1/120, 7/8, 5/8, 1/2,	**1-51**	5/1944, 1/6, 7/162
	91/120, 1/8	**1-52**	1/2
1-38	30/91, 230/273, 2/35	**1-53**	1/4, 5/16, 5/16
1-39	13/20, 7/20	**1-54**	$\frac{7}{3}\left(\frac{5}{6}\right)^5$, $13/3^6$
1-40	88/4165		
1-41	1/3, 1/2	**1-55**	$\sum_{11}^{20}\binom{20}{k}(.45)^k(.55)^{20-k}$
1-42	Both 1/221		
1-43	Both 26/51	**1-56**	$\sum_{11}^{20}\binom{45}{k}\binom{55}{20-k}/\binom{100}{20}$
1-44	7/18, 5/11, 6/10, 14/18		
1-45	5/9	**1-57**	.63
1-46	2/105, 2/5	**1-58**	.99
1-47	Both 3/13	**1-59**	$(.5)(.95)^9$
1-48	Both 26/51	**1-60**	.48, .65
1-50	1/2		

Chapter 2

2-1	$p(k) = (6 - |k - 7|)/36$, $k = 2, \ldots, 12$
2-2	Same for all three
2-3	$p(k) = \binom{10}{4-k}\binom{3}{k}/\binom{13}{4}$, $k = 0, 1, 2, 3$
2-4	$p(k) = \binom{4}{k}p^k(1 - p)^{4-k}$, $k = 0, 1, 2, 3, 4$
2-5	$p(1) = p(2) = p(3) = 1/5$, $p(4) = 2/5$
2-6	$p(k) = (1/6)(5/6)^{k-1}$, $k = 1, 2, 3, \ldots$
2-7	$p(j, k) = 1/20$, for $j, k = 1, 2, 3, 4, 5$, and $j \neq k$
2-8	$p(x_1, x_2, x_3) = p(x_1)p(x_2)p(x_3)$
2-9	$p(x) = 1$ for $x = k$
2-10	7
2-11	1/2
2-12	12/13
2-13	$4p$
2-14	14/5
2-15	6
2-17	12/13
2-19	7/3
2-20	$3p$
2-22	0
2-25	$p^{x_1+x_2+x_3}(1 - p)^{3-x_1-x_2-x_3}$, $x_i = 0, 1$
2-26	$p(x, y) = 1/4$ for $(x, y) = (-1, 0), (0, -1), (0, 1)$, and $(1, 0)$
2-28	$EY = 3/2$, $EY^2 = 3$
2-29	35/6
2-30	1/4

2-31   90/169

2-32 $4p(1 - p)$

2-33   34/25

2-35   80.1, 189

2-36   3, 3, 17/2, 2, 2, $-1/2$, 3

2-37   8/5

2-38   1

2-39 $-2/3$, 5/9

2-40 $pt + (1 - p)$

2-41   200, 10

2-43   270, 15

2-44   4/3, 8/9

2-45   7/128

2-46 $\eta_Y(t) = (pt + 1 - p)^n$

2-49 $1/5, \ \dbinom{2}{k}\dbinom{8}{4 - k}\Big/\dbinom{10}{4}, \ 4/5, \ 32/75$

2-50   13/4, 507/272

2-51   1, 12/17

2-52 $20, \ 10, \ \displaystyle\sum_{0}^{5} \dbinom{20}{k}\dbinom{40}{30 - k}\Big/\dbinom{60}{30}$

2-53   .0337, .96, e^{-5T}

2-54   .184

2-55   .082, .544, .713

2-56   .0183, .0916

2-57   .0115, 20

2-58 $e^{m(t - 1)}$

2-59 $(13/8)e^{-1/2}$

2-60 $e^{-5}, \ 5^x e^{-5}/x!, \ 1 - 6e^{-5}$

2-61 $\displaystyle\sum_{0}^{2} \dbinom{100}{k}\dbinom{400}{75 - k}\Big/\dbinom{500}{75} \doteq 3.2 \times 10^{-6}$

2-62   .140

2-63   Poisson: .0498   .149   .224   .224   .168
            Binomial: .0476   .147   .225   .227   .171

Chapter 3

3-1 $.6 \pm .035$

3-2   (a) $\dfrac{1}{16}\dfrac{M}{25}\left(1 - \dfrac{M}{25}\right)$

　　　　(b) $\dfrac{25}{36}\dfrac{1}{16}\dfrac{M}{25}\left(1 - \dfrac{M}{25}\right) + \dfrac{1}{144}\left(1 - \dfrac{2M}{25}\right)^2$

3-3 $\left(\dfrac{1}{2} - p\right)^2$, compared with $\dfrac{1}{5}p(1 - p)$

3-4 $a = 1/6$

3-6 $E(1/N) = -\dfrac{p}{q} \log p \quad \left(.693 \text{ for } p = \dfrac{1}{2}\right)$

3-7 $.48 \pm .005$

3-8

Test no.	1	2	3	4	5	6	7	8
Crit. region	Empty	{0}	{1}	{2}	{0, 1}	{0, 2}	{2, 1}	{0, 1, 2}

3-9

Test no.	1	2	3	4	5	6	7	8
Power	0	$(1-p)^2$	$2p(1-p)$	p^2	$1-p^2$	$2p^2-2p+1$	$2p-p^2$	1

3-10 Power $\equiv 0$ for Test 1, $\equiv 1$ for Test 8

3-11 Use $Y = 8, 9, 10$ for $\alpha \doteq .05$ (Reject H_0 if $Y = 9$)

3-12 .299

3-13 .0034

3-14 Crit. regions: Empty set, {0, 6}, {0, 1, 5, 6}, {0, 1, 2, 4, 5, 6}, whole space

3-15

M	0	1	2	3	4	5	6	7	8
$56(OC)$ $(c = 0)$	56	35	20	10	4	1	0	0	0
$56(OC)$ $(c = 1)$	56	56	50	40	28	16	6	0	0

3-16 $AOQL = 5/56, 45/224$

3-17 Plan 1: $PR = 3/8$, $CR = 1/14$; Plan 2: $PR = 0$, $CR = 1/2$

3-20 $AOQ \doteq e^{-25p}(p + 25p^2)$, where $p = M/N$; $AOQL \doteq .22$

Chapter 4

4-1 $1/2$

4-2 $.96$; x^2 if $0 < x < 1$

4-3 (a) $1/4$, (b) 0, (c) 0

(d) $\frac{1}{2}(1 + x)^2$ if $-1 < x < 0$, $1 - \frac{1}{2}(1 - x)^2$ if $0 < x < 1$, 0 if $x < -1$, 1 if $x > 1$

4-4 (a) .8721, (b) .6628, (c) .8415, (d) .5228, (e) .0456, (f) .9974

4-5 0

4-6 $\mu = 0$, median $= 0$, $Q_1 = -.674$, $Q_3 = .674$

4-7 $-.293, 0, .293$

4-8 median $=$ mean $= 0$

4-10 2.7, 6.7; 0.48; means

4-11 $-.727$

4-14 (a) same as 5-3(d)

(b) $F(x) = \begin{cases} 0, & x < 0 \\ 1 - e^{-2x}, & x \geq 0 \end{cases}$

(c) $F(x) = (\pi/2 + \arctan x)/\pi$

$$(d) \ F(x) = \begin{cases} 0, \ x < -1 \\ 3x/4 - x^3/4 + 1/2, \ -1 < x < 1 \\ 1, \ x > 1 \end{cases}$$

$$(e) \ F(x) = \begin{cases} 0, \ x < 0 \\ \sin x, \ 0 < x < 1 \\ 1, \ x > 1 \end{cases}$$

4-15 (a) $3e^{-3x}, \ x > 0$, (b) $[\pi(1 + x^2)]^{-1}$, (c) $(2\pi e^{x^2})^{-1/2}$

4-16 0, 1/2, 0

4-17 1/6, 1/4, 1/8

4-18 (a) $\sqrt{y}, \ 0 < y < 1$

(b) $\dfrac{1}{2\sqrt{y}}, \ 0 < y < 1$

(c) 1/3,

(d) 1/3

4-21 $\dfrac{a}{\sqrt{2\pi}} e^{-(az+b)^2/2}$

4-22 .5, .1574, .9974, 0, .0456

4-24 .0082, .8904, 0, .8426

4-25 (8, 4) or (2, 64)

4-26 About 6′ 4″

4-27 4.8 percent, nonnegative, 3.78k

4-28 1.7 percent, 127.3, 123.4 to 136.6, 85.3 percent

4-29 100 oz, .1 oz

4-30 0, 9.2 (in fourth decimal place)

4-31 2×10^6 ft^2

4-32 .30

4-33 Yes, tolerance of combination is $\pm.707$ (less than required)

4-34 .49929

4-35 1.5 inches, $\pm.00458$ inches

4-36 1.12 miles

Chapter 5

5-1 Random sampling without replacement

5-2 Random sampling ("with replacement"). The population is the probability space of values $(2, \ldots, n)$ with corresponding probabilities.

5-3 (a) Random sampling; the population is the probability space for a single spin.

(b) Random sampling; the population is a probability distribution on the positive numbers, $0 < x < \infty$.

5-4 Only (a)

5-5 (b) is better

5-13 $\bar{X} = 53.3, \ s_x^2 = 133$

5-14 Median = 52, range = 55

5-16 8.745, 1.285

5-17 (a) 4.625

(b) 4.530, 4.716, 4.656, 4.630, 4.592; same mean

(c) .0301

(d) 4.61, .63

5-18 $16\frac{1}{8}$ (oz), $1\frac{1}{4}$ (oz), 16.1 (oz), .051 (oz^2)

5-19 $ES = 6$, var $S = 3$

5-20 σ^2

5-21 $\dfrac{n\theta^2}{(n + 1)^2(n + 2)}$

Chapter 6

6-1 .3174, .0456

6-2 663, 1089

6-3 .0655

6-4 .0513

6-5 .0058

6-6 .1303

6-7 .0179, .7286, .0485

6-8 .1829

6-9 .0185

6-10 Normal .6401, Poisson .6767, binomial .6772

6-13 $\bar{X} > .4935$, $\beta \doteq 0$

6-15 $K = 1$, $n = 21.7$

6-16 .629

6-17 $K = .061$, $n \doteq 1780$

6-18 5′ 9.2″ to 5′ 10.8″

6-19 $2.3 \pm .0514$, $2.3 \pm .0392$

6-20 661

6-22 (.61, .77), (.64, .75)

6-23 (.57, .80)

6-24 (.055, .174)

6-25 (.52, .76), (.515, .747)

6-26 (1.92, 2.14)

Chapter 7

7-1 (35.3, 61.9), (34.9, 61.1)

7-2 $s_x^2 = 45.1 > 28.3$, reject $\sigma^2 = 25$ (all $\times 10^{-8}$)

7-3 $\pi(\sigma^2) = 1 - F_{\chi^2}(1981/\sigma^2)$, $\beta = 1 - \pi(36) = .1034$

7-5 $s_x^2 = 2.56 < 3.8$, accept H_0; $\beta = .68$, $\pi(\sigma^2) = 1 - F_{\chi^2}(19/\sigma^2)$

7-6 (1.15, 26.5), (1.65, 12.1)

7-8   3.70, 3.97, (2.51, 6.32), (3.02, 7.21)

7-9 $R = 4 < 5.46$, accept H_0; $\beta = .7$, $\pi(\sigma) = 1 - F_W(5.46/\sigma)$
     (.91, 22), (1.32, 10.1)

7-10 $1 - F_W(w_{.95}\sigma_0/\sigma) + F_W(w_{.05}\sigma_0/\sigma)$

7-11   (a) $1.98 < 2.14 = t_{.975}(14)$, accept
     (b) $1.98 > 1.76 = t_{.95}(14)$, reject

7-12   (3.63, 3.75)

7-13 $t = 5.59$, reject

7-14   (90.84, 96.72), (88.47, 99.09)

7-15 $t_{.90}(8) = 1.40 < 2.29$, reject

7-16 $1 - F_{\chi^2(n-k)}(nK/\sigma^2)$

7-17 $1 - \Phi\left(\dfrac{K - a_m\sigma}{b_m\sigma/\sqrt{k}}\right)$

7-18 $\tilde{s}_x{}^2 = .00077$, $(.00045, .00161)$; $(\bar{R}/a_3)^2 = .000645$, $(.000367, .001042)$

7-19 $\bar{R} > 7.2$, $\beta = .01$

7-20 $\bar{X}$: 15 ± 3.71, R: 9.98 ± 8.62; $.0143$; $.0284$

7-23   3.70; LCL 3.47, UCL 3.93; LCL 0, UCL .719

7-24 $D = .40$ (reject at either .01 or .05)

7-25 $D = .8$ (reject at either .01 or .05)

7-26   There is a difference, (.216, 2.184)

7-27   (a) $Z = -3.9 < -1.65$, reject at .05
     (c) $t = -3.5$, reject at .05
     (d) $(-.0033, -.0009)$

7-28 $Z = 6.65$, reject H_0 at .01

7-29 $5.79 > 3.01$, reject at .05

7-30 $1/2.17 < 1.6 < 2.17$, accept equality

7-31   Reject equality

Chapter 8

8-1   (a) $(2\pi v)^{-n/2} \exp\left[-\frac{1}{2}\sum X_i{}^2/v\right]$
     (b) $m^{\sum X_i{}^2} e^{-nm}/X_i{}^2$
     (c) $p^n(1 - p)^{\sum X_i}$
     (d) $\theta^n \exp\left[-\sum X_i/\theta\right]$

8-2 $M = 8$ if bead is White, $M = 0$ if Black

8-3 $Y/3$

8-4   (b) $\theta = \bar{X}$

8-5 $v = \dfrac{1}{n}\sum X_i^2$

8-6   .329

8-7   Empty set, {2}, {2, 0}, {2, 0, 1}

8-9 $s_x{}^2 > K$

8-10   Empty set, {0, 2}, {0, 1, 2}

8-11 .994

8-13 9, 5

8-14 Continue sampling if $|k - .2675n| < .631$

8-15 1.63, 2.26

8-17

Rule:	1	2	3	4	5	6	7	8	
$X = 0$	A	A	A	B	A	B	B	B	(A is to accept f_0,
$X = 1$	A	A	B	A	B	A	B	B	B is to accept f_1)
$X = 2$	A	B	A	A	B	B	A	B	
$R_0 = \alpha$	0	.1	.6	.3	.7	.4	.9	1	L.R. rules are 1,
$R_1 = \beta$	1	.8	.7	.5	.5	.3	.2	0	2, 6, and 8

8-18 Rule 6; Rule 2

8-19 Reject $\mu = 0$ if $\overline{X} > 1/2$

8-20 d_8 is minimax

8-21 Use $K = 1/2$

8-22 For $0 \le \gamma \le 1/2$, use d_2; for $1/2 \le \gamma \le 2/3$, use d_4; for $2/3 \le \gamma \le 1$ use d_5

8-24 $K = 1.193$

8-25 $K = .019$

8-26 $(1/22, 21/22)$, $(1/2, 1/2)$; B, A

8-27 $h(\theta|x) \equiv g(\theta)$

8-29 11/4

8-30 1/5, 2/5, 3/5, 4/5

Chapter 9

9-1 Reject at $\alpha = .05$

9-2 $p^9(10 - p)$

9-3 .9533

9-4 Reject

9-5 Accept at $\alpha = .05$, reject at $\alpha = .20$

9-6 Accept equality at 5 percent

9-7 $p^{10} + 10p^9(1 - p) + 10p(1 - p)^9 + (1 - p)^{10}$

9-8 Reject equality at $\alpha = .05$ in each case

9-9 Accept equality with each test at $\alpha = .05$

9-10 Accept equality with each test at $\alpha = .05$

9-11 $\chi^2 = 9 > 6.63$, reject $p = 1/2$

9-12 $D_n > .061$, reject $p = 1/2$

9-13 (a) $\chi^2 = 3.16 < 13.4$, accept, (b) $\chi^2 = .89 < 10.6$, accept
(c) $D_n = .17 > .122$, reject (but grouping has increased D_n)

9-14 $D_n = .38 > .322$, reject H_0

9-15 $D_n = .033$ for first coding, .067 for second

9-16 Left to right: 42 to 46 runs above and below median, reject
120 to 124 runs up and down, reject

Top to bottom: 79 to 85 runs above and below median, reject

134 to 136 runs up and down, accept

(Note: Number of runs depends on how ties are broken.)

9-17 51 to 59 runs above and below median

30 to 36 runs up and down. Reject at 5% level

9-18 $\Sigma it_i = 84$, accept randomness

Chapter 10

10-1 $6x - 34y + 53 = 0$

10-2 $(-.094, .278)$, yes

10-3 $\hat{\alpha} = 7.06$, $(6.47, 7.65)$, $(-.094, .278)$

10-4 $(3.34, 7.50)$

10-5 $(-.26, .62)$

10-6 Test ratio $= 49$, reject H_0

10-7 Test ratio $= 8.25 > 3.89$, reject at .05; .199

10-8 Not at .05 level (test ratio $= 2.44 < 3.34$); 11.7; no

10-9 No, test ratio $= 2.16 < 9.28$; yes, test ratio $= 14.3 > 10.1$ (5 percent level)

10-10 No, $3.51 < 3.86$; yes, $14.8 > 3.86$ (5 percent level)

INDEX

A

Acceptance number, 92
Acceptance sampling, 91
Addition law, disjoint events, 12
Addition law, general, 13
Additivity of expectations, 50, 104
Additivity of variances, 58, 118, 119
Alternative hypothesis, 85
Analysis of variance, 256ff
Arrangements, 16
Average outgoing quality, 94
Average range, 181
Average value, 44
Axioms for probability, 6, 98

B

Bayes estimates, 223
Bayes procedure, 218
Bayes risk, 217
Bayes' theorem, 28, 221
Behrens-Fisher problem, 192
Bernoulli distribution, 58
Bernoulli trials, 33, 60, 152
Binomial approximation to hypergeometric, 72, 93
Binomial coefficient, 21, 281
Binomial distribution, 60, 72, 152
Binomial expansion, 21
Binomial formula, 34, 61
Binomial probability model, 33
Binomial random variable, 61
Binomial theorem, 21
Birthday problem, 36

C

c.d.f. (*see* Distribution function)

Solutions to
Selected Problems

Introduction to
PROBABILITY
and
STATISTICS Third Edition

B. W. LINDGREN, *Department of Statistics, University of Minnesota*

G. W. McELRATH, *Bayer and McElrath, Inc., Management Consultants, and Department of Mechanical Engineering, University of Minnesota*

The Macmillan Company
Collier-Macmillan Limited, London

This solutions manual has been prepared as an aid to instructors
using our book as a text. Not every solution is given, but it is hoped
that those most likely to be needed have been included. Answers are
given for all "review problems" whose answers were omitted from the book.

We shall greatly appreciate being told of any errors, typographical
or otherwise, in either the book itself or in this manual. Please address
such correspondence to the first-named author at the Department of
Statistics, University of Minnesota, 55455.

B. W. L. and G. W. McE.

Second Printing, 1969

Earlier edition © copyright 1966 by The Macmillan Company.

THE MACMILLAN COMPANY
COLLIER-MACMILLAN CANADA, LTD., TORONTO, ONTARIO

PRINTED IN THE UNITED STATES OF AMERICA

Chapter 1.

1-13. One counterexample is $P(E \cap F) = \frac{1}{6} \neq \frac{1}{4} \times \frac{5}{12} = P(E)P(F)$.

1-14. $P(F) = P[E \cup (F \cap E^c)] = P(E) + P(F \cap E^c) \geq P(E)$,
      because $P(F \cap E^c) \geq 0$.

1-19. Number using 3 R, 1 W: $4!/3! = 4$
             using 3 R, 1 B: $4!/3! = 4$
             using 2 R, 1 W, 1 B: $4!/2! = 12$
             using 2 R, 2 B: $4!/(2!2!) = 6$
             using 1 R, 1 W, 2 B: $4!/2! = \underline{12}$
                                         38

1-20. Seat chairman, then arrange remaining 6.

1-21. Fix one person, arrange remaining six in sequence.

1-22. Two choices for each position in the sequence.

1-24. Put B's in a row, insert group of 9 A's in one of the
      11 spaces between the B's or at the ends; then insert
      the 10th A in any one of these same 11 spaces:
      $11 \times 11 = 121$ ways.

1-27. List the 36 outcomes and count.

1-29. (a) No matter which container first object falls in,
      prob. is 1/6 for each subsequent object to fall in that
      container.

1-31. $\binom{9}{2}$

1-33. (b) $\binom{6}{2}\binom{44}{4}$

1-34. $\binom{n}{k}\binom{k}{1} =$ number of ways of selecting k from n, and
                       then one from those k,
      $\binom{n}{1}\binom{n-1}{k-1} =$ number of ways of selecting 1 from n, and
                       then $k-1$ from the remaining $n-1$.

      In each case the net result is a division of the n

1-34. (cont.) objects into three piles: one with n-k objects, one with k-1, and one with 1.

1-37. (c) $1 - \binom{6}{2}/\binom{16}{2}$

(e) $\binom{10}{1}\binom{6}{1}/\binom{16}{2}$

1-38. (b) $1 - [\binom{10}{4} + \binom{5}{4}]/\binom{15}{4}$

(c) $\binom{9+4}{2}/\binom{15}{4}$

1-39. (a) $\binom{14}{3}/\binom{16}{3}$

1-40. $\binom{13}{1}\binom{12}{2}\binom{4}{3}\binom{4}{1}\binom{4}{1}/\binom{52}{5}$

1-41. (a) Given at least one H, sample space consists of three points: (H, T), (T, H), (H, H), of which just one is the desired (H, H).

(b) Given that the penny is H, the sample space consists of two points, (H, T), (H, H).

1-42. (a) $\binom{4}{2}/\binom{52}{2}$

(b) $\frac{4}{52} \times \frac{3}{51}$

1-46. (a) $\frac{\binom{6}{1}\binom{4}{3}}{\binom{10}{4}} \times \frac{1}{6}$ (b) $\frac{\binom{6}{6}\binom{4}{3}}{\binom{10}{9}}$

1-49. Elementary outcomes of composite experiment are of the form $\{u_i \text{ and } v_{ij}\}$, for $i = 1,\ldots, m$ and $j = 1,\ldots, n$.

$P(u_i \text{ and } v_{ij}) = P(u_i)P(v_{ij}|u_i) = \frac{1}{m} \times \frac{1}{n} = \frac{1}{mn}$, (all i,j).

1-51. (c) $P(7) = 1/6$, $P(11) = 1/18$,

$P(\text{neither}) = 1 - 1/6 - 1/18 = 7/9$,

so $P(\text{one } 7, \text{ one } 11, \text{ one neither})$

$= \frac{3!}{1!1!1!} (1/6)^1(1/18)^1(7/9)^1$

1-52. $\frac{4}{6} \times \frac{3}{6} + \frac{2}{6} \times \frac{3}{6}$

- 2 -

1-54. (b) $P(2 \text{ or } 3) = 1/3$, so

$$P(5 \text{ or } 6 \text{ 2's or 3's}) = \binom{6}{5}(\tfrac{1}{3})^5(\tfrac{2}{3}) + \binom{6}{6}(\tfrac{1}{3})^6$$

1-58. $P(\text{alarm sounds}) = 1 - P(\text{all three devices fail})$
$$= 1 - (.1)^3 = .999$$

1-60. (b) $(.8)(.95)(\tfrac{.6}{.7})$

1-61. $\binom{11}{8}$

1-62. 2^4

1-63. $\binom{4}{1}(\tfrac{1}{6})(\tfrac{5}{6})^3$

1-64. If brands are A, B, and C, the six equally likely
guesses are:

(A, B, C) (A, C, B) (C, B, A) (C, A, B)
(B, C, A) (B, A, C)

In three of these (2nd, 3rd, 6th) there is just one
correct identification; hence, 3/6.

1-65. (a) $P(\text{1st, not 2nd}) + P(\text{2nd, not 1st})$
$$= (.01)(.98) + (.99)(.02)$$
(b) $1 - P(\text{loses in both}) = 1 - .99$

1-66. In each of 4 suits there are 9 runs: $36\big/\binom{52}{5}$.

1-67. 4 with 3 A's, 1 B, and 6 with 2 A's, 2 B's; total 10.

1-68. (a) $1 - P(\text{both kinds}) = 1 - (.1)(.05) = .995$
(b) $1 - P(\text{not def.}) = 1 - (.90)(.95) = .145$
(c) $\dfrac{P(1 \text{ def})}{P(\text{def})} = \dfrac{.140}{.145} = .9655$

1-69. $\dfrac{(1/2)^{10}}{(1/2)^9} = 1/2$

1-70. (a) $[\binom{8}{5} + \binom{8}{6} + \binom{8}{7} + \binom{8}{8}]\big/2^8$
(b) 2^8 (each person has two choices)

1-71. (a) If he wins at any play, he has won the desired
$1,000. Thus

- 3 -

1-71. (cont.) P(wins his expenses) = 1 - P(loses in 3 plays)

$$= 1 - (.6)^3 = .784$$

(b) $\binom{10}{8}(.784)^8(.216)^2$

1-72. 1 - P(no two have the same birthday)

$$= 1 - \frac{364}{365} \times \frac{363}{365} \times \ldots \times \frac{346}{365} = .411$$

(can use log factorial table to aid in evaluation)

1-73. P(R, H, and L) = $1/4 \neq$ P(R)P(H)P(L), since

P(R) = P(H) = P(L) = 1/2, hence not independent.

But, P(R,H) = 1/4 = P(R)P(H), and similarly

P(R,L) = P(R)P(L) and P(H,L) = P(H)P(L).

1-74. (a) $\frac{1}{2} \times \frac{2}{3} \times \frac{2}{3} \times \frac{2}{3} = \frac{4}{27}$

(b) P(A wins in 5) = P(AAABA) + P(AABAA) + P(ABAAA)

$$+ \ P(BAAAA)$$

$$= 2/81 + 2/81 + 2/81 + 4/81 = 10/81$$

Chapter 2.

2-1. Example: P(total of 4) = P(1, 3) + P(2, 2) + P(3, 1)

$$= 3/36$$

[Formula given was written down after probabilities

were computed.]

2-5. p(3) = P(G, G, then D) = $\frac{4}{5} \times \frac{3}{4} \times \frac{1}{3} = \frac{1}{5}$, but if the

defective is not located at the 3rd test, it will be

located at the 4th test; if the 4th one tested is

good, the remaining one must be the defective one.

(This assumes that the presence of one defective is

known to the tester; if this is not the case, then

p(4) = p(5) = 1/5.)

2-15. $\sum_1^\infty k \frac{1}{6}(\frac{5}{6})^{k-1} = \frac{1}{6} [1 + 2(\frac{5}{6}) + 3(\frac{5}{6})^2 + \ldots]$

$$= \frac{1}{6} \cdot \frac{1}{(1 - 5/6)^2} = 6.$$

2-19. $\sum X(\omega_i)p_i = (1/6)(5 + 1 - 1 - 1 + 1 + 5)$

$\sum x_j p_X(x_j) = 5(1/3) + (-1)(1/3) + 1(1/3)$

$\sum y_k p_Y(y_k) = 5(1/3) + 1(2/3)$.

2-21. $\eta(t) = \sum t^{x_i} p(x_i)$

$\eta''(t) = \sum x_i(x_i - 1)t^{x_i-2}p(x_i)$

$\eta''(1) = \sum x_i(x_i - 1)p(x_i) = E[X(X - 1)]$.

2-23. (b) $E[(X - EX)(Y - EY)]$

$= E[XY - Y\,EX - X\,EY + EX\,EY]$

$= E(XY) - EY\,EX - EX\,EY + EX\,EY$.

2-24. $P(X = i) = \sum\limits_{j=1}^{6} P(X = i \text{ and } Y = j)$

$= 1/12 + \ldots + 1/12 = 1/2$

$P(Y = j) = P(X = 0 \text{ and } Y = j) + P(X = 1 \text{ and } Y = j) = 1/6$,

and hence

$P(X = i \text{ and } Y = j) = P(X = i)P(Y = j)$, $i = 0, 1$

$j = 1, 2, \ldots, 6$.

2-26. $P(X = 1)P(Y = 1) = (1/4)(1/4) \neq P(X = 1 \text{ and } Y = 1) = 0$.

2-27. $E(t^{X+Y}) = E(t^X t^Y) = E(t^X)E(t^Y)$.

2-28. $\eta_Y(t) = \eta_{X_1}(t)\eta_{X_2}(t)\eta_{X_3}(t) = (pt + q)^3$, where $p = P(\text{Heads})$,

$q = 1 - p = 1/2$.

$\eta_Y''(1) = 3 \times 2(p + q)^1 p^2 = 6p^2$,

$E(Y^2) = E[Y(Y-1)] + EY = 6p^2 + 3p = 3$.

2-37. Because X and Y uncorrelated, var(X+Y) = var X + var Y

2-40. $\eta(t) = t^0 p(0) + t^1 p(1)$

2-44. Let $X_i = \begin{cases} 1, & \text{if ith toss is } 1 \text{ or } 2 \\ 0, & \text{if ith toss is } 3, 4, 5, \text{ or } 6. \end{cases}$

- 5 -

2-44. (cont.) Then X_i is Bernoulli with $p = 1/3$, and $X_1 + X_2 + X_3 + X_4$ = number of 1's and 2's is binomial with $n = 4$ and $p = 1/3$.

2-46. $EY^2 = E(Y^2 - Y) + EY = n(n-1)p^2 + np$

2-51. $P(3 \text{ or } 4 \text{ Aces}) = [\binom{4}{3}\binom{48}{10} + \binom{4}{4}\binom{48}{9}]/\binom{52}{13}$

2-53. (b) Average no. per min. = 5,
$P(\text{at least } 2) = 1 - e^{-5} - 5e^{-5}$

2-57. (a) Average no. on 8-hr. mission = 8/50

2-58. $\sum_0^\infty t^k e^{-m} m^k/k! = e^{-m} \sum_0^\infty (tm)^k/k! = e^{-m} e^{tm}$

2-59. Use $\lambda t = np = (50)(.01)$

2-60. $\lambda t = (.0005)(10,000) = 5$

2-62. $p = M/N = 500/10,000 = .05$
First approximate the exact hypergeometric probability by $\binom{100}{3} p^3 q^{97}$ and then approximate this with the Poisson formula using $\lambda t = np = (100)(.05) = 5$.

2-64. (a) $\frac{.2}{.8}$ (b) $2 \times .3 + 3 \times .2 + 4 \times .3 = 2.4$
(c) $2.4 - (EX)(EY) = 2.4 - 3 \times .8 = 0$ (d) $.3$

2-65. $X = \frac{1}{2}(Y + 4)$, $EX = (8 + 4)/2$, var $X = \frac{1}{4}(4) = 1$

2-66. $E(X^2 + 2X) = EX^2 + 2EX = \text{var } X + (EX)^2 + 2EX$
$$= 8 + 144 + 24$$

2-67. $p(3) = 1/6$, $p(1) = 1/2$, $p(0) = 1/3$; $EX = \text{var } X = 1$

2-68. P(k tests needed) = P(3 def. in k-1 tries, and

4th def. on kth try)

$$= \frac{\binom{6}{k-4}\binom{4}{3}}{\binom{10}{k-1}} \times \frac{1}{11-k}$$

$$= \frac{4(k-1)(k-2)(k-3)}{10 \times 9 \times 8 \times 7},$$

for k = 4, 5,..., 10. Expected number is then 8.8.
(This assumes tester doesn't stop after 9 tests.
Cf. solution to 2-10.)

2-69. Assuming signal and noise are independent phenomena,

$$P(X + Y = 1) = P(X = 1 \text{ and } Y = 2)$$

$$+ P(X = -1 \text{ and } Y = 2)$$

$$= \frac{1}{3} \times \frac{2}{3} + \frac{1}{3} \times \frac{1}{6} = \frac{5}{18}$$

One can complete the table in similar fashion:

z_i	-3	-2	-1	0	1	2	3
$p(z_i)$	1/18	1/18	5/18	4/18	5/18	1/18	1/18

EZ = 0, var Z = 2.

2-70. No, since P(X = i and Y = j) = 0 $\neq$ P(X = i)P(Y = j).

2-71. p(6) = P(HTHTHH) + P(THTHTT) = $1/2^5$, etc.

$$EX = \sum_2^\infty k/2^{k-1} = (1 - 1/2)^{-2} - 1 = 3.$$

2-72.

Selections	X	Y	Z
1 2 3	3	1	2
1 2 4	4	1	3
1 2 5	5	1	4
1 3 4	4	1	3
1 3 5	5	1	4
1 4 5	5	1	4
2 3 4	4	2	2
2 3 5	5	2	3
2 4 5	5	2	3
3 4 5	5	3	2

z_i	$P(Z = z_i)$
2	3/10
3	4/10
4	3/10

EZ = 3, EX = 4.5, EY = 1.5

var Z = .6, var X = var Y = .45

cov(X, Y) = .15

2-73. $1 - (11/12)^4$

2-74. P(4 or 5 successes) $= [\binom{5}{4}\binom{15}{1} + \binom{15}{5}]/\binom{20}{5}$

2-75. $1 - e^{-.1}$

2-76. $P(X = 1) = M(10 - M)(9 - M)(8 - M)/\binom{10}{4}$, max. at

$$M = 2.$$

2-77. $np = 12$, $np - np^2 = 8$; so $np^2 = 4$ and $p = 1/3$, $n = 36$

2-78. $P(\text{no Aces}) = (1 - 1/13)^{20} \doteq e^{-20/13}$

2-79. $P(\text{bust}) = \binom{36}{13}/\binom{52}{13} = \frac{36!\,39!}{23!\,52!}$

(then use log factorial table)

2-80. $np = (50)(.005) = .25$

$P(\text{at most one}) = e^{-.25}(1 + .25) = .9735$

$p' = P(\text{more than one}) = .0265$, $n' = 100$,

$n'p' = 2.65$, P(no boxes with more than 1 def.)

$$\doteq e^{-2.65}$$

Chapter 3.

3-2. (a) $E(Y/10 - M/25)^2 = \text{var}(Y/10)$

$$= \frac{1}{100} \times 10 \times \frac{M}{25}(1 - \frac{M}{25}) \frac{25-10}{24}$$

$$= \frac{1}{16} \times \frac{M}{25}(1 - \frac{M}{25})$$

(b) $E((Y+1)/12 - M/25)^2 = \text{var}(\frac{Y+1}{12}) + [E(\frac{Y+1}{12}) - \frac{M}{25}]^2$

$$= \text{var}(\frac{Y}{12}) + [\frac{1}{12}(\frac{10M}{25} + 1) - \frac{M}{25}]^2$$

$$= \frac{1}{16} \times \frac{25}{36} \times \frac{M}{25}(1 - \frac{M}{25})$$

$$+ \frac{1}{144}(1 - \frac{2M}{25})^2$$

3-3. $E(\widetilde{p} - p)^2 = E(\frac{1}{2} - p)^2 = (\frac{1}{2} - p)^2$. This is smaller

for p near 1/2.

3-4. $E(aY-p)^2 = a^2 \text{ var } Y + (aEY-p)^2$

$$= \frac{5}{4} a^2 + (\frac{5}{2}a - \frac{1}{2})^2$$

$$= \frac{15}{2}a^2 - \frac{5}{2}a + \frac{1}{4}$$

which is smallest for $a = \frac{5}{4} / \frac{15}{2} = \frac{1}{6}$.

3-6. $P(N = n) = p(1-p)^{n-1}$, $n = 1, 2, \ldots$

$$E(1/N) = \sum_{n=1}^{\infty} \frac{1}{n} p(1-p)^{n-1} = \frac{p}{1-p} \sum_{1}^{\infty} \frac{1}{n}(1-p)^n$$

$$= -\frac{p}{q} \log p.$$

3-7. Using a binomial approximation:

$$\text{s.e.} = \sqrt{\frac{.48 \times .52}{10,000}} \doteq .005 .$$

More exactly,

$$\text{s.e.} = \sqrt{\frac{.48 \times .52 \times 9,000}{10,000 \times 9,999}} = .00474 .$$

3-11. $f(10) = 1/1024$, $f(9) = 10/1024$, $f(8) = 45/1024$

$P(8, 9, 10) = f(8) + f(9) + f(10).$

3-12. $P(8, 9, 10 | p = 2/3) = (2/3)^{10} + 10(1/3)(2/3)^9$

$$+ 45(1/3)(2/3)^8.$$

3-14. $P(0, 1, 2 | p = 2/3) = (1/3)^{10} + 10(1/3)^9(2/3)$

$$+ 45(1/3)^8(2/3).$$

3-16. $c = 0$: $\text{AOQ} = (M/N)P(Y = 0 | M) = \frac{M}{N} \frac{(8-M)(7-M)(6-M)}{8 \times 7 \times 6}$.

3-17. $\text{PR} = 1 - \text{OC}(1/8)$, $\text{CR} = \text{OC}(4/8)$.

3-20. $\text{AOQ} = \frac{M}{N} P(Y = 0) + \frac{M-1}{N} P(Y = 1) = pe^{-25p} + 25p^2 e^{-25p}$.

4-1. $P(|X - 1| > .5) = 1 - P(-.5 < X - 1 < .5)$

$$= 1 - P(.5 < X < 1.5).$$

4-3. (d) For x between 0 and 1, the desired area can be computed as 1-(unshaded area).

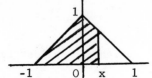

4-5. 0 is a point of symmetry.

4-7. Area to left of Q_1 is $1/4 = (Q_1 + 1)^2/2$,

so $Q_1 = \sqrt{1/2} - 1$.

4-8. 0 is a point of symmetry.

4-9. Divide the interval from 0 to 1 into n pieces, defining rectangles of heights

$$3/4,\ 3(1 - 1/n^2)/4,\ldots,\ 3(1 - ([n-1]/n)^2)/4.$$

Areas of these rectangles have the sum

$$\frac{3}{4} \times \frac{1}{n} [n - (1/n^2 + 4/n^2 +\ldots+ (n-1)^2/n^2)]$$

$$= \frac{3}{4n} [n - n(2n^2 - 3n + 1)/(6n^2)]$$

$$= 1/2 + 3/(8n) - 1/(8n^2) \to 1/2.$$

4-19. $\psi'(t) = \frac{d}{dt} \int_{-\infty}^{\infty} e^{tx}f(x)dx = \int_{-\infty}^{\infty} x\, e^{tx}f(x)dx,$

$$\psi'(0) = \int_{-\infty}^{\infty} x\, f(x)dx = EX.$$

4-20. $\psi'(t) = (1 - t)^{-2}, \psi''(t) = 2(1 - t)^{-3}; EX^2 = \psi''(0).$

4-21. $f_X(x) = \frac{d}{dt} P(aZ + b \le x) = \frac{d}{dx} P(Z \le \frac{x - b}{a})$

$$= \frac{d}{dx} F_Z(\frac{x - b}{a}).$$

4-23. (a) $1 - P(-k < X < k) = 1 - \Phi(k) + \Phi(-k)$

$$= 1 - \Phi(k) + 1 - \Phi(k).$$

4-25. $\sigma^2 + \mu^2 = 68$, $(10 - \mu)/\sigma = 1 = z_{.8413}$

(then solve for σ and μ).

4-26. $h = 70" + (z_{.98})3" = 76.15"$.

4.27. $E(kd^3) = k \int_{-\infty}^{\infty} x^3 e^{-(x - 1.5)^2/.18} dx/\sqrt{.18\pi}$

$$= \frac{k}{\sqrt{.18\pi}} \int_{-\infty}^{\infty} (y + 1.5)^3 e^{-y^2/.18} dy$$

(then expand the cube and drop terms with odd
powers of y, these integrals being zero).

4-31. Assume a coin is tossed to decide whether to round up
or down, when last digit is a 5:

Last digit	0	1	2	3	4	5	6	7	8	9
Error	0	1	2	3	4	5	-5	-4	-3	-2	-1
Probability	.1	.1	.1	.1	.1	.05	.05	.1	.1	.1	.1

4-32. $E(X^2 + Y^2) = (\sigma_X^2 + \mu_X^2) + (\sigma_Y^2 + \mu_Y^2) = 2 \times 10^6$ ft^2

$P(X^2 + Y^2 > 1550^2) = 1 - P[(X^2 + Y^2)/10^6 < 2.4] = .30.$

4-33. $T^2_{series} = 1 + 1$, $T_{series} = .707$ percent of 200 ohms.

4-34. $.01 = P(\text{clearance} < 0) = \Phi(\frac{0 - [.5 - x]}{.00307})$,

so $\frac{x - .5}{.00307} = -2.326 = z_{.01}$.

4-36. $\sigma_\epsilon^2 = (2.5)(.01) + (400)(.0025) = (1.12 \text{ mi.})^2$.

Chapter 5.

5-4. (b) Crates are sometimes packed with good items on top.
(c) Students not studying are apt to differ in dating
habits from those who are.

5-5. A watched observation tends to be nontypical.

5-19.

Sample	1,2	1,3	1,4	1,5	2,3	2,4	2,5	3,4	3,5	4,5
S	3	4	5	6	5	6	7	7	8	9

(Probability 1/10 is assigned to each sample).

s	3	4	5	6	7	8	9
$P(S = s)$	.1	.1	.2	.2	.2	.1	.1

5-20. $EX_i^2 = \text{var } X_i + (EX_i)^2 = \sigma^2$, for $i = 1, \ldots, n$.

5-21. $EY^2 = \int_0^\theta y^2(ny^{n-1}/\theta^n)dy = \dfrac{n\,y^{n+2}}{(n+2)\theta^n}\Big|_0^\theta = \dfrac{n\theta^2}{n+2}$

$\text{var } Y = EY^2 - (EY)^2 = \theta^2(\dfrac{n}{n+2} - [\dfrac{n}{n+1}]^2)$.

Chapter 6.

6-1. $1 - \Phi(\sqrt{n}\,/\,5) + \Phi(-\sqrt{n}\,/\,5)$.

6-2. $.5\sqrt{n}\,/\,\sigma = 2.58$ for (a), $= 3.29$ for (b).

6-3. $\Phi([190 - 210]/\sqrt{175})$.

6-4. $1 - \Phi([488 - 480]/\sqrt{24})$.

6-5. $P(\text{sum of 98 wts.} > 10) = 1 - \Phi(\dfrac{10 - 9.8}{\sqrt{98}\,(.008)})$.

6-7.   (b) $P(25 \leq X \leq 35) = P(24 < X \leq 35)$

$$= F_X(35) - F_X(24)$$

$$= \Phi(5.5/5) - \Phi(-5.5/5).$$

6-10. Normal: $\Phi([2.5 - 2]/\sqrt{70/36}$

Poisson: $e^{-2}(1 + 2 + 2^2/2!)$

Binomial (exact): $\displaystyle\sum_0^2 \binom{72}{k}(\dfrac{1}{36})^k(\dfrac{35}{36})^{72-k} = .6772$.

6-13. $.05 = 1 - \Phi(\dfrac{K - 0}{3/10})$, $\beta = \Phi(\dfrac{K - 2}{3/10})$.

6-15. $\sqrt{n}\,K/2 = 2.33 = \sqrt{n}\,(K - 2)/2$.

6-16. $\pi(\mu) = 1 - \Phi([K - \mu + 2]/.005) + \Phi([2 - K - \mu]/.005)$.

6-17. $\dfrac{K}{1/\sqrt{n}} = 2.57$, $.05 = \Phi(\dfrac{K-.1}{1/\sqrt{n}}) - \Phi(\dfrac{-K-.1}{1/\sqrt{n}})$.

Assuming that $\sqrt{n}(-K-.1) < -4$ one can drop the last term, so that $1.645 = \sqrt{n}(K-.1)$ and then solve this together with the first relation. (The results then justify the assumption.)

6-20. Length of interval $= 2(2.58)(.005)/\sqrt{n} = .001$.

6-26. Let $X_i =$ number of counts in the ith second.

Then $\displaystyle\sum_1^{60} X_i$ is Poisson with parameter 60λ, and

is approximately normal with this as mean and variance. Hence,

$$P([\Sigma\, X_i - 60\lambda]/60\lambda \le 1.96) = .95.$$

Then square the inequality:

$$(\Sigma\, X_i)^2 - 120\lambda\Sigma\, X_i + (60\lambda)^2 \le 60\lambda(1.96)^2,$$

and solve for λ with $\Sigma\, X_i = 120$; the resulting limits are

$$2 + \frac{(1.96)^2}{120} \pm \frac{1.96}{60}\sqrt{120 + (1.96)^2/4}\ .$$

Chapter 7.

7-5. Choose $\sigma^2 = 4$ if $s_x^2 > K$; then

$$\pi(\sigma^2) = 1 - F_{\chi^2}(5K/\sigma^2),\ \pi(2) = .05.$$

7-7. (b) $\operatorname{var}(ns_x^2/[n-1]) = n^2\, \operatorname{var}(s_x^2)/(n-1)^2$.

7-8. $R = 11$, $s_x = 3.97$.

7-9. $\pi(\sigma) = 1 - F_W(K/\sigma)$, $\alpha = \pi(\sqrt{2})$, $\beta = 1 - \pi(2)$.

7-12. $s_x = .1527$, $\overline{X} = 3.691$; confidence interval is

$$3.691 \pm (.1527)(1.73)/\sqrt{20}\ .$$

7-13. $t = \dfrac{3.691 - 3.5}{.1527/\sqrt{20}} = 5.59 > 1.33 = t_{.90}(19)$.

- 13 -

7-14. $\overline{X} = 93.78$, $s_x = 4.47$.

7-19. $.10 \doteq 1 - \Phi(\dfrac{K - a_n\sigma}{b_n\sigma/\sqrt{k}})$, $\beta \doteq \Phi(\dfrac{7.20 - 2.704\sqrt{10}}{.833\sqrt{10}/\sqrt{20}})$.

Chapter 8.

8-3. $L(p) = p^3$, if $Y = 3$,

$\qquad 3p^2(1-p)$, if $Y = 2$,

$\qquad 3p(1-p)$, if $Y = 1$,

$\qquad (1-p)^3$, if $Y = 0$.

8-4. (b) $\log L = \log[\theta^{-n}\exp(-\Sigma X_i/\theta)] = -n\log\theta - \Sigma X_i/\theta$.

8-6. $\alpha = 1 - \Phi(\dfrac{K-0}{1/5})$, whence $5K = 1.645$ (for $\alpha = .05$).

8-7.

x	f_0	f_1	f_0/f_1
0	.3	.5	3/5
1	.6	.3	2
2	.1	.2	1/2

$\Lambda(2) < \Lambda(0) < \Lambda(1)$.

8-9. $\Lambda = \dfrac{(2\pi v_0)^{-n/2}\exp[-\dfrac{1}{2v_0}\Sigma(X_i - \overline{X})^2]}{(2\pi v_1)^{-n/2}\exp[-\dfrac{1}{2v_1}\Sigma(X_i - \overline{X})^2]}$

$\qquad = (\dfrac{v_1}{v_0})^{n/2}\exp[-ns_x^2(\dfrac{1}{v_0} - \dfrac{1}{v_1})]$.

8-10.

Y	M 0	1	2	3	4	Λ
0	1	1/2	1/6	0	0	1/3
1	0	1/2	2/3	1/2	0	4/3
2	0	0	1/6	1/2	0	1/3

$\Lambda(0) = \Lambda(2) < \Lambda(1)$.

8-15. $EZ = p\log 9 + \log(5/9) = \begin{cases} .222 \text{ under } H_0 \\ -.160 \text{ under } H_1 \end{cases}$

$E(\log \Lambda_n) = \begin{cases} -\alpha\log 4 + (1 - \alpha)\log 4, \text{ under } H_0 \\ -(1 - \beta)\log 4 + \beta\log 4, \text{ under } H_1 \end{cases}$

8-19. Set $\alpha = \beta$: $1 - \Phi(5K) = \Phi(5(K-1)) \Rightarrow -5K = 5(K-1)$.

8-22.

Rule	1	2	3	4	5
Bayes risk	$5-3\gamma$	3γ	$1+3\gamma$	$2-\gamma$	$4-4\gamma$

8-24. $-1 = \dfrac{\Phi'(K-1)}{2\Phi'(-K)}$, or $2e^{-K^2/2} = e^{-(K-1)^2/2}$, $K = \dfrac{1}{2} + \log 2$.

8-26. $P(Y = 0) = .3 \times .09 + .7 \times .81 = .594$, $\dfrac{.3 \times .09}{.594} = \dfrac{1}{22}$,etc.

$P(Y = 1) = .3 \times .42 + .7 \times .18 = .252$.

8-27. $h(\theta|z) = \begin{cases} 0, \text{ if } \theta \neq \theta_1 \\ f(\theta_1|z)/f(\theta_1|z) = 1, \text{ if } \theta = \theta_1 \end{cases}$

8-28. $h(\theta|z_i) = \dfrac{a_i g(\theta)}{a_i \Sigma\, g(\theta)} = g(\theta)$, since $\Sigma\, g(\theta) = 1$.

8-30. $\Sigma\, f(2|m)g(m) = 0 \times \dfrac{1}{4} + 0 \times \dfrac{1}{4} + \dfrac{2}{90} \times \dfrac{1}{4} + \dfrac{6}{90} \times \dfrac{1}{4} = \dfrac{1}{45}$

$h(m|2) = \begin{cases} 0, \text{ for } m = 0, 1 \\ 1/4, \text{ for } m = 2 \\ 3/4, \text{ for } m = 3 \end{cases}$

Bayes est. is $E_h M = 0 + 0 + 2 \times \dfrac{1}{4} + 3 \times \dfrac{3}{4} = \dfrac{11}{4}$.

Chapter 9.

9-1. $(88.5 - 75)/\sqrt{150}/4 = 2.2 > 1.96$; rej. at 5% level.

9-2. Power fn. $= P(9 \text{ or } 10|p) = 10p^9(1 - p) > p^{10} = \pi(p)$

$\alpha = \pi(1/2) = .0093$, $P(\text{acc.}|p = 2/3) = 1 - \pi(2/3) = .896$.

9-3. $\displaystyle\sum_{40}^{59} \binom{100}{k}/2^k$.

9-5. If $\alpha = .05 = 1 - \Phi(\dfrac{K > 1/2 - 29/2}{\sqrt{29/4}})$,

$K = 14 + 1.645\sqrt{29/4} = 18.43$.

9-6. For $\alpha = .05$:

$\alpha = 2P_{H_0}(X \leq K)$, $K + 1/2 - 20 = \sqrt{10}\,(-1.96)$,

$K = 13.31$.

9-6. (cont.) Thus, at this level, reject H_0 if the number of +'s exceeds 26.69 or is less than 13.31. For the given data, it is 20 to 25, depending on how ties are broken.

9-8. (a) Critical region of Example 9-e can be used; the number of A's to the right of the median is 2 to 6 (depending on ties), less than 7. Rej. at .056.

9-9. (a) Two sided test at $\alpha = .05$ rejects H_0 if

$$|Z - 20|/2.25 > 1.96,$$

where

$$2.25 = \sqrt{40 \times \frac{1}{2} \times \frac{1}{2} \times \frac{80 - 40}{80 - 1}} \,,$$

and Z is the appropriate statistic.

(b) Two sided test at $\alpha = .05$ rejects H_0 if

$$|U - 800|/80.5 > 1.96.$$

9-11. $\chi^2 = \dfrac{(230 - 200)^2}{200} + \dfrac{(170 - 200)^2}{200}$

9-12. With either coding $D_n = 30/400 > 1/22/\sqrt{400}$

9-18. Most extreme rank permutations, and values of Σit_i, are

1	2	3	4	5	6	91
2	1	3	4	5	6	90
1	3	2	4	5	6	90
1	2	4	3	5	6	90
1	2	3	5	4	6	90
1	2	3	4	6	5	90
2	1	4	3	5	6	89
2	1	3	4	6	5	89

Clearly the most extreme 1 percent of the 720 permutations would have a value of Σit_i at least 89. So given permutation (84) calls for acceptance.

- 16 -

Chapter 10.

10-1. Solve for α, β: $\begin{cases} 8 = 4\alpha + 10\beta \\ 23 = 10\alpha + 42\beta. \end{cases}$

10-2. $.092 \pm 1.96 \sqrt{\dfrac{4.6}{(10.24)(50)}}$ (using $\hat{\sigma}^2$ for σ^2).

10-3. New $\hat{\alpha} = \overline{Y} = (\text{old } \hat{\alpha}) + \hat{\beta} (\text{old } \overline{x}) = 6.31 + (.092)(8.2)$

Confidence limits for α are $7.06 \pm 2\hat{\sigma}/\sqrt{50}$.

10-4. $50\hat{\sigma}^2/\sigma^2$ is chi-square (48), so confidence interval is

$$\frac{50\hat{\sigma}^2}{\chi^2_{.975}(48)} < \sigma^2 < \frac{50\hat{\sigma}^2}{\chi^2_{.025}(48)}$$

(these percentiles are 69.0 and 30.7, resp.).

10-5. $.1765 \pm (1.89)\sqrt{.935}/\sqrt{17}$, where

$$.935 = \hat{\sigma}^2 = \frac{1}{4} \sum_{1}^{4} (Y_i - \frac{6}{34} x_i - \frac{53}{34})^2.$$

10-6. Sum of squares about $\overline{X} = 11$ is $312 = 294 + 18$. The appropriate F-ratio is then

$$F = (294/2)/(18/6) = 49.$$

10-7. $\overline{X} = 3.75$, $F = \dfrac{(5/2)(.67)}{(1/12)(2.44)} = 8.25$, $\hat{\sigma}^2 = .203$.

10-8. (a) $\overline{X} = 5.05$, $F = \dfrac{(1/3) \Sigma n_i(X_i - \overline{X})^2}{(163.28)/14} = \dfrac{28.6}{11.7}$.

10-9. $\overline{X} = 3.475$, sum of squares about $\overline{X}$ is 2.695 which is decomposed into $1.62 + .735 + .340$. F-ratios are $(1.62/1)/(.34/3)$, and $(.795/3)/(.34/3)$.